MW00637169

Science in the Scientific Revolution

by

Dr. Jay L. Wile

Science in the Scientific Revolution

Published by
Berean Builders
Muncie, IN
www.bereanbuilders.com

Manufactured in the United States of America
Second Printing 2019

ISBN: 978-0-9890424-4-4

All Scripture verses are taken from the New American Standard translation.

Introduction

In the year 1543, two revolutionary books were published. One was about how the sun, the planets, and the stars are arranged in the heavens. The other was about the marvelous design of the human body. The publication of these two books is considered by most historians to mark the beginning of a period in history known as "The Scientific Revolution." Why? More than any other work up to this point in history, these two books were willing to question the teachings of ancient authorities and instead concentrate on what could be observed in the present. As a result, these books started a process that would revolutionize the study of the natural world. Instead of referring to people from the past, natural philosophers (that's what scientists were called back then) would start making observations in the present and would use those observations to explain how the world around them worked.

If you've studied much science at all, you have probably heard names like Copernicus, Galileo, Newton, and Pascal. These men lived in this time period. They were eager to learn how nature worked because they thought that by studying nature they could learn more about God. For example, in a letter to the Grand Duchess of Tuscany in 1615, Galileo wrote, "…for the holy Bible and the phenomena of nature proceed alike from the divine Word." After discussing what he meant by that, he quoted Tertullian, a Christian author who lived from about AD 160 to about AD 225:

> We conclude that God is known first through Nature, and then again, more particularly, by doctrine, by Nature in His works, and by doctrine in His revealed word. [http://www.fordham.edu/halsall/mod/galileo-tuscany.asp, retrieved 11/01/2013]

This, of course, echoes what Romans 1:20 says. There is no excuse for people who reject God. Even if they have never read the Bible or heard the Good News of Jesus Christ, God's handiwork (the created world) makes His presence and His nature clear to everyone.

The Christian faith of those who started and continued The Scientific Revolution had a profound impact on their science, and you will learn a lot about that as you move through this course. I personally think this is one reason The Scientific Revolution was such an astounding success. Because science was being done in the context of the Christian faith, it was incredibly effective. Lots of progress was made because those studying the world around them realized that in order to fully understand nature, you had to understand the characteristics of its Creator.

As you study this course, I want you to keep in mind something that was said by Robert Boyle, another great natural philosopher from this time period. In a speech he gave to other natural philosophers of his day, he said, "Remember to give glory to the One who authored nature." [Dan Graves, *Scientists of Faith*, Kregel Resources 1996, p. 63]

How To Use This Book

This book contains 90 lessons, split into six sections. However, there are two kinds of lessons. Twelve of the lessons in each section are the "normal" lessons, and the other three are "challenge" lessons. To remind you of this fact, the titles look different from one another. Normal lessons are titled in black type, while the challenge lessons are titled in red type. There are two ways to schedule these lessons:

1. You can do a lesson every other day. This allows you to cover all 90 lessons in a typical academic year, which usually consists of 180 days of school.

   or

2. You can do two lessons each week. If you follow this schedule, you will be skipping the challenge lessons. There is no harm in skipping the challenge lessons, since nothing in the normal lessons refers to what is learned in the challenge lessons.

Which do you choose? It just depends on how much science you want to do. If your children enjoy what they are doing and ask to do it a lot, you can do science every other day. If not, you can do science twice per week. Of course, if you want this book to last more than a year, you can do science even less often than twice per week. It all depends on what works best for your specific situation.

Each lesson in this book contains a hands-on activity, usually an experiment. The hands-on activity often starts the lesson, but sometimes it appears later on in the lesson. In addition, each lesson contains reading. I have designed this course so that *all* elementary-age children can use it together, so the best thing to do is to have all your elementary-age children participate in the hands-on part of the lesson, and you or the oldest child should read the lesson aloud to everyone else. The lessons are short (less than three pages of reading each), so even the youngest student should be able to get through the lesson without too much discomfort.

At the end of each lesson, there is a review assignment that is split up according to the age of the students. The youngest students review the lesson by orally answering two questions. The older students have a notebooking exercise to complete, and the oldest students have a more difficult notebooking exercise to complete. How will you know which review exercise your student should do? It is really up to you. If a student is having difficulty writing, then the notebooking assignments are probably not a good fit, unless you want to use them to help the student develop writing skills. Thus, non-writers should do the review exercises for the youngest students. Whether a student does the review exercises for the "older students" or the "oldest students" is up to you. The exercises for the oldest students require more critical thinking and more writing than the ones for the older students.

In my opinion, all you need to do is the lesson and the review exercises. If you want to give your student a grade for the course, you can use the notebook or the oral questions as an evaluation tool. However, if your child is at the upper end of the elementary years, and you would like to get him or her used to taking tests in science, there are some tests available in the "Helps and Hints" book that accompanies this book. I don't think these tests are necessary, but I have made them available in case you decide they are. In order to study for each test, the student should review the notebook that was made. The tests assume that the student has done the review exercises for the oldest students.

Question/Answer Service

One of the most important things you need to remember while using this course is that there is a way to get help if you are stuck or confused. Just go to:

http://www.askdrwile.com/

To use this website, you will need to register, but registration is free. Once you have registered, you can log in to use the website. The website allows you to ask questions about the material, and it also allows you to search for the answers to questions that have been asked previously. Please feel free to ask as many questions as you like!

Experiments and Activities

There are a lot of experiments and activities in this course, but most of them are purposely kept fairly simple. Ideally, the students should be doing most of the work in the experiments and activities, but *they must be supervised by an adult*. While most of the experiments and activities are very safe, some use flames, heat, or sharp instruments. In addition, some specifically ask for the aid of an adult. Thus, *you should have the children do all of the experiments under constant adult supervision*.

Most of the experiments in the course don't take much time, but some are more long-term experiments. However, you don't have to worry about looking ahead to see whether an experiment is long-term or short-term. If a long-term experiment is coming up, you will be notified of it with a note that is set off in a yellow box. It will warn you to look ahead at the upcoming long-term experiment, and it will tell you when that experiment needs to be started. Thus, you need not read ahead in the book. Everything you need to know will be presented as you need to know it.

********* **Please Do The Experiments With Common Sense And Adult Supervision**. *********

You will not find these experiments to be any more dangerous than cooking or cleaning, but that doesn't mean children can't get hurt. Supervise your children and coach them that oven burners and open flames should be treated with extreme care, and unless you are specifically told otherwise in the book, you should *never* eat or drink anything that comes from an experiment! You should also avoid having food and drink around when you are doing experiments to reduce the risk of contamination.

Experiment Supplies

The experiments use only common household items, but of course, some items are more "common" than others. Here is a list of the things that are a bit unusual and might take some time to find. The supplies listed in red are used for the challenge lessons. If you are not doing those lessons, you don't have to worry about those supplies.

Materials That Might Take Some Time to Acquire

- For **Section 1** (challenge lesson): Some ink (Stamp pad of ink would be ideal, but you can use fingerpaint or watercolor paint and a brush as well.)
- For **Section 2**: Two distinctly different flowers, such as a daisy and geranium (If you are doing this during a time of year when flowers are not in bloom, you can usually get flowers fairly cheaply from a supermarket. The flowers can be of any variety, as long as they are very different from one another in terms of the number of petals, whether or not there are stalks at the center of the flower, etc. If you simply don't have the time or money, pictures will work, as long as they show the flowers in some detail.)
- For **Section 2**: A sunflower seed in its shell
- For **Section 2**: A peanut with the shell intact
- For **Section 2**: Hydrogen peroxide (Drugstores carry it.)
- For **Section 2**: Active dry yeast (Grocery stores sell it for making bread.)
- For **Section 2** (challenge lesson): Weak reading glasses (A power of 1.50 is ideal.)
- For **Section 3**: Root Kill (It is found in the plumbing section of a hardware store. The ingredients list should have "copper sulfate" or "copper sulfate pentahydrate" as the main ingredient. If you can look inside the package, it should be full of blue crystals.)
- For **Section 5**: A flower with petals that are light in color (White would be ideal, but any light color will do. A flower bought from a store will work or pick one from outside if you can find one.)
- For **Section 5**: A string of Christmas tree lights (It probably won't be the Christmas season when you cover this section.)

Here is a list of everything you need to do the experiments, separated by the section that contains the lesson. Each section is six weeks' worth of lessons if you are scheduling a year for the course, so making sure you have everything for a given section ensures that you have six weeks of science supplies ready. Note that the things listed above are also contained in the list below:

Supplies for the First Section (Lessons 1 – 15)

- A square or rectangle of cardboard that is larger than a paper plate
- Five paper plates
- A nail
- Scissors
- Crayons, colored pencils, or markers
- Modeling clay, like Play-Doh
- Two metersticks, yardsticks, or thin pieces of wood
- Two blank sheets of paper
- A Bible
- A fresh chicken drumstick (uncooked)
- A knife
- A cutting board
- A pushpin
- A pen
- Paper towels
- A fresh chicken wing (uncooked)

- A magnifying glass
- A mirror
- Water
- Flour
- Cream of tartar
- Vegetable oil
- Salt
- A large bowl
- A mixing spoon
- A saucepan
- A stove
- Glue (A glue stick works best, but any glue will do.)
- Two coffee filters
- A funnel
- A handful of dirt
- A pitcher or large glass that has a pouring spout on it
- Two small glasses (like juice glasses)
- A window
- Ice (If your freezer makes crushed ice, that's what you want.)

If your freezer can't make crushed ice, you need the following three items:

  - Ziploc bag
  - Hammer
  - Cutting board

- A tennis ball you can ruin
- Three slices of bread
- An old sock that you aren't going to use anymore (the longer, the better)
- A gallon-sized Ziploc bag
- White vinegar
- A ½-cup measuring cup
- Some nylon stockings that you can cut up
- A sink
- A camera (optional and only for those who do the "older" and "oldest" student assignments)
- Some ink (Stamp pad of ink would be ideal, but you can use fingerpaint or watercolor paint and a brush as well.)

<u>Supplies for the Second Section (Lessons 16 – 30)</u>

- Six noodles
- Vanilla
- Two dinner plates
- A paper napkin
- Paper towels
- Two bowls that are big enough to cover the dinner plates when turned upside down
- A measuring tablespoon
- A pan for boiling the noodles
- A strainer for the noodles
- A drinking glass
- Water

- A small lump of charcoal
- A pencil "lead" (The easiest thing to do is get a piece of "lead" from a mechanical pencil. However, you can whittle down a pencil to get some of the "lead." The piece only needs to be about 2 centimeters – just under an inch – long.)
- A candle that can stand on its own or is in a holder
- A metal pie pan or other metal container that is bigger than the candle
- Metal tweezers
- A hammer
- Some paper
- A stove
- Matches or something else you can use to light a candle
- A winter glove
- A sink with running water
- Two rather different flowers, such as a daisy and geranium (If you are doing this during a time of year when flowers are not in bloom, you can usually get flowers fairly cheaply in a supermarket. The flowers can be of any variety, as long as they are very different from one another in terms of the number of petals, whether or not there are stalks at the center of the flower, etc. If you simply don't have the time or money, pictures will work, as long as they show the flower in some detail.)
- A dried bean
- A sunflower seed in its shell
- A peanut with the shell intact
- A pair of pliers
- A stopwatch or timer
- Two shiny pennies (They should be really clean and shiny. If you can't find any shiny pennies, use a hard toothbrush and tomato ketchup to scrub them to the point where they are shiny.)
- White vinegar
- Salt
- Thread
- Scissors
- Tape
- Hydrogen peroxide (Drugstores carry it.)
- Two ½-liter plastic bottles (like the kind bottled water comes in)
- Active dry yeast (Grocery stores sell it for making bread.)
- Aluminum foil
- A ½-cup measuring cup
- A ¼-cup measuring cup
- A 1-cup measuring cup
- A ¼-teaspoon measuring spoon
- A funnel
- A small glass
- A flashlight that uses two batteries (It is best to use a flashlight with a single bulb. Flashlights with several LED lights will not give good results.)
- Two white pieces of paper
- Two Styrofoam cups (One needs to be large.)
- Flour
- A measuring tablespoon
- Kitchen tongs

- A hand-held hair dryer.
- String
- Two washers or nuts
- Two cardboard tubes from two rolls of paper towels
- A flat piece of cardboard that is at least 20 centimeters by 20 centimeters (8 inches by 8 inches)
- A flat board that is at least a meter (39 inches) long
- A marble
- Two large books
- Two ½-liter bottles, like the kind water comes in
- A large glass
- Food coloring
- A spoon
- A large pot for heating water
- Weak reading glasses (A power of 1.50 is ideal.)
- A meterstick or yardstick

Supplies for the Third Section (Lessons 31 – 45)

- A flashlight that has a face which is at least 1.5 inches across
- A magnifying glass that is larger than the flashlight's face
- A baseball or some other hand-sized ball that is white or at least brightly colored
- Black construction paper
- Scissors
- Clear tape (like cellophane tape)
- A blank sheet of white paper
- A thick piece of cardboard or a table to which your parents will allow you to tape three pieces of paper.
- Three blank sheets of paper
- A pencil
- String
- Cellophane tape
- A ruler
- A ball that is about the size of a baseball or tennis ball
- A marker that can be used to make a mark on the ball
- A rubber band that can fit around the ball and still be stretched
- Vegetable oil
- Water
- Salt in a saltshaker
- Two tall glasses that you can see through
- Apple cider vinegar (You can use clear vinegar if you like, but the experiment will be slightly more disgusting as a result.)
- Water
- Antacid tablets (Any brand will do. Unflavored tablets would be ideal, but they are hard to find.)
- An aluminum pie pan (or a shallow dish that will not break when repeatedly hit by a hammer)
- Paper towels
- A hammer
- Three small glasses

- Two spoons for stirring
- A ¼-cup measuring cup
- Some newspapers or old towels
- A large bowl
- A measuring glass that can measure at least 2 cups
- Water
- A stopwatch
- The phone numbers or E-MAIL addresses of your pastor and at least three other adults in your church. It is best to contact people who are knowledgeable about the Bible and matters that relate to the creation account as given in the book of Genesis.
- Root Kill (It is found in the plumbing section of a hardware store. The ingredients list should have "copper sulfate" or "copper sulfate pentahydrate" as the main ingredient. If you can look inside the package, it should be full of blue crystals.)
- Steel wool
- A measuring teaspoon
- A measuring cup
- A spoon for stirring
- Blue food coloring (any dark color will work)
- Three straws (Two of them need to be able to bend near one end.)
- Wooden Matches
- A plastic, ½-liter bottle with a lid, like the kind water comes in
- A coin that has an easy-to-recognize "heads" side and an easy-to-recognize "tails" side
- Two candles, one of which needs to be able to stand on its own or be put in a holder
- Matches or something else to light the candles
- Vinegar (any kind)
- Baking soda
- A spoon for stirring
- A counter that is above a floor you can make a mess on

Supplies for the Fourth Section (Lessons 46 – 60)

- Ice
- Water
- A small glass
- A metal paper clip
- A plastic garbage bag that is tall enough so that you can stand inside it and the top will reach up to your waist (the thicker the plastic, the better)
- A vacuum cleaner with a hose and a small attachment that has bristles around the edge
- A balloon (Any shape will do, but it should be larger than your hand when it is inflated.)
- Clean, dry hair (yours or someone else's)
- Thread
- Scissors
- A tennis ball or baseball
- Two straight pins
- A pen or marker
- A paper plate
- A Ziploc bag

- Tape
- A large ball that bounces well. The ideal ball is a basketball, but it can be a soccer ball or any other ball that is pretty large and has a nice bounce to it.
- A ball that is much smaller than the first one – the smaller the better. A golf ball, for example, would be great.
- String
- Two washers or nuts
- A stopwatch
- A flashlight
- A straight piece of cardboard that is as wide as your bathtub and at least 10 centimeters (4 inches) tall
- A bathtub
- A turkey baster
- Milk (Whole milk is best, but any cow milk other than skim milk will work.)
- A pan and a stove for boiling water
- Four colors of food coloring (They need to be liquid, not gels.)
- A Q-tip
- Dishwashing soap
- A small bowl
- A large plate that can hold a thin layer of milk
- Two round balloons of the same size (Somewhere between 5-8 inch diameters work best)
- A hex head nut (This is the kind of nut that fits on a bolt and is tightened with a wrench. The nut has six flat sides on the outside.)
- A penny
- An old compact disc (CD) that can be completely ruined
- A candle that can stand on its own or is in a holder (It should make a large flame.)
- Something to light the candle
- A magnifying glass
- A 1½ meters (5 feet) length of string
- A plastic bottle (1-liter bottles are best, but a ½-liter bottle will do. It should be one you can ruin.)
- Some paperback books
- Two plastic bags
- A small jar, like a baby food jar.
- A funnel whose large opening is bigger than the jar
- Some Play-Doh
- A small balloon (It needs to fit inside the jar when it is just barely inflated.)
- A wall mirror
- A kitchen sponge it is okay to ruin
- Epsom salt (available at any drugstore)
- A pan
- A stove
- A spoon for stirring something hot
- Two bowls
- Two small plates
- Two small rocks
- A Slinky (It can be small or large, plastic or metal.)

🖐 A stepladder or platform that is a couple of meters (six feet) high and an easy place from which to drop objects.

Supplies for the Fifth Section (Lessons 61 – 75)

🖐 A mug used for hot beverages or a very well-insulated cup and a glove.
🖐 Water
🖐 A pan and stove for boiling water
🖐 A flashlight
🖐 A 30-centimeter (12-inch) length of string
🖐 A fresh tomato
🖐 A large pot for boiling water
🖐 A knife
🖐 A plastic container with a lid (like a Tupperware container) that is small enough to fit into the pot but large enough to hold half a tomato
🖐 Kitchen tongs
🖐 A piece of cardboard (no bigger than 18 cm [7 in] by 10 cm [4 in])
🖐 Clear plastic wrap
🖐 Tape
🖐 Scissors
🖐 A medicine dropper
🖐 A flower with petals that are light in color (White would be ideal, but any light color will do. A flower bought from a store will work, or you can pick one from outside.)
🖐 A small glass (like a juice glass)
🖐 Food coloring
🖐 Scissors
🖐 A spoon
🖐 A flower that looks something like a lily. It should have obvious stalks in the center, and one should be noticeably different from the rest (see picture on page 203).
🖐 Two plain white sheets of paper
🖐 A magnifying glass
🖐 A string of colored Christmas tree lights
🖐 A tapered candle that is 15 centimeters (6 inches) long or can be cut down to that length.
🖐 A lighter
🖐 Two tall glasses that are the same height
🖐 Aluminum foil
🖐 Two straight pins
🖐 A serrated knife (like a steak knife)
🖐 A pie pan or the top from a round storage tin
🖐 Two cardboard tubes from the center of a roll of toilet paper
🖐 Three cardboard tubes from rolls of paper towels
🖐 Eight uncooked eggs
🖐 A Ping-Pong ball
🖐 A metal hanger
🖐 A small plastic bottle, like the kind water comes in
🖐 A ¼-cup (or about 60 mL) measuring cup
🖐 A funnel

- A marker
- A stopwatch or a watch with a seconds hand
- A marble (A "shooter" marble that is larger than a standard marble is best. However, a standard marble will work.)
- A golf ball
- A straw (the kind you use to drink)
- A ruler
- A bag of small candies like Reese's Pieces, M&Ms, or Skittles
- A ½-cup measuring cup
- A measuring tablespoon
- An index card
- A pushpin
- A lamp that can be moved
- A wagon or anything else with wheels that you can stack things on and push (Even a chair with wheels will work.)
- A driveway or other long, flat surface over which the wagon can roll
- Several books that can be easily stacked on top of one another

Supplies for the Sixth Section (Lessons 76 – 90)

- A handheld hair dryer (It is best if the hair dryer has at least two settings, like "low" and "high.")
- A Ping-Pong ball
- A golf ball
- A paper or Styrofoam cup
- A stepladder
- A pen
- Water
- A long piece of string (Ideally, it should be long enough to stretch out along the longest hallway you have. You need something stronger than thread, but it needn't be really thick string.)
- A straw
- Two balloons
- Tape
- Several (at least 5) coins of the same value
- Two rulers (You can use just a single ruler if it has a thin groove in the center that will act as a track down which marbles can be rolled.)
- At least five marbles, all the same size
- A few heavy books
- A Styrofoam cup
- A stopwatch
- Water
- Karo corn syrup (Other brands would probably work.)
- A sink
- A pan
- A spoon for stirring
- A stove
- A pitcher, measuring cup, or some other container with a pour spout
- A square of aluminum foil that is about 5 centimeters x 5 centimeters (2 inches x 2 inches)

- A sewing needle
- A lump of Play-Doh or modeling clay
- Two paperback books that are roughly the same size and thickness
- An empty CD case
- About two meters (about six feet) of string
- A small plastic bag (like a Ziploc bag)
- At least 30 pennies
- A small plastic bottle with a lid (like the ones water comes in)
- A funnel
- A ¼-cup measuring cup
- A thin piece of cardboard (like you find on the back of a pad of paper)
- A toy car that doesn't have a motor
- Two chairs of the same height (or other heavy items to which string can be tied)
- A metal pot with a handle
- A metal spoon
- A coffee mug (The experiment is more dramatic if its breakable!)
- A length of string that is about as tall as you and strong enough to stop the mug if it falls
- Scissors
- A nut (the kind that threads on to a screw)
- A pencil
- A Styrofoam plate that has enough of a raised edge that it is a bit like a very shallow bowl
- A Styrofoam cup (the larger the better, but any size works)
- A pen
- A bathtub

Science in the Scientific Revolution
Table of Contents

end of 2ⁿᵈ quarter

Section 1: The Revolution Begins

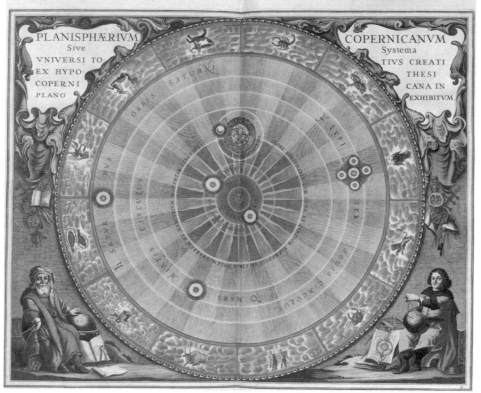

These drawings contrast the ancient view of the universe championed by Ptolemy (top) and the view that was a part of The Scientific Revolution, as championed by Copernicus (bottom).

Lessons 1-15: The Revolution Begins

Lesson 1: Nicolaus Copernicus (1473 – 1543)

Many science historians think that the 16th century (the era of the 1500s) marks the beginning of the **Scientific Revolution**. That's because a lot of great scientific discoveries were made and publicized during that time, and more importantly, those scientific discoveries would seriously change the way natural philosophers thought about the world around them. Some say they can even pinpoint the very year when the Scientific Revolution began: 1543. That's because two very important books were published that year.

This statue of Nicolaus Copernicus is in Toruń, the Polish city where he was born. Note the sun is at the center of the model he is holding.

The first book I want to discuss was written by **Nicolaus** (nik uh lay' us) **Copernicus** (koh pur' nih kus), a Polish astronomer. His book was titled *On the Revolutions of the Celestial Spheres*. If you studied Aristotle, you should understand the title. Aristotle thought that the planets were embedded in spheres that revolved around the earth. While Copernicus agreed with Aristotle about the spheres, he made a significant change to Aristotle's view: he put the sun at the center of the universe, while Aristotle had put the earth at the center.

The sun-centered system, called the **heliocentric system**, was not new. If you studied a natural philosopher named Aristarchus, you might remember that he suggested a sun-centered system around 230 B.C. However, the earth-centered system, also called the **geocentric system**, was considered the correct view by almost all natural philosophers in the 16th century. As a result, what Copernicus suggested was very controversial. In fact, it was so controversial that Copernicus was hesitant to publish it. However, most of his close friends and even one of the most important men in the Roman Catholic church at that time (former Cardinal Nikolaus von Schönberg) urged him to publish it. Because of the delay, however, he died either shortly after or just as the book was published. Historians are not sure which. There is no historical evidence to back this up, but legend has it that the first printed copy of the book was placed in his arms while he lay dying. According to the legend, he awoke from his coma, looked at the book, and then died peacefully.

Why did Copernicus suggest that the sun is at the center of the universe, instead of the earth? One key reason was that he believed God created the universe, and therefore, he thought that the universe should be very orderly. In his book he wrote that the machinery of the world "has been built for us by the Best and Most Orderly Workman of all." However, the geocentric view of the universe was very messy. If you studied the work of the ancient natural philosopher known as Ptolemy (c. AD 90 – c. AD 168), you know that the geocentric view of the universe had to have several epicycles added to it in order to make it consistent with most of the observations astronomers had made. That made it very complicated, which didn't fit well with Copernicus's view of God as an "Orderly Workman." Copernicus's arrangement of the universe was more orderly and pleasing to the eye.

Also, Copernicus's arrangement could explain some observations that had always puzzled astronomers who believed in the geocentric system. For example, the planets that astronomers knew about during the 16th century were Mercury, Venus, Mars, Jupiter, and Saturn. They noticed that Mars, Jupiter, and Saturn could appear in the eastern sky right after the sun set in the west. However, Mercury and Venus never appeared in the eastern sky after sunset. When they appeared in sky after sunset, it was always in the west. That was hard to explain in the geocentric system. Do the following activity to understand why.

Where are Mercury and Venus?

What you will need:
- A square or rectangle of cardboard that is larger than a paper plate
- Three paper plates
- A nail
- Scissors
- Crayons, colored pencils, or markers
- A small amount of modeling clay, like Play-Doh
- An adult to help you

What you should do:
1. Draw a large red dot near the edge of one of the paper plates.
2. Cut a circle out of the other paper plate that is about half as big around as the plate.
3. Draw a large blue dot near the edge of the circle you just cut out of the paper plate.
4. Cut a circle out of the third paper plate that is about half as big around as the one you cut in step 2.
5. Draw a large green dot near the edge of that circle.
6. Have an adult help you stick a nail through the center of the square of cardboard.
7. Have an adult help you stick the paper plate with the red dot on it into the point of the nail so that the nail goes through the center of the plate.
8. Repeat step 7 for the circle with the blue dot and then the circle with the green dot.
9. Make a small ball of clay and stick it on the pointed end of the nail. Your model should now look like the picture above.
10. Let's start by thinking about a geocentric system. In that case, the ball of clay is the earth, the green dot is a planet, the blue dot is the sun, and the red dot is another planet.
11. Spin the circles so that all three dots line up above the ball of clay, as shown in the picture above.
12. Imagine the sun is setting in the west. If you are on the ball of clay (the earth) and face towards the sun (the blue dot) and wait for it to get dark, where will the planets appear when they are arranged like this? You will be facing them, so they will appear in the western sky, where the sun just set.
13. Keeping the blue dot where it is, move the red and green dots so they are below the ball of clay.
14. Once again, imagine that the sun is setting in the west. When the planets are arranged like this, where will they appear in the night sky? Think about standing on the earth (the ball of clay) and facing the sun (the blue dot). The planets will be behind you, so they will appear behind you in the eastern sky.
15. Now let's assume this is a heliocentric system. In that case, the ball is the sun, the green dot is a planet, the blue dot is earth, and the red dot is another planet.
16. Arrange the circles so all the dots are lined up like they are in the picture above.
17. Now where will the two planets appear in the sky when the sun sets? Remember, you are on the blue dot (earth). Imagine standing on that blue dot and facing the sun (the ball of clay). You are facing the green dot, so it will appear in the western sky. However, the red dot is behind you, so it will appear in the eastern sky.

18. Keeping the blue dot (the earth) where it is, move the red and green dots so they are below the ball of clay.
19. Now where will the two planets appear in the night sky right after sunset? If you think of yourself standing on the blue dot and facing the ball of clay, both dots will be in front of you, so they will appear in front of you, or in the west.
20. Play with the model a bit and notice that while the red dot can appear in the eastern sky at sunset, because you can arrange it to be behind the blue dot, the green dot cannot. There is just no way to arrange things so the green dot is behind the blue dot.
21. Keep your model, because you will use it again in the next lesson.

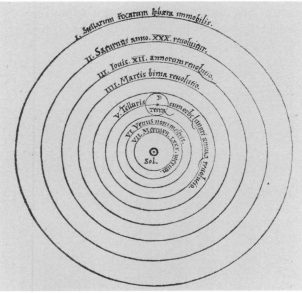

This drawing comes from Copernicus's book. It shows his view of the universe, with the sun (Sol) at the center, and the planets orbiting the sun in circles in the following order: Mercury (closest to the sun), Venus, earth, Mars, Jupiter, and Saturn. In his view, the stars were farthest from the sun and did not move.

Why did I have you do all that? Well, as you saw, if the earth is at the center, when the planets are arranged correctly, they can be seen in the eastern sky at sunset. Ancient astronomers could find Mars, Jupiter, and Saturn in the eastern sky at sunset during certain times of the year. However, Venus and Mercury *never* appear in the eastern sky at sunset. Mercury appears low in the western sky at sunset when it does appear, and Venus appears a bit higher in the western sky at sunset. Neither of them ever appears in the eastern sky at sunset, however.

This was a real puzzle for the geocentric system, but it made perfect sense in the heliocentric system. Venus and Mercury never appear in the eastern sky at sunset because they are between the sun and the earth. As a result, there is never a time when the sun is on one side of the earth and Mercury or Venus is on the other side. Because of this, Mercury and Venus can never be in the opposite sky as the sun. Since Mercury usually appeared lower than Venus in the western sky at sunset (closer to the sun), Copernicus decided that it was the planet closest to the sun. This provided an arrangement of planets that allowed astronomers to finally understand why finding Mercury and Venus at sunset was so different from finding the other planets that were known at the time.

LESSON REVIEW

Youngest students: Answer these questions:

1. What was controversial about Copernicus's book? Heliocentrical

2. Fill in the blank: Copernicus put the planet mercury closest to the sun.

Older students: Make a drawing of Copernicus's view of how the sun, planets, and stars are arranged. Explain how it was different from the view of most natural philosophers of that time.

Oldest students: Do what the older students are doing. In addition, use the heliocentric system to explain why Mercury and Venus never appear in the eastern sky just after sunset.

Lesson 2: More Evidence for the Heliocentric System

As I told you in Lesson 1, Copernicus believed in the heliocentric system because it was a more orderly, elegant system than the geocentric system, which was the accepted view in his time. In addition, it could explain certain observations that the geocentric system could not explain. You learned one of those observations in the previous lesson. Now, let's learn another.

Astronomers of Copernicus's day understood that the planets which were known at the time (Mercury, Venus, Mars, Jupiter, and Saturn) shine in the night sky because they reflect light from the sun. Astronomers also knew that their brightness in the night sky varies. Mars, Jupiter, and Saturn are brightest when they appear in the eastern sky just after the sun sets, and they are dimmest when they appear in the western sky just after the sun sets. In the geocentric system this is puzzling, but it makes sense in a heliocentric system. Do the following activity to understand why.

Planetary Brightness

What you will need:
- The model you used in the previous lesson
- An adult to help you

What you should do:
1. Have an adult help you remove the ball of clay (which might be hard – that's fine) from the nail.
2. Remove the smallest circle (the one with the green dot) from the model so that it has only the red and blue dots on it, as shown on the right.
3. Replace the ball of clay so it is on top of the nail.
4. Line the dots up as you see in the picture, with the blue dot and red dot right above the ball of clay.
5. Imagine that the ball of clay is the earth, the blue dot is the sun, and the red dot is Mars. That's how the geocentric system had them arranged. Obviously, there are a lot more planets, but we are just concentrating on Mars for now. Since Mars travels around the earth in a circle in this model, it is always the same distance from the earth. However, since the sun also travels around the earth, the distance between the sun and Mars changes. As you have your model arranged right now, the sun is closest to Mars, right? That's when Mars should be the brightest, because it is closest to the sun. As the sun sets in the west, where will Mars appear in the night sky? Think about standing on the ball of clay and looking at the sun as it sets. When it finally sets, Mars will appear right in front of you, because you are facing Mars. That means it will appear in the western sky. In the geocentric system, then, Mars is *brightest* when it appears in the *western* sky at sunset.
6. Move the circle with the blue dot so that it is directly below the ball of clay. If the plate with the red dot moved, move it back so the red dot is still directly above the ball of clay. In this arrangement, Mars is still the same distance from earth, but it is now far from the sun, which means it will be dim. Where will Mars appear in the night sky as the sun sets? Think about standing on the ball of clay and looking at the sun as it sets. When the sun sets, Mars will be behind you, so it will appear in the eastern sky. In the geocentric system, then, Mars is *dimmest* when it appears in the *eastern* sky at sunset.
7. Reset your model so that both dots are above the ball of clay. Now imagine that the ball of clay is the sun, the blue dot is the earth, and the red dot is Mars (as they would be in the heliocentric system). In this arrangement, Mars is always the same distance from the sun, but its distance from earth changes. It will appear brightest, then, when it is closest to the earth. That's what you have

right now. The blue dot (earth) and the red dot (Mars) are as close as they can get to one another. So Mars will appear brightest with this arrangement. Where will it appear in the sky at sunset? Think about standing on the blue dot and looking at the sun as it sets. When the sun sets, Mars will be behind you, so it will appear in the eastern sky. In the heliocentric system, then, Mars will be *brightest* when it appears in the *eastern* sky at sunset.

8. Move the circle with the blue dot so that it is below the ball of clay. If the plate with the red dot moved, move it back so the red dot is still directly above the ball of clay. Now think about the brightness of Mars. It is the farthest it can be from the earth, so it will look dim. Where will it appear in the sky right after sunset? Think about standing on the blue dot and looking at the sun. When the sun sets, Mars will be right in front of you, because it is in the same direction from earth as the sun. So it will appear in the western sky right after sunset. In the heliocentric system, then, Mars will be *dimmest* when it appears in the *western* sky at sunset.

9. After you are done with the lesson, you can put your model away or tear it apart and clean up your mess.

Now remember, astronomers knew that Mars appears brightest when it is in the *eastern* sky at sunset, and it appears dimmest when it is in the *western* sky at sunset. The heliocentric system explained why, but the geocentric system could not. In fact, the geocentric system suggested the opposite. If you had included Jupiter and Saturn in your model as well, you would have found the same thing. For any of those planets, the heliocentric system explained when they were brightest and when they were dimmest, while the geocentric system suggested the opposite of what was observed. This added more evidence to Copernicus's view that the heliocentric system was the correct arrangement of the universe.

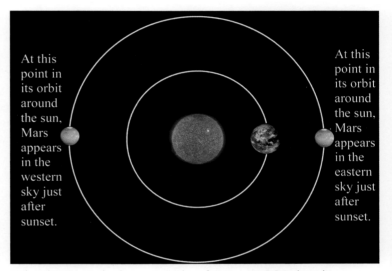

At this point in its orbit around the sun, Mars appears in the western sky just after sunset.

At this point in its orbit around the sun, Mars appears in the eastern sky just after sunset.

When it appears in the eastern sky after sunset, Mars is at its brightest, because it is closest to the earth. When it appears in the western sky after sunset, it is dimmer, because it is farther from the earth. This can only be understood in the heliocentric system. In scientific terms, we would say that Mars is in opposition to the sun on the right side of this illustration.

When a planet is on the opposite side of the earth as the sun, scientists say that it is in **opposition** to the sun. That doesn't mean it's fighting against the sun, of course. It just means that the earth is between the planet and the sun, so when the sun sets in the west, the planet appears in the opposite sky: the eastern sky. In scientific terms, then, scientists would say that Mars, Jupiter, and Saturn are brightest when they are in opposition to the sun.

If you studied Ptolemy's geocentric system, you might remember the problem of **retrograde motion**. When astronomers followed the planets' motion across the night sky for a long period of time, they noticed that a given planet would start out traveling in one direction, but then it would appear to stop and reverse direction for a while. Then it would stop again and reverse direction again! In order to explain this problem, Ptolemy added epicycles to his system. Those epicycles made the geocentric system messy, which bothered Copernicus. He was able to get rid of a lot of those epicycles, because retrograde motion would be a natural consequence of observing the planets from a moving earth.

Think, for example, about Mars and what it would look like from earth in a heliocentric system. Mars takes about 687 days to make one orbit around the sun, while earth takes just over 365 days. This means that the earth travels around the sun faster than Mars. So, while Mars is making its orbit, earth will overtake and pass Mars. Think about what that means for someone observing Mars from earth.

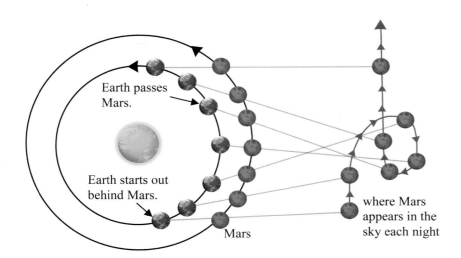

Look at the diagram on the left. It shows earth and Mars during several specific times in their orbits around the earth. Near the bottom of the drawing, earth is behind Mars. However, because it is traveling faster, it eventually catches up with Mars and passes it. The blue lines show the direction a person at the same place on the earth would have to look to see Mars, and the red curve shows how this would make Mars's motion appear in the night sky.

Because earth travels faster in its orbit than Mars, someone observing Mars from earth will see Mars move in one direction in the night sky, reverse direction, and then reverse direction again. That's why planets have retrograde motion.

Do you see what the diagram shows? If someone were looking at Mars from the earth, he would see it moving one way, reversing direction, and then later on, reversing direction again. In other words, it shows retrograde motion! This told Copernicus that retrograde motion is a consequence of the fact that the earth is moving. Rather than requiring a "fix" like epicycles, as the geocentric system did, the heliocentric system actually explained retrograde motion directly. Combined with the behavior of Venus and Mercury in the night sky and the fact that Mars, Jupiter, and Saturn were brightest in the eastern sky after sunset, this produced what Copernicus saw as a strong case for his heliocentric system.

LESSON REVIEW

Youngest students: Answer these questions:

1. Fill in the blank: Mars is _____ when it appears in the eastern sky right after sunset.

2. What do we call it when a planet appears to be moving one direction in the night sky, then changes direction, and then later on changes direction again?

Older students: Make a drawing that represents your model during steps 4 and 5. Make another drawing for step 6, another for step 7, and another for step 8. Label the sun, earth, and Mars in each drawing, and under each one, indicate the brightness of Mars and where it appears in the sky right after sunset. Indicate that the last two drawings, which are based on the heliocentric system, are the ones consistent with what is observed.

Oldest students: Do what the older students are doing. In addition, make a drawing like the one above to show why the heliocentric system explains retrograde motion.

Lesson 3: Objections to the Heliocentric System

As you learned in the previous lessons, Copernicus was convinced that the heliocentric system was the correct way to understand the universe. Not only was it simpler and more elegant than the geocentric system, it could also explain some observations that the geocentric system could not explain, such as why Mars, Jupiter, and Saturn were brightest when they appeared in the eastern sky just after sunset.

While this was nice, one of the most important things astronomers wanted to do at the time was to predict where the planets would be in the future. They thought that if they could accurately predict where the planets would be several years in the future, that would show they had a good understanding of how the sun, moon, planets, and stars behaved. Unfortunately, the heliocentric system as developed by Copernicus did no better at predicting the future positions of the planets than the geocentric system did. It was no worse, but it was also no better.

This made natural philosophers skeptical of Copernicus's view. After all, if his view were correct, shouldn't it predict the future positions of the planets better? Well, it turns out that the heliocentric system Copernicus constructed wasn't quite correct. You will learn why later. For right now, you just need to know that the errors in his system made it just as unreliable as the geocentric system when it came to predicting the future positions of the planets in the night sky.

There was another reason natural philosophers were skeptical of his view. If Copernicus were correct, natural philosophers understood that they should observe something called **parallax** (pehr' uh lacks) when they looked at stars during different times of the year. To understand what that is, do the following experiment.

Parallax

What you will need:
- Two metersticks, yardsticks, or thin pieces of wood
- A hallway
- Someone to help you

What you should do:
1. Have your helper hold a meterstick in each hand.
2. Have your helper stand at one end of the hallway.
3. Stand half a meter (about one and a half feet) down the hallway from your helper.
4. Have your helper hold the metersticks at arm's length to one side of his or her body. They should be held so that their thin sides face toward you. You, your helper, and the metersticks should now be arranged as you see in the picture on the right.
5. Close one eye. It doesn't matter which.
6. Move to the left or right (but not towards or away from your helper) until the metersticks are perfectly lined up. When this happens, the meterstick nearest you should completely block the view of the other meterstick.
7. Once you have the two metersticks perfectly lined up, open your other eye and close the one that was open.

8. Are the metersticks still perfectly lined up?
9. Walk backwards (looking behind you as you walk) so you are farther from your helper and about halfway down the hall.
10. Repeat steps 5-8. How is the result different from what you saw before?
11. Walk as far backwards as the hallway will allow so that you are as far from your helper as possible.
12. Repeat steps 5-8. How is the result different this time?
13. If you can't tell a difference, walk towards your helper so that you are once again just half a meter from him or her and repeat steps 5-8. You should notice a big difference from when you were far from your helper.
14. Put away the metersticks.

What did you see in your experiment? You should have seen that when you lined up the two metersticks with one eye, they were not lined up when you used the other eye to look at them. However, the effect should have lessened the farther you got away from your helper. When you were close to your helper, the metersticks appeared far apart from one another when you used your other eye to look at them. When you were far from your helper, however, the metersticks were not nearly as far apart when you looked at them with your other eye.

What does this have to do with the heliocentric system? In the experiment, the two metersticks represented two stars that, according to Copernicus, never moved. Your eyes represented the earth, which orbits around the sun. When you looked at the metersticks with one eye, it was like you were looking at two stars when the earth was at one point in its orbit around the sun. When you used the other eye, it was like you were looking at the same two stars when the earth was at a different point in its orbit around the sun. Because you were looking at them from a slightly different angle, the result was that they seemed to change their positions compared to one another.

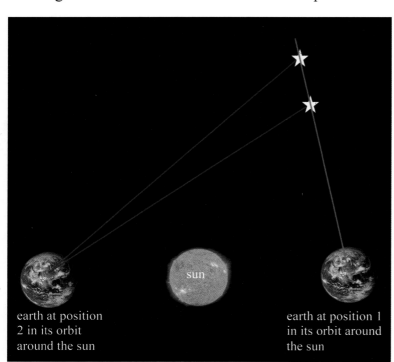

earth at position 2 in its orbit around the sun

sun

earth at position 1 in its orbit around the sun

Because the earth orbits the sun, the stars seem to change positions relative to each other. This is called parallax.

This is called parallax, and it is illustrated in the drawing on the left. Imagine you are on the earth at position 1 and are looking at the two stars in the drawing. The first star will be right in front of the second one, which means you probably won't even see the second star. However, if you wait six months, the earth will be on the opposite side of the sun (position 2), because it makes one complete orbit around the sun every year. If you looked at the first star at that time, you would see that it appears to be to the right of the second star instead of directly in front of it.

Natural philosophers pointed out that when they viewed the stars, the stars did not change positions in this way as the year progressed. In other words, the heliocentric system should produce parallax when viewing the stars, but according to observations back then, it didn't. Most considered this strong evidence against the heliocentric system.

Copernicus had an answer against this objection, however. Remember what happened in your experiment when you moved away from your helper and repeated the procedure. The shift in position decreased, didn't it? The farther you were from your helper, the less the two metersticks shifted position when you looked at them with the other eye. That's because the farther away you are from the things you are observing, the smaller the effect of parallax becomes.

Copernicus said that the reason natural philosophers couldn't see the parallax that the heliocentric system predicts is because the stars are very, very far away from the earth. As a result, the effect of parallax is very, very small, and they simply couldn't notice it. While that turned out to be the correct answer, most natural philosophers at the time thought the universe was pretty small. Because of this, they were unwilling to believe the stars were really that far from the earth. As a result, they used the lack of parallax as a reason against believing in Copernicus's heliocentric system.

Now, please understand that with today's scientific instruments, we can, indeed, see the parallax that is predicted in the heliocentric system. In fact, we can use that parallax to actually measure how far away certain stars are from the earth. As a result, it has helped us to get a good idea of how big the universe is!

This telescope image shows three stars whose distances from earth have been measured by parallax. Altair is 160 trillion kilometers (100 trillion miles) from the earth, Vega is 240 trillion kilometers (150 trillion miles) from the earth, and Deneb is 2,500 trillion kilometers (1,500 trillion miles) from earth. No one in Copernicus's time thought stars could be so far from the earth.

LESSON REVIEW

Youngest students: Answer these questions:

1. (Is this statement True or False?) Copernicus's system predicted the future positions of the planets better than the geocentric system.

2. Fill in the blank with just one word: The heliocentric system predicts that you will see _____ if you view two stars at different times of the year.

Older students: In this lesson, you learned two arguments that natural philosophers used against Copernicus's system. Summarize them.

Oldest students: Do what the older students are doing. In addition, make a drawing like the one on page 8 and then use it to explain parallax in your own words. Also indicate why natural philosophers didn't see parallax in Copernicus's day.

Lesson 4: Another Objection to the Heliocentric System

As you learned in the previous lesson, most of the natural philosophers of Copernicus's day had problems with the heliocentric system. Since it didn't do any better than the geocentric system when it came to predicting the motion of the planets, they thought it couldn't have been any more correct. Also, they thought that the heliocentric system should produce parallax when viewing the stars, but they saw none. There was one other objection, however, and among some natural philosophers, it was the most important. At that time, most Christians thought the Bible taught that the earth does not move. Do the following activity to see why.

What the Bible Says About the Earth Moving

What you will need:
✋ A Bible

What you should do:
1. Read 1 Chronicles 16:29-30.
2. What do these verses say about the earth moving? *it will & be moved*
3. Read Psalm 93:1-2.
4. What do these verses say about the earth moving? *firmly est.*
5. Read Psalm 96:10.
6. What does this verse say about the earth moving? *shall & be moved*

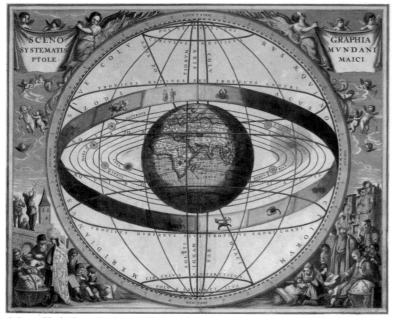

Most Christians in Copernicus's day thought the geocentric view was supported by Scripture, as they thought Scripture says the earth doesn't move. Also, putting earth at the center of the universe increased its importance, as demonstrated by how big the earth is in this drawing of the geocentric system.

Can you see why Christians didn't like the idea of the heliocentric system back in Copernicus's day? When you read each of the verses in the activity above, what was the impression you got? Those verses really seem to say that the earth doesn't move, don't they? Indeed, virtually all theologians of Copernicus's day thought the Bible taught that the earth doesn't move. In the heliocentric system, however, the earth does move. Not only does it orbit the sun, but it rotates so that night turns into day. That's two kinds of motion! Most Christians in Copernicus's day simply could not accept the idea of a moving earth, because it seemed to go against the verses of Scripture you read.

There was another Biblical issue as well. The Bible clearly states that people are very important to God. In Psalm 8:5, we read this about man: "Yet You have made him a little lower than the angels, and You crown him with glory and majesty!" So the Bible says that man has been given an honored place in creation. In addition, people are so important to God that He sent His only Son to die for us (John 3:16). Since people are so important to God, it only makes sense to conclude that the place they live (earth) would be at the center of the universe. So not only does the Bible seem to teach that the earth doesn't move, but it also seems to imply that earth should occupy a special place in the heavens.

However, it is important to understand that there is another way to interpret the verses you read in the activity. To see what I mean, consider a song that was popular in the 1930s. It is called "We Shall Not Be Moved," and it is thought to have been written during the time of slavery in the United States. It was sung by slaves, but in the 1930s, it was adapted to be used by workers who thought that they were being taken advantage of by the companies that employed them. They formed a union of workers to fight for their rights, and they often sang the song to inspire their fellow workers. Here is a part of the song:

> The union is behind us,
> We shall not be moved.
> Just like a tree that's standing by the water,
> We shall not be moved.
> We will stand and fight together,
> We shall not be moved.

The song was later changed again and used by people in the United States' Civil Rights movement during the 1960s.

What is the message of the song? Is it that the people who are singing it will never move? Are they really saying that they will stand still like a tree and never walk, run, or dance? Of course not! They are saying that they will not be moved from their purpose, which was to fight for the rights of the workers (or later on, for civil rights). Indeed, the workers often waved their arms and swayed when they sang that song. So they were physically moving even as they sang, "We shall not be moved." In the end, saying they will not be moved was simply a poetic way of saying that they were not going to abandon their purpose.

This picture was taken at the famous "March on Washington" that was held in 1963. The man at the center is Martin Luther King, Jr., who was a major figure in the Civil Rights movement. During this march, the people sang, "We Shall Not Be Moved." Obviously, they were moving, because they were marching on Washington. The phrase meant that they would not abandon their purpose of gaining civil rights for all Americans.

Now let's think about the verses you read again. Do you know what the book of Psalms is? The word "psalm" actually means "a sacred song or hymn." So the book of Psalms is actually a collection of songs! That means two of the verses you read in your activity come from a collection of songs. What about the verse from 1 Chronicles 16? If you go back and look at verse 7, you will read, "Then on that day David first assigned Asaph and his relatives to give thanks to the LORD." The following verses (8-36) make up a psalm of thanksgiving that was offered to the Lord.

So all the verses you read really come from songs. As a result, you can expect the words to be poetic. Since the idea of something being unmoving is a poetic way of saying that it will not abandon its purpose, another very proper way to understand these verses is to understand that the earth will not abandon its purpose. Since its purpose is to provide a home for people, those verses can mean that earth will never stop being a home for people.

Each light in this picture taken by the Hubble telescope represents a huge collection of stars in a small portion of the universe. The universe is enormous, but God is everywhere in the universe, because He is omnipresent.

What about the idea that the earth has to be at the center of the universe in order to indicate that people are special to God? There is no reason to think that the center of the universe is any more important to God than anywhere else. Remember, God is **omnipresent** (Jeremiah 23:24, Psalm 139:7-10). What does that mean? It means He is everywhere all the time. As a result, it's not at all clear that God thinks the center of the universe is any more special than anywhere else, because He is everywhere.

So in the end, the Biblical objections that people raised in Copernicus's day weren't really accurate. The Bible is a very deep, very meaningful book. After all, it is God's revelation to man. Because of this, it is important to be careful in how you interpret it. As you will see later on in this book, most Christians eventually put away the incorrect interpretations of the Bible that led them to believe that the earth doesn't physically move. However, it took quite a while for that to happen.

LESSON REVIEW

Youngest students: Answer these questions:

1. (Is this statement True or False?) The Bible teaches that the earth does not physically move.

2. What does the word "omnipresent" mean? Who is omnipresent?

Older students: Explain in your own words why the Bible doesn't teach that the earth is stationary in space. Also, explain why there is probably nothing special to God about the center of the universe.

Oldest students: Do what the older students are doing. In addition, read Joshua 10:1-13. Those who argued against Copernicus often used this verse to say that the Bible teaches the sun moves in space. Talk to a pastor or parent to learn why that's not a proper interpretation of the verse. Write the explanation in your own words.

Lesson 5: Andreas Vesalius (1514 – 1564)

Copernicus's work was not really appreciated when it was published. However, future natural philosophers were influenced by his book, and they went on to provide more evidence for the heliocentric system. We now turn to the other important book that was published in 1543, *On the Fabric of the Human Body*, which was written by a Belgian physician named **Andreas** (ahn dray' us) **Vesalius** (vih say' lee us), who taught human anatomy at a few different universities.

This portrait of Andreas Vesalius appears in his book, *On the Fabric of the Human Body*.

You might have learned about a natural philosopher named Galen (AD 129 – c. AD 200). He tried to understand anatomy, but he did so by dissecting (cutting up and looking inside) dead animals. He wanted to dissect dead people as well, but the Roman government (under which he lived) didn't allow that. Since he assumed that his observations of animals could be directly applied to people, he made a lot of mistakes. During Vesalius's time, Galen was still considered the main authority on human anatomy, but Vesalius started noticing his mistakes. When he pointed these out, many people got angry, because they didn't like the idea of some young man (Vesalius was 28 when his book was printed) correcting the work of someone who had been well respected for more than 1,300 years!

Vesalius didn't care what such people thought, however. He wanted his students (and anyone who dealt with medicine) to know the truth about human anatomy. As a result, he wrote a series of corrections to Galen's main work, and he decided to write his own textbook on human anatomy so that students could learn from a more accurate source. To emphasize the mistakes in Galen's work, Vesalius publicly dissected the body of a dead felon from the city of Basel, Switzerland and used the dissection to show that Galen was wrong about a lot of things! Perform the following experiment to see one of the many things Galen was wrong about.

The Length of Certain Bones

What you will need:
- A meterstick, yardstick, or ruler
- Someone to help you

What you should do:
1. Have your helper bend his or her arm at the elbow and hold it out to one side.

2. Measure the distance between your helper's elbow and shoulder, and write the number down, indicating what it is.
3. Have your helper sit on a chair with his or her feet resting flat on the floor.
4. The way your helper is sitting, his or her knees should be bent. This makes it very easy to see where the knee is.
5. Measure the distance between your helper's knee and hip, and write the number down, indicating what it is.
6. Measure the distance between your helper's knee and ankle, and write the number down, indicating what it is.
7. Put away the meterstick.

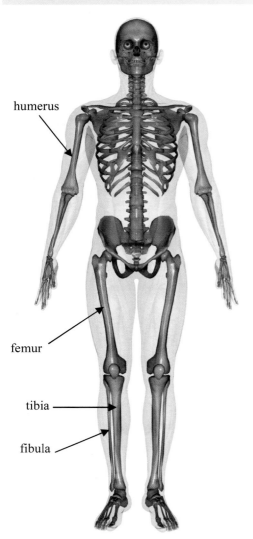

humerus

femur

tibia

fibula

This drawing shows the major bones in the human skeleton.

Even though you couldn't see them, you and your helper actually measured the length of certain bones. If you look at the drawing of the skeleton to the left, you will see that the bone between the shoulder and elbow is called the **humerus** (hyoo' muh rus). So measuring the distance between the shoulder and elbow is one way to estimate the length of the humerus. In the same way, the bone that goes between the hip and the knee is the **femur**, so by measuring that distance, you estimated the length of the femur. There are two bones that go between the knee and ankle: the **tibia** (tib' ee uh) and **fibula** (fib' yuh luh). The fibula is not as long as the tibia, however, so measuring the distance between the knee and ankle estimates the length of the tibia. Now, of course, none of the lengths you measured are perfect, because you couldn't see the actual bones to measure them. Nevertheless, what you did gives a good estimate for the bone lengths.

Which bone was the longest? You should see that the longest distance you measured was between the hip and the knee. That tells you the femur is the longest bone in the body. You should have seen that the distance between the knee and ankle was the second longest, which tells you that the tibia is the second longest of the three bones whose lengths you estimated. Finally, the distance between the shoulder and elbow was the shortest, so of those three bones, the humerus is the shortest.

Why is this important? Well, Galen's work says quite specifically that the femur is the longest bone in the body, and the humerus is the next longest bone in the body. However, Vesalius knew this just wasn't correct. By dissecting dead people, Vesalius was able to remove the bones and measure each one quite carefully. When he did so, he always found that the tibia and fibula were longer than the humerus. Thus, while Galen said that the humerus was the second-longest bone in the body, it is not. Why did Galen make such a mistake? Because he couldn't directly measure human bones. However, he could directly measure the bones of apes. He tried to apply what he learned about apes to humans, but it didn't always work.

Galen was also wrong about the human **sternum** (stur' num), which is commonly called the breastbone. In adult apes, the sternum is made up of seven different bones. As a result, Galen taught that the sternum in adult people is also composed of seven different bones. However, based on his dissections, Vesalius knew this wasn't correct. Instead, the human sternum is composed of only three bones: the manubrium (muh noo' bree uhm), gladiolus (glad ee oh' lus), and xiphoid (zif' oyd) process.

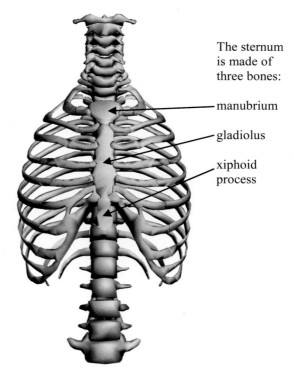

The sternum is made of three bones:

manubrium

gladiolus

xiphoid process

Since I am talking about a bone that is found on the ribcage, I might as well mention something else that Vesalius corrected. It wasn't one of Galen's ideas, but it was a very common belief in his day. Because the Bible says that God took a rib from Adam in order to make Eve (Genesis 2:21-22), it was commonly believed that men had one fewer rib as compared to women. Vesalius showed that this simply was not the case. Women and men have the same number of ribs.

This drawing shows a human ribcage, including the sternum.

Knowing what we know now about modern medicine, there is no reason to think that women and men have a different number of ribs. Suppose that before you were born, your father had gone through a surgical procedure in which one of his ribs had to be removed. Does that mean you would be born with one less rib than your friends? Of course not! When someone's body is modified by surgery, those modifications aren't passed on to his or her children. So even though Adam did have one of his ribs removed, there is no reason to think that his male children would also be missing a rib.

Of course, the people of Vesalius's time didn't understand that, but they couldn't deny the plain fact that when Vesalius actually counted the number of ribs in the dead men and women he dissected, the number of ribs was the same.

LESSON REVIEW

Youngest students: Answer these questions:

1. Order the following bones in terms of their lengths in the human body, starting with the shortest: femur, humerus, tibia.

2. (Is this statement True or False?) Men and women have the same number of ribs.

Older students: Write about how Vesalius corrected Galen regarding the length of the humerus and the number of bones in the sternum. Explain why Galen made those mistakes and how Vesalius discovered that Galen was wrong.

Oldest students: Do what the older students are doing. In addition, write about how Vesalius corrected the mistaken idea that men have one less rib than women. Explain where the idea came from and why it doesn't make sense based on what we know now.

Lesson 6: Cartilage and Bones

In the previous lesson, you learned about two mistakes that were made by Galen and corrected by Vesalius. Vesalius corrected many other mistakes made by Galen, and you'll learn about another one in this lesson. Before you learn about that, however, you probably noticed that so far, I have been talking about the skeleton. That's because the first part of Vesalius's book was all about the skeleton. Vesalius was fascinated by bone. In fact, here's how he described it at the beginning of his discussion of the skeleton:

> Bone is the hardest and driest of all parts of the human body, the most earthy and cold, and, with the sole exception of the teeth, most lacking in sensation. God, the supreme maker of things, rightly made its substance of this temperament so as to supply the entire body with a kind of foundation. For what walls and beams provide in houses, poles in tents, and keels and ribs in ships, the substance of bones provides in the fabric of man. [*On the Fabric of the Human Body*, translated by Daniel Garrison and Malcolm Hast, Book 1, Chapter 1]

So Vesalius correctly understood that bone was made by God in order to provide support for the body, much like walls and beams provide support for a house.

At the same time, however, Vesalius understood that there was more to the skeleton than just bone. In fact, the second chapter in his section on the skeleton is all about **cartilage** (kar' tih lej). To give you a good idea of what cartilage is, perform the following experiment.

Hyaline Cartilage

top (part of the knee joint)

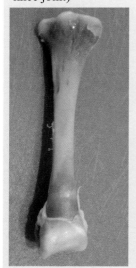

bottom (part of the ankle joint)

What you will need:
- A fresh chicken drumstick (uncooked)
- A knife
- A cutting board
- A pushpin
- An adult to help you

What you should do:
1. Have an adult help you remove the skin and meat from the drumstick. In the end, the only thing you want left is the large bone that is found at the very center of the drumstick. It should look something like the picture on the left.
2. This is the tibia of the chicken. If you noticed a thin bone that broke off as you were pulling the meat away from the bone, that was the fibula.
3. Look at the top end of the bone and the bottom end of the bone. Do you see that the bone is "capped" on both ends by white tissue?
4. Slide your finger along the white tissue and then along the rest of the bone. Do you feel any difference?
5. Push the pushpin into the white tissue on one end of the bone. **Be careful!** If the pushpin slips, it could stick one of your fingers! Repeat this on the white tissue at the other end of the bone.
6. Try to push the pushpin into the bone at several places where there is no white tissue. Do you notice a difference between this and what happened in step 5?
7. Clean up your mess and dispose of the chicken meat and bone as instructed by your parent/teacher.

What did you notice about the ends of the bone compared to the rest of it? If your fingers were sensitive enough, you should have noticed that the white tissue at the ends of the bone was smoother than the bone itself. In addition, you should have noticed a big difference between how the pushpin went into the white tissue and the rest of the bone. While you probably couldn't get it to sink into the bone (at least not without a lot of effort), it sank more easily into the white tissue, didn't it?

As you've probably already guessed, the white tissue on the ends of the bone is cartilage. Vesalius noted that cartilage is hard, but not nearly as hard as bone. Because it is soft, it is more flexible than bone. What does cartilage do in the skeleton? Well, there are three different kinds of cartilage, and they perform different functions in the body.

The cartilage you saw in your experiment is called **hyaline** (hi' uh lun) **cartilage**. It is found in joints. As you've probably already learned, the joints in your skeleton allow you to move and bend your body. They are the places where two bones come together and move relative to one another. Because the bones move in the joints, they rub against each other. If the joint had bone rubbing on bone, it would not move well and would quickly become painful, because bone is hard. To keep this from happening, God capped the ends of the bones in joints with hyaline cartilage. Because it is smoother and softer than bone, it moves more easily and painlessly in a joint.

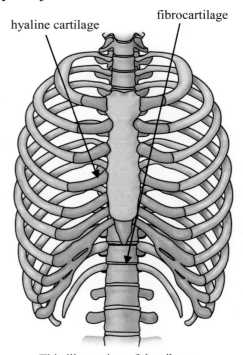

hyaline cartilage

fibrocartilage

Hyaline cartilage is also used to make certain structures in your body. For example, look at the ribcage illustrated on the right. The purple tissue that connects the ribs to the sternum is made of hyaline cartilage. Since the cartilage is flexible, it allows the ribcage to expand when you breathe in and contract when you breathe out.

A second type of cartilage is **fibrocartilage** (fye' broh kar' tih lej). It is found in joints that require the bones to be held together but cushioned. The individual bones in your spine (which you probably know are called vertebrae) are cushioned with fibrocartilage, as shown by the pale purple tissue in the illustration on the right.

Finally, there is **elastic cartilage**. It is the most flexible form of cartilage, and it is found on parts of the body that need to be really flexible. Grab the top of your ear. Pull down so the top of your ear bends. Now release it. What happens? Your ear pops right back into its normal shape, right? That's because your external ear (the part of the ear that is on the outside of your head) is made of elastic cartilage.

This illustration of the ribcage shows two types of cartilage.

You can feel the difference between bone, hyaline cartilage, and elastic cartilage by pinching your nose right between your eyes, where it attaches to your face. That's bone between your fingers. Now pull your fingers down but keep pinching. You should eventually feel a ridge. That's the end of your nasal bone. Directly below that ridge, your nose is made of hyaline cartilage. Pull your fingers down farther and you will come to the part of your nose that wiggles. That's elastic cartilage.

There is one other thing that is interesting about cartilage. Your body can make it into bone! In fact, when you are developing inside your mother, your skeleton starts out as cartilage. However,

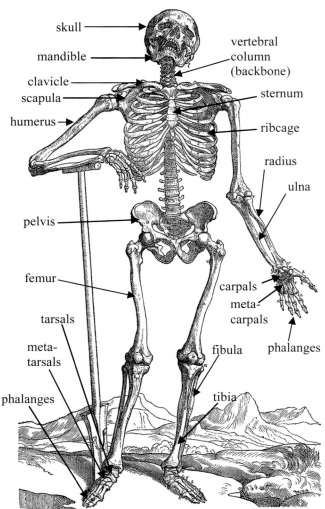

skull

mandible

clavicle

scapula

humerus

vertebral column (backbone)

sternum

ribcage

radius

ulna

pelvis

femur

carpals

meta-carpals

tarsals

meta-tarsals

fibula   phalanges

phalanges

tibia

This drawing from Vesalius's book illustrates a human skeleton. The drawings often showed the subjects in natural poses, such as this skeleton, which is leaning on a shovel.

over time, much of it turns into bone through a process called **ossification** (os' uh fih kay' shun). This process continues most of your life, because your bones have to grow with you and change as you change. Any new bone that is formed starts out as cartilage and is then ossified into bone.

Now, of course, Vesalius's main focus in the first part of his book was bones. He had several very detailed illustrations of a complete human skeleton made, such as the one shown on the left. We aren't really sure who made most of the illustrations, and many historians think that they are the work of several different artists. Many of the illustrations are so detailed and accurate that it is thought the artists were actually present for many of the human dissections upon which the book is based.

You have probably learned about most of the bones pointed out in the illustration already, but you might want to review them again to help you remember them better. In addition, notice the bone labeled **mandible**. This is commonly called the jawbone, and it is the bone that moves up and down when you talk and chew. This drawing corrected another mistake that had been made by Galen. Based on animal dissection, Galen thought that the human mandible was made of two separate bones that were fused together. Vesalius showed it as being made from a single bone, which is correct.

LESSON REVIEW

Youngest students: Answer these questions:

1. What is the soft "cap" at the end of a bone that moves in a joint made of?

2. What does the term "ossification" mean?

Older students: List the three types of cartilage found in the human skeleton, and give examples of where each is found. In addition, explain that cartilage can be turned into bone, using the word "ossification" in your explanation.

Oldest students: Do what the older students are doing. In addition, write about how Vesalius corrected Galen when it came to the mandible. Explain what the mandible is.

NOTE: The activity in the next lesson (a challenge lesson) requires a long time for clay to dry. You should do the first five steps of the activity now so the clay can dry for a couple of days.

Lesson 7: Vesalius and His "Muscle Men"
Remember from the introduction that lessons titled in red are "challenge lessons." You do not have to cover them, but they are interesting and allow you to learn more science.

This drawing from Vesalius's book shows the superficial muscles in a man as seen from the side.

In the second part of his book, Vesalius discussed the muscles in the human body. In some ways, this is the part of his book for which he is most famous. He didn't increase scientific knowledge of the muscles nearly as much as he did the rest of the human body, but this part of his book contains incredibly detailed drawings of the muscles in the human body, such as the one shown on the right. It shows the muscles you would see if you could remove a man's skin from his body.

Vesalius showed a lot more than that, however. The drawing on the right shows the **superficial muscles** of the human body. In other words, these are the muscles that are "on top." That might sound strange, because the muscles are found *underneath* the skin. However, your body is so full of muscles that some muscles are on top of other muscles! That's what the superficial muscles are. The muscles below the superficial muscles are called the **deep muscles**, and Vesalius understood that they were very important as well. As a result, his book also contains drawings of the deep muscles. In fact, many of the drawings actually showed the superficial muscles peeled back so that the reader could see the deep muscles just as if he were dissecting a person himself.

These drawings were revolutionary for their time, because they were not only incredibly detailed and very artistic, they were made in a way that they could be reproduced. If you studied Leonardo da Vinci (1452 – 1519), you learned that he produced very good drawings of the human body as well, including the muscles of the human body. However, these drawings were done with a pen and ink or charcoal. While they were very good, they could not be easily reproduced back in the 1500s, so they could not be included in a mass-produced book. Vesalius had all of the drawings in his book done so that they could be mass-produced. How? Do the following activity to find out.

A Play-Doh "Woodcut"

What you will need:
- Play-Doh
- A pen
- Some ink (A stamp pad of ink would be ideal, but you can use fingerpaint or watercolor paint and a brush as well.)
- A blank sheet of white paper
- Paper towels

What you should do:
1.   Grab a handful of Play-Doh and roll it into a round ball.
2.   Hold on to one part of the ball and push it down on a smooth, flat surface so that it gets flattened

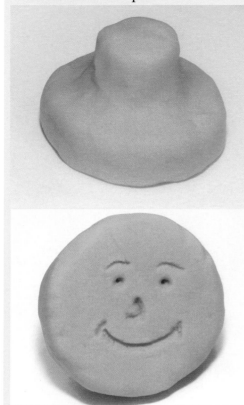

out. As you do that, work the part you are holding into an easy-to-grip handle. The shape should look something like the picture on the top left. If you are using a stamp pad, make sure the flattened end is small enough to fit on the stamp pad.
3.   Using the handle you just fashioned, hold the Play-Doh so that the flat side is facing you.
4.   Use the pen to "draw" something on the flat side of the Play-Doh. Do this by pushing the pen into the clay so that it makes deep grooves that outline what you are trying to draw. For example, I used the pen to make a "smiley face" in the clay, as shown in the picture on the bottom left.
5.   Use a paper towel to clean the Play-Doh off the pen.
6.   Let the clay sit until it is dry.
7.   Once the clay is dry, cover the flat side of it with ink or paint. You can do this by pushing it on a stamp pad or using a brush to paint the flat side of the clay.
8.   Push the flat side (that is now covered with ink or paint) down onto the plain white piece of paper.
9.   Lift the Play-Doh thing off the paper. What do you see?
10. Repeat steps 7-9.
11. Clean up your mess and put everything away.

What you saw probably didn't surprise you very much. The paint or ink went on the paper everywhere the Play-Doh was flat, but the grooves you made didn't put any ink on the paper. As a result, you saw the same drawing you made in the Play-Doh transferred to the paper. In other words, you made a stamp. When you covered the flat part with ink or paint again, you stamped another copy of your drawing on the paper. If you kept doing that, you could reproduce your drawing over and over again.

Does any of this sound familiar? If you learned about Johannes Gutenberg and his world-changing device known as the moveable-type printing press, it should. Gutenberg invented his printing press around 1450, and by Vesalius's time, it was used throughout Europe. In order to print something, metal letters were arranged on the press to spell out the words for a given page in a book. The letters were then covered in ink, and paper was pressed into them. When the paper was pulled back, the words had transferred their ink to the paper, making a printed copy of that page of the book. The stamp you made works on the same principle.

This revolutionized the bookmaking industry, because it allowed books to be mass-produced. As a result, it made them affordable and allowed the information they contained to be spread throughout the world. When Vesalius's book was printed, then, it was printed on a moveable-type printing press.

But how were the drawings in the books printed? The artists who made the drawings for Vesalius's book did something very similar to what you did in your activity. However, they didn't use clay; they used wood. So rather than drawing their pictures with pen and ink, they cut them into a block of wood. Any groove that they cut in the wood would not put ink on the page, while the uncut parts of the block would. A block of wood made in this way is called a **woodcut**. Imagine the skill that these artists had! They could make detailed drawings of muscles such as the one shown on the previous page by cutting grooves into wood!

Using the drawings that were printed in this way, Vesalius was able to show most of the muscles in the body. He was even able to show the muscles of the eyes! Does it surprise you that your eyes have muscles? It shouldn't. After all, you can move your eyes, can't you? Without moving your head, you can look up, down, or even side-to-side by just moving your eyes. How do you do this? You do it with muscles that are attached to your eyeballs!

Now even though Vesalius was mostly correct when it came to the muscles of the human

This is a woodcut that has an illustration (the martyrdom of Saint Sebastian) and some text. Notice how dark the raised parts are. Those are the parts that put ink on the paper.

body, he got some things wrong. For example, the illustration of the eye muscles in his book shows an extra muscle that is found in some animals (like the ox) but not in people. He also thought that the heart wasn't a muscle, even though now we know that it is. Despite these small mistakes, his work was a very important step forward in our understanding of the muscles of the human body.

LESSON REVIEW

Youngest students: Answer these questions:

1. Where are the superficial muscles located in the human body?

2. (Is this statement True or False?) When printing from a woodcut, the grooves in the wood do not put any ink on the page.

Older students: Explain the difference between deep muscles and superficial muscles. In addition, make a drawing of the stamp you made in your activity, and explain how it ended up transferring ink to the paper.

Oldest students: Do what the older students are doing. In addition, explain how the same process you used in the activity can be modified to make illustrations for a printed book.

Lesson 8: Muscles, Tendons, and Ligaments

Vesalius not only provided detailed illustrations of the superficial and deep muscles, but he also studied the makeup of muscles and how they interact with the skeleton. After all, the muscles that he took such great pains to have illustrated in his book move the bones in our skeleton. As a result, we call them **skeletal muscles**. Of course, the reason our muscles can move our bones is because the skeleton has lots of joints in it. As a result, our skeletal muscles and joints work together. However, this led Galen to make a mistake that Vesalius had to correct. To learn about this, perform the following experiment.

Muscles, Tendons, and Ligaments

What you will need:
- A fresh chicken wing (uncooked)
- A knife
- A cutting board
- An adult to help you

What you should do:

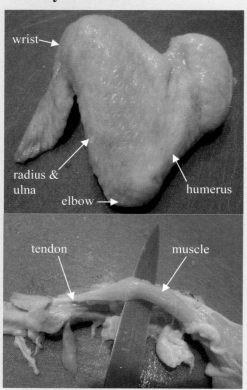

1. Put the chicken wing on the cutting board.
2. Using the picture on the left as a guide, find the parts of the wing that contain the humerus, elbow, radius & ulna, and wrist.
3. Have an adult help you use the knife and your fingers to pull the skin off the chicken wing. Don't worry about getting all the skin off; just get rid of enough skin so you can see a lot of the meat underneath. Try not to disturb the meat.
4. Once you get a lot of the skin off, look at the meat that you have revealed. In case you aren't aware, when we eat meat, we are eating an animal's muscles. So the meat you are looking at right now is actually the muscles the chicken uses to move the bones of its skeleton.
5. Have an adult help you use the knife to probe the meat. Notice that the meat is not made up of just one muscle. There are several muscles in the wing.
6. See if you can use the knife to lift one of the muscles like I have done in the picture on the left. The muscle you see there is one that lies on top of the radius and ulna.
7. As you examine the muscle you just lifted up, notice that it is composed of two different kinds of tissues: a pinkish or reddish muscle, and a white **tendon**. As you might have already learned, the tendon is what attaches the muscle to the bone.
8. Pull on the muscle and see what happens. If the tendon is still connected to the bone, some part of the wing should move when you pull on the muscle. By doing this, you are determining what bone that particular muscle has been designed to move. For example, when I pulled on the muscle shown in the picture above, the wing below the wrist moved up. That told me the muscle controls that part of the wing.
9. Feel free to find other muscles and repeat step 8.

10. When you are done working with the muscles, grab the wing above and below the wrist.
11. Bend the wing at the wrist and twist the bones until they pull apart from each other at the wrist. Notice how hard this is to do.
12. Examine the bones that were connected in the wrist. Notice the cartilage that caps those bones. This is more hyaline cartilage, which you saw in Lesson 6.
13. Now look for stringy white tissue that comes from the ends of the bone that were a part of the wrist joint. In some cases, you might even find the stringy tissue still attached to both sets of bones, as shown in the picture on the right.

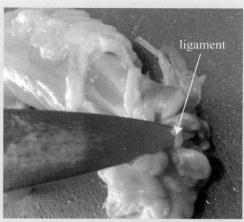

14. If you can't find any stringy white tissue coming from the bones of the wrist, do the same thing with the bones of the elbow and look for some stringy white tissue there.
15. The stringy white tissue is called a **ligament** (lig' uh munt). Its job is to hold the bones together in the joint. While it is flexible, it is also strong. Do you notice how similar the ligament is to the tendon you saw in step 7?
16. Clean up your mess and dispose of the wing as instructed by your parent/teacher.

In your experiment, you should have seen three different structures: muscle, tendon, and ligament. They are all related in some sense, since they all deal with joints and moving the bones of the skeleton. The tissue that makes up the muscle is clearly different from the tissue that makes up the tendon. However, the tendons and ligaments looked pretty similar, didn't they? Galen noticed this a long time ago, and he actually thought that tendons were just ligaments that had nerves in them.

If you studied Galen, you might have learned that he was the first major natural philosopher who showed that nerves control muscles. Since he noticed that ligaments and tendons look the same, he figured they must have basically the same function. However, since he knew muscles were controlled by nerves, he decided the tendons must be how the nerves get to the muscles, so he decided that tendons must just be ligaments that have nerves in them.

Vesalius showed that this was not correct. Instead, he demonstrated that ligaments were different from tendons, and that nerves were not part of the tendons at all. As a result, he recognized that tendons and ligaments had different functions. He agreed with Galen and da Vinci that tendons connect the muscles to the bones, allowing the muscles to move them. However, he decided that the ligaments did something entirely different.

What is the function of the ligaments? They hold the bones in the joints together. In your experiment, you twisted and bent the chicken's wrist joint (and perhaps its elbow joint) in order to pull the bones apart. Did you notice how hard that was? Now remember, the purpose of a joint is to allow bones to move in relation to one another. Your wrist joint, for example, allows you to move your hand independently of the radius and ulna in your arm. You can bend your hand up and down without moving your arm at all, because your wrist allows the carpals of your hand to move independently of the radius and ulna of your arm. If you are having trouble following what I am saying because I am using the actual names of the bones, look at the human skeleton drawn on page 18. Find the bones I am talking about in the drawing so that you can better understand what I am saying.

So in order for a joint to do what it is supposed to do, it has to allow the bones to move. However, if the bones move too much, there would be a problem. Have you ever heard about someone dislocating his or her shoulder? When this happens, the bones that are in the shoulder joint move too far, and that messes up the joint. The result is that the person experiences a lot of pain and cannot move his or her arm properly. So the bones in a joint need to be able to move, but they cannot be allowed to move *too far*.

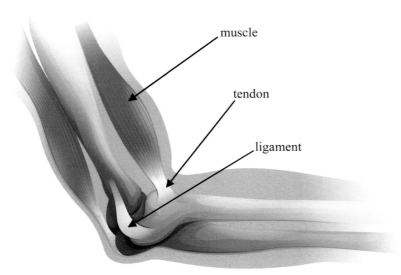

muscle

tendon

ligament

This drawing shows muscles, tendons, and a ligament in the elbow. Notice how the tendons connect muscle to bone, while the ligament connects one bone to another bone.

That's where ligaments come in. Ligaments hold the bones in a joint together. Ligaments are flexible, so the bones in the joint can move. At the same time, however, they aren't too flexible. As a result, they only allow a certain amount of movement. They also restrict the direction of the movement. Under normal conditions, then, the ligaments in a joint ensure that the bones do not move too much and don't move in the wrong direction. Of course, there is a limit to what ligaments can do. If bones are pulled with enough force, the ligaments can be overcome, and the joint can be dislocated.

Because there is a limit to what ligaments can do, they can actually tear if they are stretched too much. A torn ligament can be painful, and it often leads to swelling and an inability to move the joint. If a tear is small, it can generally heal on its own. However, severe tears can require surgery.

LESSON REVIEW

Youngest students: Answer these questions:

1. What do we call the muscles that move the bones of the skeleton?

2. What do we call the tissue that holds together the bones of a joint?

Older students: Make a drawing of an elbow joint, such as the one above. Point out the muscle, tendon, and ligament. Below the drawing, explain the function of each. Also, explain why the muscle in the drawing is called a skeletal muscle.

Oldest students: Do what the older students are doing. In addition, do a little research to find out what kinds of muscles your body has in addition to skeletal muscles. Describe them in your notebook.

Lesson 9: Arteries and Veins

In the third part of his book, Vesalius turned his attention to the blood vessels known as **arteries** and **veins** in the body. You may have learned a bit about them already. For example, you might have learned that other natural philosophers, like Galen, noticed that there is a difference between arteries and veins. The blood they both carry looks slightly different, and the vessels themselves are different. Arteries, for example, have thicker walls than veins.

Vesalius detailed these differences, as well as some others. Do the following activity to notice two more differences between arteries and veins.

Arteries and Veins

What you will need:
- A magnifying glass
- A mirror

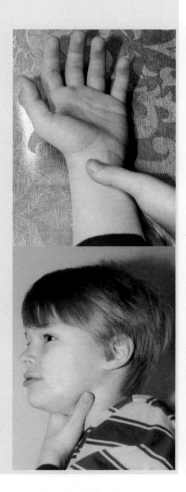

What you should do:
1. Put the thumb of your right hand on the left side of your left wrist, as shown in the picture on the right.
2. Push your thumb gently into your wrist and move it around until you feel the throbbing of your pulse.
3. Note where your thumb is.
4. Lift up your thumb and look at your wrist where your thumb was. Do you see anything but skin and perhaps some hair?
5. Use the magnifying glass to look more closely. Do you see anything throbbing? Probably not.
6. Note the blood vessels you see near the place your thumb felt your pulse. Are they throbbing? No.
7. Put the thumb of your left hand on the left side of your neck, as shown in the picture on the right.
8. Press down gently with your thumb and move it around until you feel the throbbing of your pulse again. This time, it should feel much stronger.
9. Use the mirror to look at that part of your neck. Do you see it throbbing? Probably not.
10. Repeat steps 7 & 8 to once again find your pulse with your left thumb.
11. Keeping your left thumb on the pulse in your neck, find the pulse in your left wrist with your right thumb, as you did in steps 1 & 2.
12. You should now be feeling a pulse on each thumb. What do you notice about them?
13. Put the magnifying glass and mirror away.

In the activity, you should have noticed that even though you could clearly feel your pulse throbbing in your wrist and neck, you couldn't see anything throbbing. In addition, even though you could see blood vessels in your wrist, they were clearly not throbbing. So what did you feel throbbing, and why couldn't you see it happening, despite the fact that you saw blood vessels in your wrist?

The answers to these questions lie in a distinction between arteries and veins. Arteries pulse, but veins do not. When you felt the pulse in your wrist, then, you were feeling an artery in your wrist. When you felt the pulse in your neck, you were feeling an artery in your neck. But why didn't you see anything pulsing in your wrist or neck? That's because of another distinction between veins and arteries: arteries are usually found deeper in the body than are the veins.

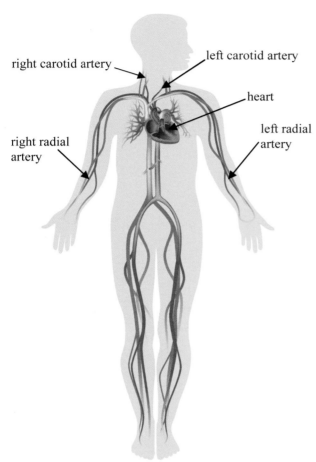

right carotid artery

left carotid artery

heart

left radial artery

right radial artery

In this drawing, the veins are colored blue, and the arteries are colored red. Please note that veins are not really blue; they are dark red. They only appear to be blue because your skin distorts their color.

Do you remember learning about the difference between superficial muscles and deep muscles? The superficial muscles are closer to the skin, while the deep muscles are underneath the superficial muscles. Well, the words "superficial" and "deep" are used a lot when studying anatomy. In general, "superficial" means "closer to the surface," while "deep" means "deeper in the body." Using that terminology, then, anatomists say that arteries are deep, while veins are superficial.

What does that tell you about the blood vessels you can see through your skin? They are veins, because veins are close to the skin, while arteries are much deeper. As a result, if you push on certain parts of your skin, you can *feel* the arteries, but because they are deeper inside the body, you can't *see* them through the skin. You can see only your veins, which don't pulse. That's why you don't see your pulse.

With that knowledge under your belt, look at the drawing on the left. It shows the largest arteries (colored red) and veins (colored blue) in the human body. There are a *whole lot* more arteries and veins in the body, but the drawing shows you the major ones. When you felt the pulse in your wrist, you were feeling your **radial artery**. Specifically, you were feeling your left radial artery. Can you tell me why it is called the radial artery? Look back at the skeleton drawn on page 18. Can you tell me now? It's because this artery travels along the bone known as the radius. When you felt the pulse in your neck, you were feeling your **carotid** (kuh rot' id) **artery**. Specifically, you were feeling your left carotid artery.

When you felt both your radial and carotid arteries together, what did you notice? They were pulsing at exactly the same time, weren't they? It turns out that's true of all your arteries. They pulse together. Think about that for a moment. All your arteries are pulsing together, but your veins don't pulse at all. Also, most of your arteries are deeper in your body, and most of your veins are superficial. Finally, the blood your veins carry is dark red, while the blood your arteries carry is bright red. As a result, the system of veins in your body is very different from the system of arteries in your body. It's not surprising, then, that Vesalius (as well as other natural philosophers before and after him) thought the arteries and veins were two different systems, carrying two different kinds of blood.

Because of this, Vesalius discussed veins and arteries as if they were two completely different systems. Look, for example, at the drawing on the right. It is taken directly from Vesalius's book, and it represents the veins in the upper part of a person's body. Do you notice anything missing? There is no heart! Why would Vesalius have the veins in the human body drawn but leave out the heart? Think about it. The heart beats in time with the pulse. As a result, it was thought that the system of arteries in a person's body originated in the heart. However, since the veins do not pulse, and since the blood they carry is a slightly different color from the blood in arteries, it was thought that the system of veins started somewhere else.

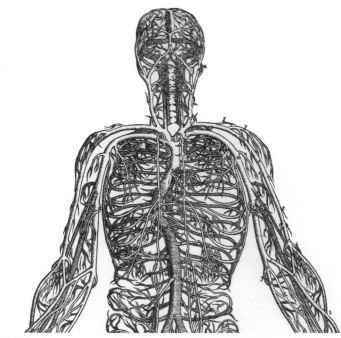

This is the upper portion of Vesalius's diagram of the veins in the human body. Notice that the heart is missing.

Galen taught that the system of veins in a person's body started in the liver. Vesalius offered several arguments against this idea, but he didn't come right out and say that it was wrong. Instead, after giving his arguments against Galen's idea, he then said that he would discuss the veins in the human body as if they did start in the liver. This was because despite all the great things Vesalius had discovered about the human body, he couldn't figure out exactly how blood flowed through the body. As a result, he thought that he should teach blood flow in the traditional way and simply mention his observations that led him to question that teaching.

Of course, the arguments he listed inspired someone else to study the veins, arteries, and heart even more carefully, and eventually, blood flow in the body was figured out. So even though Vesalius didn't get it exactly right, his observations led natural philosophers down the path of eventually figuring it all out.

LESSON REVIEW

Youngest students: Answer these questions:

1. Which type of blood vessel pulses?

2. Which is usually found more superficial in the body: arteries or veins?

Older students: Make a drawing of where you found your pulse on your wrist and neck. Name the arteries that you were feeling, and explain why you don't see them pulsing through your skin. Also, explain why you can see some of your veins, but you can't see them pulsing.

Oldest students: Do what the older students are doing. In addition, try to think of a reason why arteries have thicker walls than veins. Check your answer, and correct it if it is wrong.

Lesson 10: Nerves and the Brain

In the fourth part of his book, Vesalius discussed nerves and the brain. As you may already know, it was common knowledge back then that the nerves controlled the muscles. Galen demonstrated that way back in the late second century. There was still some controversy in Vesalius's time regarding where the nerves came from, but most natural philosophers agreed that they came from the brain. As you may have learned, Leonardo da Vinci showed that the spinal cord comes from the brain, and Vesalius made it clear in his book that all nerves start either in the spinal cord or in the brain itself.

In his drawings, he showed that the nerves come out of the brain and spinal cord in pairs. One member of the pair goes to the right side of the body, while the other goes to the left side of the body.

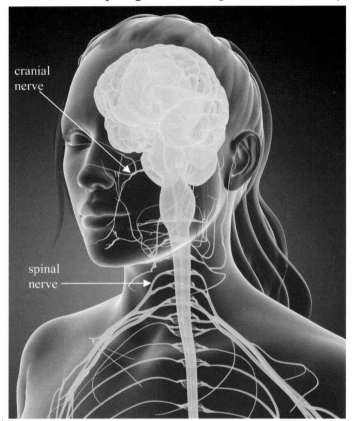

cranial nerve

spinal nerve

The cranial nerves come directly from the brain, while the spinal nerves come from the spinal cord.

He counted 30 pairs of nerves coming out of the spinal cord, but he actually missed one. Today, we recognize that there are 31 pairs of nerves coming from the spinal cord, and we call them **spinal nerves**. He also counted 7 pairs of nerves coming directly from the brain. We now know that there are 12 pairs of nerves that come directly from the brain, and we call them **cranial nerves**.

Vesalius recognized that nerves had two specific functions: to control things or to sense things. For example, nerves that went to the muscles were meant to control the muscles, allowing us to move. Other nerves, however, were for the purpose of providing sensations. In other words, when you feel something touch you, the nerves that give you that feeling (sensation) are not controlling anything. They are simply giving you the ability to feel what is touching you. Today, we say that the nerves which control your muscles are your **motor nerves** (they make your muscles move), while the nerves that allow you to sense things are called **sensory nerves**.

Galen, and those who followed him, thought that the nerves carried either air or some fluid, and therefore they needed a channel through which the air or fluid could travel. However, most people who actually looked at nerves said they couldn't find any kind of channel in them. Galen claimed that he saw the channel in the **optic nerve**, which is the nerve that travels from the eye directly to the brain. However, he admitted that he could not find it in other nerves. His explanation for this was that the optic nerve is very wide. Since the channels are so small, they are only visible in very wide nerves like the optic nerve.

Vesalius, on the other hand, could not find any channel, even in the optic nerve. He reported several different ways in which he studied many different optic nerves, but he never saw the channel that Galen claims to have seen. However, he wasn't willing to say that Galen was wrong on this point.

All he said was that he had never seen such a channel himself. Today, we understand that nerves carry electrical signals, so like a wire, they don't need a channel. Galen, therefore, was wrong, and it is easy to understand why Vesalius never saw a channel in the optic nerve – there isn't one!

In addition to discussing the nerves in the body, Vesalius discussed quite a bit about the brain. Some of the discussion takes place in the fourth part of the book (along with his discussion of the nerves), and the rest takes place in the seventh part. In the fourth part of his book, he discussed the general structure of the brain. He showed that it has three basic sections: the **cerebrum** (suh ree' brum), the **cerebellum** (ser' uh bel' uhm), and the **brain stem**. Each of those sections comes in two halves.

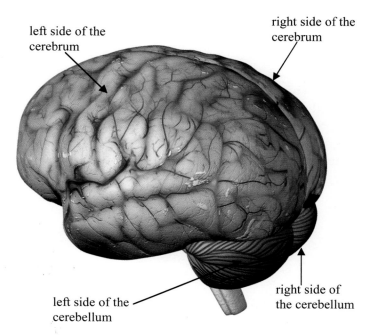

left side of the cerebrum

right side of the cerebrum

left side of the cerebellum

right side of the cerebellum

This illustration shows the human brain from the back left side. The brain stem is not shown, as it is underneath the cerebellum. The yellow structure at the bottom is the spinal cord.

To get some more experience with the shape of the brain, do the following activity.

A Model Brain

What you will need:
- 2 cups of water
- 2 cups of flour
- 4 teaspoons cream of tartar
- ¼ cup vegetable oil
- 1 cup salt
- A large bowl
- A mixing spoon
- A saucepan
- A stove
- A paper plate
- An adult to help you

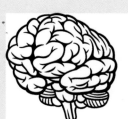 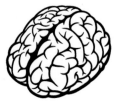 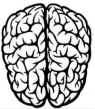 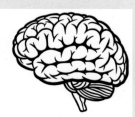

View from the bottom and front

View from the top and front

View from the top

View from the side

These are four more drawings of the brain from different views to give you an idea of how to make your model.

What you should do:
1. Mix the water, flour, salt, and cream of tartar together in the bowl until it has very few lumps in it.
2. Add the vegetable oil and mix again.
3. Put the contents of the bowl into the saucepan.
4. Have the adult help you cook the contents of the saucepan and stir over low heat.
5. Eventually, the mixture will get harder and harder to stir and will eventually have the consistency of wet clay. At that point, take the saucepan off the stove.
6. Use the spoon to clump the mixture up as best you can, and then put it all on the paper plate.

7. Use your hands to mold the "clay" into the shape of a brain. Use the pictures on the previous page as a guide. Be sure to make the cerebrum and cerebellum different from each other, and make it clear that there are two parts to each.
8. If you made the measurements correctly when it came to the ingredients, the brain model you made is roughly the size of the average adult brain.
9. Allow your brain to dry, and clean up your mess.

Now, your model can't show you everything about the brain. For example, the inside of the brain has **ventricles** (ven' trih kulz), which are open spaces. Yes, your brain actually has holes (well, at least spaces) in it! Da Vinci knew this, and so did Vesalius. However, they had a completely wrong idea of what these holes are for. They thought that the blood carried by the arteries somehow mixed with the air that a person breathes to produce an "animal spirit" that filled the ventricles. This animal spirit was supposed to be the stuff that traveled through the nerves that controlled the muscles. Vesalius was skeptical of this idea, and we now know that he was right to be skeptical. The ventricles in your brain actually hold a very important fluid that not only cushions your brain but also carries nutrients to different parts of your brain and gets rid of waste that your brain produces.

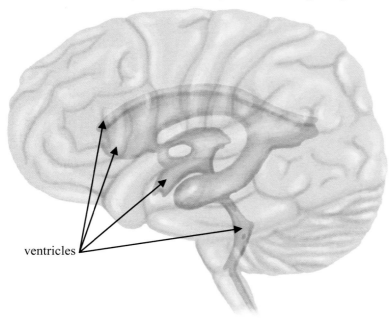

ventricles

The brain has four ventricles inside it. These spaces were not understood by Vesalius, but because he discussed them at length, other scientists were able to figure out what they are for.

LESSON REVIEW

Youngest students: Answer these questions:

1. What are the two functions of nerves, and what do scientists call the nerves that perform each function?

2. What are the three basic sections of the brain?

Older students: Take a picture of your model and tape it into your notebook. If you can't do that, draw a picture of it. Label the cerebrum and cerebellum. Also, discuss the two functions of nerves and what the nerves that perform those functions are called.

Oldest students: Do what the older students are doing. In addition, define "cranial nerves" and "spinal nerves." Indicate what the optic nerve is and whether it is a cranial nerve or spinal nerve.

Lesson 11: The Digestive Organs

In the fifth part of his book, Vesalius discussed several organs found in the body, including the organs related to nutrition. He actually called them "the organs of nutrition," but nowadays, we call them the **digestive system**. One reason you eat food is so you can use the chemical energy that is contained in that food. Your body converts that chemical energy into the energy you need to do all the things you want to do. However, in order to get to the point where it can do this, your body first has to break down the food into specific chemicals that it can use. This process is called **digestion**, and the organs that do it make up the digestive system.

To get some experience with the digestive system, do the following activity.

The Digestive System

What you will need:
- A photocopy of page A1 from the Appendix of your parent/teacher's Helps and Hints book
- Scissors
- Glue (A glue stick works best, but any glue will do.)
- Your notebook or, for the youngest students, a piece of paper

What you should do:
1. Use the scissors to cut out the outline of a human body that you find on page A1 of the Appendix. Don't cut through any of the organs on that page when you do this, because you will be using them as well.
2. Start a new page in your notebook and label it "The Digestive System."
3. Paste the human outline on that page of your notebook.
4. Use the scissors to cut out all the organs on A1 of the Appendix. You don't have to cut them out perfectly. If there is white space around the organ, don't worry about it. If you are having trouble, get an adult to help you.
5. Without using any books or resources, place each organ in the outline of the body where you think it is in a real human body. Don't glue them onto the outline yet. Just lay them there. Some parts will lie on top of other parts. That's fine. Just put them where you think they should go.
6. When you are done, check your work against the drawing that you will find on the next page.
7. Fix any mistakes you made, and then glue the organs in the right place.
8. Clean up your mess.

How did you do when it came to putting the organs in their proper places? It doesn't really matter. I just wanted to give you some experience in working through their positions. In the end, as long as you have them in their correct positions now, that's all that matters.

When you look at the digestive system and think about what happens when you eat food, it should be clear what path the food follows as it is digested. It starts in the **mouth**, where you chew it. This mixes the food with your **saliva** (also called "spit") and concentrates it into a small package called a **bolus** (boh' lus). The bolus moves down the **esophagus** (ih sof' uh gus) and into the **stomach**. When it is empty, the stomach is about the size of an adult's closed fist. However, as it fills with food, it can expand, becoming much larger. The food sits in the stomach for up to a few hours, depending on what you have eaten. While it is there, the food is broken down by the churning action of the muscles in the stomach as well as the juices produced by the stomach.

After it has been processed by the stomach, the food goes into the **small intestine** a little bit at a time. Vesalius called this the "thin intestine," and in my opinion, that is a better name. The small intestine is small not because it is short. Instead, it is called "small" because it is not very big around. In other words, its *diameter* is small. If it were stretched out, the small intestine would be somewhere between 4.5 meters (15 feet) to 9 meters (30 feet) long!

The food takes several hours to pass through the small intestine before coming to the **large intestine**. The large intestine has a larger diameter than the small intestine, but it is a lot shorter. If it were stretched out, the large intestine would be only about 1.5 meters (5 feet) long. The large intestine ends in the **rectum**. Any solid material that makes it all the way to the rectum is eventually released as **feces**. Vesalius distinguished the rectum from the large intestine by calling the large intestine the **colon**. In his mind, then, the large intestine was made up of the colon and the rectum. Today, the word "colon" is often used to mean the same thing as "large intestine."

Vesalius didn't know the details of what happened to the food in the stomach, small intestine, and large intestine, but he had the right idea. He knew that the stomach converted the solid food in the bolus to a liquid mixture that he simply called "juice from the food." He also knew that the intestine removed useful stuff from this juice so that it could be used by the body, and anything that was leftover in the end had to be eliminated from the body. When it came to the details, however, he got several things wrong. For example, he thought that the materials the intestines removed were all sent to the **liver**, which used those materials to make blood. We now know that he was right about all the materials going to the liver. However, he was wrong about the liver making blood.

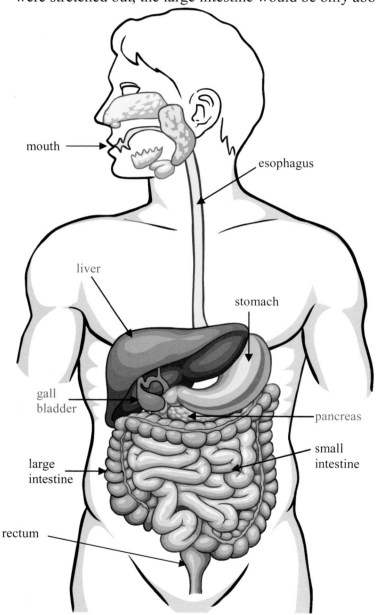

This diagram has the organs of the digestive tract labeled in black and the accessory organs labeled in blue.

Speaking of the liver, notice that I didn't talk about food moving through the liver. That's because it doesn't. Likewise, the food doesn't move through the **gall bladder** or **pancreas** (pan' kree us). These three organs are a part of the digestive system, but the food doesn't move through them. As a result, many scientists make a distinction between these organs and the rest of the digestive system. Anything the food moves through (mouth, esophagus, stomach, small intestine, and large intestine) is called the **digestive tract** or the alimentary (al' uh men' tuh ree) canal. The digestive organs that the food does not pass through are called the **accessory organs**.

What do the accessory organs do for digestion? Well, I don't want to give you the complete story, since Vesalius got a lot of it wrong. However, he did get some things right. For example, he recognized that the liver makes **bile**. If you studied Hippocrates (c. 460 BC – c. 370 BC), you know that he thought there were two kinds of bile in people: yellow bile and black bile. Vesalius thought that both of these biles were byproducts of how the liver made blood. Thus, he recognized that bile is made in the liver. He also correctly concludes that yellow bile is sent from the liver to the gall bladder, which then injects the bile into the intestines.

Not surprisingly, Vesalius was wrong on a few points. First, bile is not a byproduct. It is something the liver purposely makes. Second, black bile doesn't exist. Finally, he was completely wrong about the function of yellow bile. He says that it helps to "clean out" the intestines, and that just isn't correct.

Vesalius was also wrong about what the pancreas does. He thought it protected the stomach from damage in some way, but we now know that's not correct. Interestingly enough, the name "pancreas" comes from the Greek word *pankreas*, which can be translated as "all flesh." It probably gets that name from the fact that it is a soft organ, with no cartilage or bone.

Even though he got a lot of things wrong when it comes to the digestive system as a whole, Vesalius got the big picture correct. In the first part of his discussion of the digestive organs, he says, "…the almighty Creator of the world provided not only man and the other animals but even plants with certain innate faculties that ever seek to replace what is lacking and therefore needed." [*On the Fabric of the Human Body* Volume 4, translated by William Frank Richardson and John Burd Carman, Norman Publishing 2007, p. 50]

In other words, living things keep using up what they need. However, God has given them what they need so that they can replenish what they use. For people and animals, God provided a well-designed digestive system that allows them to replenish their energy and nutrients from the food they eat.

LESSON REVIEW

Youngest students: Answer these questions:

1. What is the difference between the organs of the digestive tract and the accessory organs?

2. Which is longer: the small intestine or the large intestine?

Older students: Use the drawing on the previous page to label all the organs on the picture you made in the activity. Indicate which are organs of the digestive tract and which are accessory organs. Indicate the difference between them.

Oldest students: Do what the older students are doing. In addition, write a story from the point of view of some food someone has just eaten. Describe, from the food's point of view, where it travels and what happens to it as it travels.

Lesson 12: A Trip Through the Digestive Tract

Note: All Vesalius quotes in this lesson come from *On the Fabric of the Human Body*, Volume 4, translated by William Frank Richardson and John Burd Carman, Norman Publishing, 2007. The page numbers are listed with each quote.

In the previous lesson, you learned about the organs of digestion and the distinction between the digestive tract and the rest of the digestive system. In this lesson, I want you to get a real "hands-on" view of digestion. Do the following activity, which makes up the majority of the lesson. A word of warning: the last part of this activity gets very messy!

The Digestive Tract

What you will need:
- Three slices of bread
- An old sock that you aren't going to use anymore (the longer, the better)
- A gallon-sized Ziploc bag
- White vinegar
- A ½-cup measuring cup
- Scissors
- Some nylon stockings that you can cut up
- A sink
- Someone to help you
- A camera (optional and only for those who do the "older" and "oldest" student assignments)

What you should do:
1. If you can, have someone take pictures of you as you do this activity. It will make your notebook assignment more interesting.
2. Hold the three slices of bread in your hands. In this activity, they represent the food that you eat.
3. Use your hands to smash the slices of bread until they are just one big lump of bread. This is similar to what your teeth and tongue do – they form the food into a lump, or bolus.
4. What happens to the bolus? It goes down your throat and into your esophagus. I want you to make

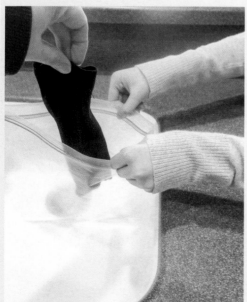

something to represent the esophagus. Use the scissors to cut the end off the sock so that it is now a "tube" that is open on both ends.
5. Open the Ziploc bag and have your helper hold it over the sink.
6. Hold the sock vertically so that it hangs directly over the opening of the Ziploc bag, as shown in the picture on the left. At this point, the sock represents your esophagus, while the Ziploc bag represents your stomach.
7. Put the wad of bread in the top opening of the sock. It should be big enough that the bread won't just fall down the sock and into the Ziploc bag. Instead, it should get "stuck" in the sock.
8. Once the ball of bread is completely inside the sock, use your hands on the outside of the sock to work it down the sock towards the Ziploc bag. Do not put your hand inside the sock and push it.

9. Did you figure out how to do it? You need to squeeze the sock right above the ball of bread. That pushes it down, and the lower part of the sock expands to allow it to do so. Believe it or not, this is exactly how your esophagus pushes food into your stomach. Here is how Vesalius described it: "[The esophagus] takes up the food that is pushed along and as it were packed down by the vigorous movements of the tongue and sends it on downwards by expanding its parts below what is being swallowed and contracting those above." (p. 60) In other words, the esophagus gets wider below the bolus and gets smaller above the bolus. That pushes it down, just like you saw happening with the sock and the lump of bread.

10. Once the lump of bread (which has probably had some scraps broken off it as it traveled down the sock) is in the Ziploc bag, put the sock down and take the Ziploc bag from your helper.

11. The Ziploc bag represents your stomach. Before you actually use it, I want to point out that the stomach is something else on which Vesalius had to correct Galen. Galen said that the stomach was at the center of the body, but as you can see from the drawing on page 32, it is offset to the left side.

12. Add ½ a cup of white vinegar to the bag. That will represent what Vesalius calls the "juices" of the stomach.

13. Notice that space inside the Ziploc bag expands to allow the addition of things like the bread and the vinegar. Your stomach does something similar. As Vesalius put it: "In size the stomach varies greatly…This means that it adjusts its size in proportion to what is put into it; it can make room for a great deal (so that the person does not have to be perpetually eating) and yet, if offered only a little, can embrace and concoct that too." (p. 67) In other words, the stomach changes size to allow for a lot of food or a little food, depending on what you eat. When you eat just a little, you don't feel "full," because your stomach can still get bigger to allow for more food. As you eat more, you eventually feel "full," because your stomach is reaching the limits of what it can hold.

14. Zip the Ziploc bag closed.

15. Use your hands to repeatedly squeeze the bread and vinegar. This will allow the bread to mix with the vinegar, making a gross-looking concoction. Do this for several minutes so that the bread and vinegar are thoroughly mixed together. This represents something your stomach does – it churns the food to mix it with digestive juices. This turns the bolus into a liquid slurry that is usually called **chyme** (kyme).

16. Cut one of the legs off the nylon stockings, and then cut the foot end off as well so that, like the sock you used before, it is now a "tube" with openings at both ends.

17. If the sink isn't dry, dry it.

18. Hold the Ziploc bag so that the slurry of bread and vinegar collects in one of the bottom corners.

19. Have your helper hold the "tube" made from the nylon stocking so that it is in the sink and one end is open.

20. Hold the Ziploc bag so that the corner where the "chyme" has collected is right over the opening, as shown in the picture on the right.

21. Use the scissors to cut the corner of the Ziploc bag where your "chyme" has collected.

22. Allow the "chyme" to leak out of the bag and into the nylon tube. Squeeze the bag gently to make this happen more quickly. This is like what happens when the stomach pushes the chyme into the small intestine.

23. Once all the "chyme" is in the small intestine, use your hands on the outside of the nylon tube to push the "chyme" down

the nylon tube, similar to how you pushed the bolus of bread down the sock tube. This time, however, the results should be different. As you start pushing the "chyme" through the nylon tube, what happens? Some of it leaks out from the nylon tube doesn't it? That's because the nylon tube represents your small and large intestines. As the chyme passes through them, the materials that the body can use are pulled out of the chyme and sent to the liver.

24. Of course, once the chyme travels all the way through the small and large intestines, there is nothing useful left. Did you get anything to come out the other side of the nylon tube? I suspect that there was a lot of stuff that came out the other side. Whatever is left at the end of the nylon tube represents waste, which is stored in the rectum and then eliminated as feces.

25. The last part of this activity was probably pretty messy, so be sure to do a good job cleaning up after yourself and putting everything away.

Hopefully, you now have a better idea of what happens as food travels through the digestive tract. Now, before I end this lesson, I have to tell you that while the activity was a reasonable representation of what happens as you digest food, it is a bit too simplistic. For example, the juices in your stomach are acidic. Since vinegar is also acidic, it can be used to represent them. However, the juices in your stomach are a very complicated mixture of chemicals designed to help break down your food, and they are also much more strongly acidic than vinegar.

In addition, the nylon tube was *much* shorter than your intestines. The small intestine, for example, is so long that it must be twisted and curved to fit in the body. Why is it so long? Vesalius says, "[The intestine]…is coiled up in innumerable circles, spirals, and convolutions (so that the human nutriment shall not pass through too quickly and so fail to be sucked completely dry)…" (p. 96) In other words, the small intestine needs to be long because it takes time to draw all the necessary material out of the chyme. If it were short and not coiled like it is, the chyme would travel through it too quickly, and lots of useful material would never get to the body. One more thing: your intestines don't "leak" like the nylon tube did. Instead, there are intricately designed systems that interact with the chyme as it passes through the intestine and then pull out anything the body can use.

LESSON REVIEW

Youngest students: Answer these questions:

1. What is the slurry of food and juices called when it comes out of the stomach and goes to the small intestine?

2. Why are the intestines so long?

Older students: If you took pictures of the experiment, glue or tape them into your notebook, and caption the photos to explain what you are doing in each of them and why it represents a part of the digestive process. If you didn't take pictures, make drawings of what you did and caption those drawings.

Oldest students: Do what the older students are doing. In addition, write down the parts of the digestive system that weren't covered in the activity.

Lesson 13: The Kidneys and Bladder

In the same part of his book where he discusses the organs of digestion, Vesalius also discussed the **kidneys** and the **bladder**, which are part of the body's **urinary system**, which is sometimes called the renal system. At that time, all natural philosophers understood that the kidneys produce **urine**, and the urine is sent to the bladder. The bladder, like the stomach, expands to hold a lot of urine, and eventually, a person urinates to empty the bladder. However, because very few natural philosophers before Vesalius had spent the time dissecting dead people and looking at their organs, most had a completely incorrect view of how the kidneys produce urine. While Vesalius didn't come to the completely correct conclusion, he was able to get closer to the truth than any other natural philosopher of his time.

To understand the incorrect idea that most natural philosophers before Vesalius believed, you need to understand what a filter is and how it works. Perform the following experiment.

A Filter

What you will need:
- Two coffee filters
- A funnel
- A handful of dirt
- A pitcher or large glass that has a pouring spout on it
- Two small glasses (like juice glasses)
- A magnifying glass
- Water
- A sink
- A window
- Someone to help you

What you should do:
1. Do steps 2-14 in a sink, because some of them can get messy.
2. Put the handful of dirt in the pitcher.
3. Fill one of the small glasses with water and then dump it into the pitcher.
4. Repeat step 3 twice more so that you have three glasses' worth of water in the pitcher.
5. Swirl the pitcher around so that the dirt mixes with the water as much as possible.
6. Have your helper hold the funnel over one of the small glasses.
7. Put the coffee filter into the funnel. It will probably be too big for the funnel. That's fine. Just have your helper hold it with his or her other hand so that the filter completely covers the inside of the funnel.
8. Pick up the pitcher, swirl it around to mix the dirt and water again, and *carefully* pour some of the water into the funnel so that it has to pass through the coffee filter before it drips into the glass.
9. Wait for the water to drain through the filter and collect in the glass below the funnel.
10. Repeat steps 8 and 9 until the juice glass is at least ¼ of the way filled with water.
11. Now swirl the pitcher one more time and pour an equal amount of dirty water into the other small glass without using the funnel or the filter.
12. Compare the water in the two glasses. What's the difference?
13. Look at the filter in the funnel. What do you see?
14. Take the unused coffee filter and push it flat against a window. The window should **not** have direct sunlight. You will eventually be using a magnifying glass, and direct sunlight could hurt your eyes. So there should be sunlight coming through the window, just not *direct* sunlight.

15. If you look at the filter, you should see light coming through it.
16. Use the magnifying glass to examine the coffee filter while it is flat on the window. What do you see? You should see some dark strands in the filter, but you should also see a lot of holes. They will appear as tiny points of light.
17. Pour all the dirty water out into the yard, and thoroughly clean the pitcher and glasses. Then, put everything away.

What did you see in the experiment? You should have seen that the dirty water that passed through the coffee filter was still a bit dirty, but it was *a lot* cleaner than the dirty water you poured directly from the pitcher into the glass. It was cleaner because the filter trapped a lot of dirt, keeping it from falling into the glass. Indeed, when you looked at the filter in the funnel, what did you see? You saw the dirt that the filter trapped.

How did the filter trap the dirt? Well, when you looked at the filter with a magnifying glass, you saw a lot of tiny holes. The molecules that make up the water were small enough to easily fit through those holes, so the water dripped through the filter and into the funnel. However, most of the dirt was in clumps that were bigger than the holes. As a result, most of the clumps of dirt couldn't fall through the filter – they were just too big for the holes. Of course, *some* of the dirt was in tiny clumps, and those clumps *could* fit through the holes. As a result, *some* of the dirt got through, but only the tiny clumps.

That's how a filter works. It has tiny holes that allow small things (like water and tiny clumps of dirt) to pass through, but big things (like most clumps of dirt) can't get through. When you use a coffee filter for its intended task (making coffee), the holes allow the water and the coffee that has dissolved in the water to pass through, but they stop the coffee grounds. That way, after you use the coffee filter, you won't be drinking the coffee grounds along with the water and the dissolved coffee.

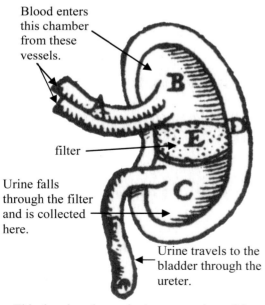

Blood enters this chamber from these vessels.

filter

Urine falls through the filter and is collected here.

Urine travels to the bladder through the ureter.

This drawing shows the *incorrect* view of the kidneys that was believed in Vesalius's time.

What does this have to do with the kidneys? Well, as I said, all natural philosophers of Vesalius's day knew that the kidneys produced urine. They figured the urine was liquid waste that came from the blood. Thus, it made sense to them that the kidneys filtered the blood, and the part that passed through the filter was urine. Since they all knew how filters worked, they assumed that the kidney was made up of two chambers. The upper chamber received blood, and there was a filter between the upper chamber and the lower chamber. The filter's holes were so small that blood could not drip through it, but urine could. As a result, urine would fall into the lower chamber, and it would then travel to the bladder to be held until the person urinated. This idea is shown in the drawing on the left, which Vesalius put in his book to illustrate the *wrong* idea of how the kidneys worked.

Vesalius showed that this idea was wrong by simply drawing what the kidneys actually looked like. He showed that there weren't two chambers in each kidney, and there was no filter either. Instead, each kidney had "rays" of tissue that spread out in numerous directions. As a result, he said that what natural philosophers in his day believed couldn't possibly be true. In fact, he called the idea "blessed nonsense." [*On the Fabric of the Human Body* Volume 4, translated by William Frank Richardson and John Burd Carman, Norman Publishing 2007, p. 132] He also said that the reason natural philosophers believed it was because most of them would not take the time to actually do dissections themselves and see what a kidney really looks like! The drawing on the right shows the urinary system in a person and a close-up of what a kidney actually looks like. Obviously,

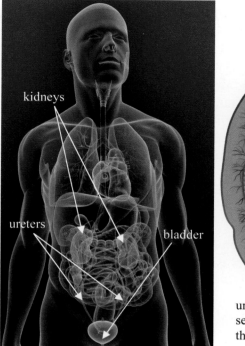
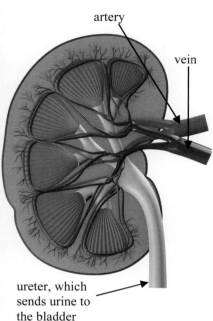

This diagram shows you the urinary system and where it is in a person (red parts in the drawing on the left) as well as a longitudinal section of a kidney (on the right) so that you can see it looks nothing like what the natural philosophers of Vesalius's time thought.

it doesn't look anything like the drawing on the previous page, which is why Vesalius knew the idea held by most natural philosophers of his day was wrong.

Even though Vesalius said that the current idea for how the kidneys work couldn't be true, he didn't really explain how the kidneys worked. Instead, he just said that the nature of the kidney was to filter out the urine from the blood. Nowadays, we know that the process by which urine is made is incredibly complicated. It's a lot more than just a simple filtering process. However, you can't learn about that yet, because we haven't gotten to the point in history where scientists figured it out!

LESSON REVIEW

Youngest students: Answer these questions:

1. What do the kidneys produce?

2. How does a filter work?

Older students: Write an explanation in your notebook of how a filter works. Then explain how the natural philosophers of Vesalius's day thought the kidneys make urine. Explain how Vesalius showed that their idea had to be wrong.

Oldest students: Do what the older students are doing. In addition, explain what the other two parts of the urinary system (the ureters and bladder) do.

Lesson 14: The Heart and Lungs

In the next part of his book, Vesalius spent time discussing the heart and lungs. Remember, he did not include the heart when he discussed the veins and arteries, because he didn't understand that the heart is the reason the blood flows through the body. One reason was that he didn't think the heart was a muscle. We now know that it is, and that muscle is responsible for pushing the blood through the arteries. However, Vesalius thought that a muscle had to be something you could control by thinking about it. You can move your arm, for example, by thinking about it, so the arm is controlled by muscles. In Vesalius's mind, since you can't control your heart beating, it must not be a muscle.

So what did Vesalius think the heart did? To get an idea, perform the following experiment.

You're Full of Hot Air

What you will need:
- Ice (If your freezer makes crushed ice, that's what you want.)
- Paper plate
- A knife

If your freezer can't make crushed ice:
- Ziploc bag
- Hammer
- Cutting board
- An adult to help you

What you should do:
1. If your freezer can make crushed ice, put about a tablespoon's worth of crushed ice on the paper plate and then skip to step 7.
2. If your freezer cannot make crushed ice, put two cubes of ice in the Ziploc bag.
3. Put the bag on the cutting board, but don't zip it closed.
4. Make sure the ice cubes are near the bottom of the bag, and use one of your hands to hold the top of the bag closed without zipping it.
5. Have an adult help you hit the ice cubes over and over again with the hammer, until they are both crushed into lots of little bits.
6. Pour about a tablespoon's worth of crushed ice on the paper plate.
7. Use the knife to separate the ice into two equal piles as far apart from each other as possible on the paper plate.
8. Position the plate so that one of the ice piles is right under your mouth.
9. For two minutes straight, inhale through your nose and exhale through your mouth right onto that pile of ice.
10. Compare the two piles of ice once you are through. What's the difference between them?
11. Clean up your mess and put everything away.

Before I use this experiment to tell you what Vesalius thought the heart does, I want to explain something about the experiment you just did. It was designed to show you the effect of breathing on a pile of crushed ice. I could have just had you breathe on one pile of ice, but that wouldn't have told you very much, because the effect of breathing on ice is best demonstrated when you compare it to what happens to a pile of ice that you aren't breathing on. We call that pile of ice the **control** of the experiment. It demonstrates what happens to ice when it just sits. The pile of ice on which you breathed demonstrates what happens when you breathe on ice. By comparing the ice on which you breathed to the control, you learn more about exactly what happens to ice when you breathe on it.

So what did you learn? The ice on which you breathed melted more quickly than the other pile of ice, right? What does that tell you? It tells you that the air you exhale is warmer than the air you inhale. We know that ice melts as it warms. The fact that it melted faster when you breathed on it tells us that it was exposed to more heat. Thus, your exhaled breath is hotter than the air to which the other pile of ice was exposed.

Do you see the value of a control in an experiment? If you had just breathed on a pile of ice, you would have seen it melt. However, you also know that the ice would have melted even if you hadn't breathed on it. So how could you tell what effect your breath was having? You compared it to a pile of ice that was sitting on the same plate and being exposed to the same air but not being breathed on. In that way, you found that the ice melted faster when you breathed on it, indicating that your exhaled breath is hotter than the air you inhale.

Vesalius, of course, knew that the air a person exhales is warmer than the air he inhales. In addition, he knew that the body is warm on the inside, even when it is cold outside. As a result, he understood that the body had to be heated in some way. That's what he thought the heart did. He thought the heart warmed the blood so that as the blood spread throughout the body, it could warm the insides of a person. In Vesalius's mind, then, the heart was the source of heat in the body. He thought the lungs brought in the air and then prepared it for the heart so that the heart could use it to warm the blood.

Now even though Vesalius didn't understand what the heart does in the body, he did correct a misconception that many people had about the heart. Many thought that the heart was at the very center of the body, but Vesalius demonstrated that this wasn't correct. Instead, he showed that there is more of the heart on the left side of the body than on the right side of the body.

Vesalius also did a good job of explaining how people breathe and how the air travels to the lungs. He knew that air came from the nose or mouth, traveled through the **trachea** (tray' kee uh), and then went into the lungs through tubes that branch out from the trachea. Interestingly enough, he didn't use the term "trachea." He called it the "rough artery." Do you know why he called it that? It looks like an artery, because it is a hollow tube. However, it has rings of cartilage in it, which make it harder and rougher than a normal artery.

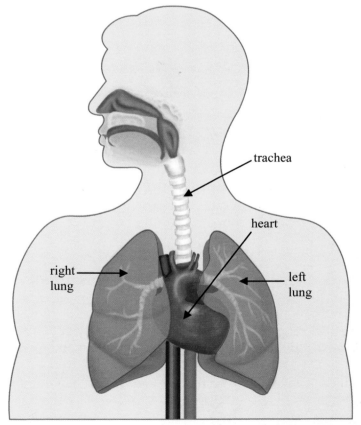

In this drawing, you can see that the heart is more on the left side of the body than the right. Also, notice the rings of cartilage on the trachea.

Now because the heart is more on the left side of the body than the right, the left lung doesn't have as much room as the right lung. If you look back at the drawing on the previous page, you should see that. Vesalius knew this. He even said that the shape of the lungs was determined by the other things (like the heart and ribcage) that are around them. However, even though he recognized that the left and right lungs are not exactly the same, he missed something important about the difference.

Each lung is a bit like a balloon, because it can be inflated with air, and the air can then be pushed out of it. However, it is different from a balloon in many ways. One difference is that while a balloon has only one region that inflates, a lung has more than one. As you can see from the drawing on the left, the right lung has three different inflatable regions, called **lobes**. The left lung, however, has only two lobes. This, of course, is because the left lung has to make room for more of the heart, so it can't hold quite as much air. As a result, it has one less inflatable region than the right lung.

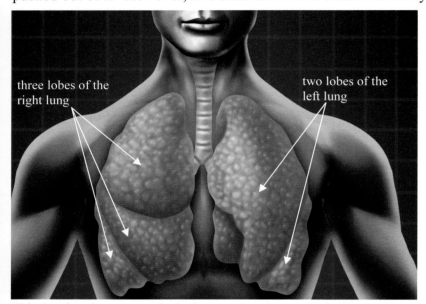

three lobes of the right lung

two lobes of the left lung

This drawing shows you only the lungs and trachea to emphasize the lobes of the lungs.

Believe it or not, Galen actually knew this. He taught that the right lung has three lobes and the left lung has two lobes. However, Vesalius could not find the third lobe on the right lungs of the people he dissected, so he said that it didn't exist. So even though Vesalius corrected Galen on a lot of matters, here is a case in which Vesalius's "correction" was wrong. This brings up an important point about the nature of science: *Newer is not always better.* Vesalius did his work more than a thousand years after Galen. He was definitely more careful than Galen, and he had the benefit of studying the anatomy of people, not just animals. As a result, you would think his teachings would always be superior to Galen's. In the case of the lobes of the lungs, however, it was most definitely not!

LESSON REVIEW

Youngest students: Answer these questions:

1. What happens to the temperature of the air when you breathe it into your lungs?

2. Why is there one less lobe on the left lung as compared to the right lung?

Older students: Make a drawing of the lungs like the one that is on this page. Point out the lobes and explain why there is one less lobe on the left lung as compared to the right lung.

Oldest students: Do what the older students are doing. In addition, point out the trachea in your drawing and explain why Vesalius called it the "rough artery."

Lesson 15: Heart Valves

If you studied the work of Leonardo da Vinci, you might have learned that he had a hard time understanding how blood flowed within the heart. However, he did show that the heart has valves that keep the blood flowing in a specific pattern. He just didn't understand what the pattern was. Vesalius didn't really understand how blood flowed within the heart either, but he did notice the valves in the heart and understood they kept the blood flowing in the proper direction.

Part of Vesalius's problem in understanding the heart was that he didn't really know where the veins and arteries ended and where the heart began. Look, for example, at the picture on the right. It shows a model heart that is used to teach students what a human heart really looks like. The heart and the blood vessels are shown cut open so you can see the insides. Modern science recognizes that the heart has four chambers: a left atrium (aye' tree um), a right atrium, a left ventricle (ven' trih kul), and a right ventricle. I have labeled each of them in the picture. Just so you understand, the terms "left" and "right" refer to the person whose heart is being studied. So the left atrium and left ventricle are on *the person's* left side.

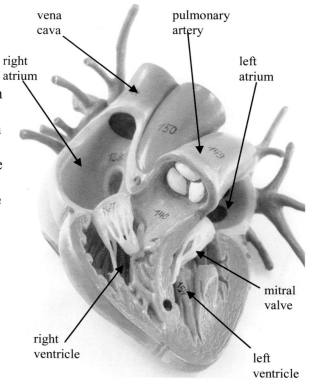

This is a model that shows a realistic view of the human heart. The pulmonary vein cannot be seen, as it is behind the heart.

Imagine, however, that you are Vesalius looking at a heart that has been cut open like this. Without any guidance at all, how many chambers would you say it has? Vesalius said the heart has two chambers (the ones labeled left ventricle and right ventricle). What about each atrium? Vesalius thought those were just the ends of the blood vessels! He thought the right atrium was not a part of the heart; it was just the end of the vena (vee' nuh) cava (kah' vuh). Similarly, he thought the left atrium was just the end of the pulmonary (pul' muh nehr' ee) veins, which cannot be seen in the picture because they are behind the heart.

Now even though he didn't understand that these structures are a part of the heart, he understood that blood flowed into the right ventricle from the right atrium (which he thought was the end of the vena cava), and it flowed into the left ventricle from the left atrium (which he thought was the end of the pulmonary veins). Why? Because he saw the valves. He understood that the valves forced the blood to flow in only one direction – from the atria into the ventricles. How do the valves do that? Perform the following experiment to see for yourself.

Valve Control

What you will need:
- A tennis ball you can ruin
- A very sharp knife
- A funnel
- A sink with running water
- An adult to help you

What you should do:

1. Have the adult cut a slit in the tennis ball by pushing a sharp knife into it. (The ball will not explode or anything like that.) It will be hard to push the knife into the ball, so the adult should position the ball at the corner of the sink, as shown by the picture on the top right. That way, the sink will hold the ball in place. The adult **should not** hold onto the ball! If the knife slips, it could cut the hand holding the ball. With the sink corner holding the ball, the adult should be able to push the knife into the ball with a lot of force. In the end, the knife should make a single slit in the ball, as shown by the picture on the bottom right.
2. Push the end of the funnel into the slit of the ball.
3. Put the funnel under the tap and use it to fill the tennis ball with water. You will know when the ball is full because water will start running out of the slit and into the sink.
4. Once the ball is full of water, pull the funnel out of the slit.
5. Keeping the ball over the sink, turn it over so the slit is now facing the bottom of the sink. Notice that little (if any) water falls out of the ball.
6. Keeping the slit pointed at the bottom of the sink, use both hands to squeeze the tennis ball. What happens?
7. Squeeze the ball a few times to see how this works.
8. Clean up your mess and put everything away.

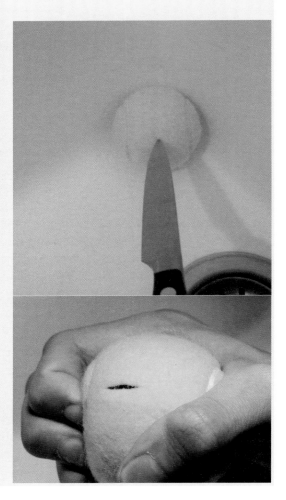

What happened in the experiment? If all went well, you should have noticed that water did not come out of the tennis ball until you squeezed it. As you squeezed the ball, water squirted out, but as soon as you stopped squeezing the water stopped squirting out. That's because when the slit was closed, it was tight enough to keep water from flowing through it. When you squeezed the ball, however, the pressure you created inside the ball pushed the slit open, and water came squirting out.

The heart valves operate in a similar way. When they are closed, blood cannot flow through them. However, when there is extra pressure behind the valves, they open, and blood flows through them. Since they only open when there is extra pressure on a specific side of the valve, that means blood can only flow one way. So blood can flow from the right atrium and into the right ventricle, but not the other way. In the same way, blood can flow from the left atrium and into the left ventricle, but not the other way.

If you look back at the picture on the previous page, you will notice that there are what appear to be three white stones in the blood vessel known as the pulmonary artery. That's actually a valve as well. After all, the pulmonary artery can't allow blood to flow the wrong way. As a result, it has a valve as well.

Vesalius noted the differences among the valves of the heart, and he tried to describe them in words. For the valve that controls the blood flow from the left atrium to the left ventricle, he said that it consisted of two parts, and "…one might not inappropriately liken them to a bishop's mitre (my' tur)." [*On the Fabric of the Human Body* Volumes 6-7, translated by William Frank Richardson and John Burd Carman, Norman Publishing 2007, p. 87].

If you don't know what a bishop's mitre is, take a look at the picture on the right. It shows a man dressed up as Sinterklaas, a traditional winter holiday character in the Netherlands, Belgium, Luxemborg, and parts of Germany. The character is based on an actual person, Saint Nicholas, who was a bishop in the fourth century. He had a reputation for secretly giving gifts to people, especially children, and that's what Sinterklaas is supposed to do. He is supposed to give gifts to people in celebration of St. Nicholas's eve, which is generally celebrated on the evening of December 5th and the morning of December 6th.

For the purpose of this discussion, all you need to do is look at the hat he is wearing. It is a formal hat worn by bishops in the Roman Catholic church, and it is called a mitre. Look at the hat, and then go back and look at the model of the heart on page 43. Do you see a resemblance? Vesalius did. The reason I am telling you this is because that description ended up sticking. Although there are other names for that valve, many scientists to this day call it the **mitral** (my' trul) **valve**.

The hat this man is wearing is a bishop's mitre, after which the mitral valve is named.

Now once again, Vesalius didn't figure out how blood flowed within the heart. He admitted so in his book. However, his discovery of the valves in the heart and their differences helped later natural philosophers figure it out. You will learn what they figured out in a later lesson.

LESSON REVIEW

Youngest students: Answer these questions:

1. How many chambers did Vesalius see in the heart? Was he correct?

2. What is the mitral valve shaped like?

Older students: Explain your experiment in words and then discuss why it demonstrates what the valves in the heart do.

Oldest students: Do what the older students are doing. In addition, explain the origin of the term "mitral valve."

NOTE: The next lesson has an experiment that must sit for several hours. Start your day with the experiment and then come back to it as the last subject of the day.

Section 2: The Revolution from the Mid-1500s to the Early 1600s

This is the Astronomer's Monument, which is at the Griffith Observatory in Los Angeles, California. It pays tribute to six great astronomers of the past, including Galileo.

Lessons 16-30: The Revolution from the Mid-1500s to the Early 1600s

Lesson 16: Girolamo Fracastoro (c. 1476 – 1553)

Girolamo (jee roh' lah moh) **Fracastoro** (frak as tor' oh) actually made his first contributions to our knowledge of the natural world several years before Copernicus published his book. This Italian-born natural philosopher taught at the same university as Copernicus and wrote a book about the motion of the planets. It influenced Copernicus, and his contribution to astronomy has been honored by naming a crater on the moon after him. They call it "Fracastorius." Like most natural philosophers of his era, however, he was interested in a great many things, including geology (the study of earth's structure and rocks), math, and music.

This statue of Girolamo Fracastoro is in his hometown of Verona in Italy.

Despite the fact that Fracastoro studied a great many things, his career was built on medicine. He taught logic and anatomy at a major university in Italy, and his medical advice was sought throughout Italy. When the Roman Catholic church held its Council of Trent in Italy, he was named physician to the council members. Obviously, Fracastoro was a very good physician for his day, and his greatest contribution to science was in that field. This contribution came after Copernicus and Vesalius published their books, which is why I chose to discuss him after I discussed them. To learn about this contribution, let's start with an experiment.

Noodles "Catching" Vanilla

What you will need:
- Six noodles
- Vanilla
- Two dinner plates
- A paper napkin
- Paper towels (you might not need them)
- Two bowls that are big enough to cover the dinner plates when turned upside down
- A measuring tablespoon
- A pan for boiling the noodles
- A strainer for the noodles
- A drinking glass
- Water
- An adult to help you

What you should do:
1. Have an adult help you boil the noodles as if you were cooking them for dinner.
2. Once the noodles are nice and soft, have the adult help you pour them into the strainer and rinse them with cold water.
3. Fold the napkin in half, and then fold it in half again.

4. Lay the napkin on one side of one dinner plate.
5. Pour a tablespoon of vanilla onto the napkin so that the napkin soaks it all up. If excess vanilla runs onto the plate, use a paper towel to clean it up. In the end, you want the napkin soaked with vanilla, but you don't want vanilla to be anywhere else.
6. Lay a single noodle on the napkin. If it is longer than the napkin, just make it twist and turn so that it is completely lying on the vanilla-soaked napkin.
7. Lay a single noodle on the dinner plate close to the napkin but not on the napkin.
8. Lay another single noodle on the dinner plate farther from the napkin than the noodle in step 7.
9. Put the dinner plate somewhere it will not be disturbed and cover it with a bowl.
10. Put the remaining three noodles on the other dinner plate.
11. Put that dinner plate somewhere it won't be disturbed and cover it with the other bowl.
12. Allow the plates to sit for at least three hours.
13. Once the plates have been sitting for at least three hours, fill the drinking glass with water.
14. Uncover both plates.
15. Eat a noodle from the plate that doesn't have the vanilla-soaked napkin on it. That's what a plain, cooked noodle tastes like.
16. Eat the noodle that has been sitting on the vanilla-soaked napkin. What's the difference?
17. Take a drink of water from the glass and swish the water around in your mouth before swallowing.
18. Eat another noodle from the plate that doesn't have the vanilla-soaked napkin on it.
19. Eat the noodle that you laid near but not touching the vanilla-soaked napkin. Is there a difference in taste between it and the plain noodle?
20. Take a drink of water from the glass and swish the water around in your mouth before swallowing.
21. Eat the last noodle on the plate that doesn't have the vanilla-soaked napkin on it.
22. Eat the last noodle on the other plate. Is there a difference in taste between it and the plain noodle?
23. Clean up your mess.

This is a bundle of vanilla beans.

Did you notice any difference in the taste of the noodles? The one that had been lying on the vanilla-soaked napkin probably tasted different from the plain noodle, didn't it? The flavor probably wasn't pleasant, but it should have been noticeably different. What about the other noodles? If you tasted the noodles carefully, you should have noticed a difference between the tastes of the noodles on the empty plate and the ones on the plate with the vanilla-soaked napkin. It was not as clear as the difference in taste between the first two noodles, but you should have been able to notice it.

Why did the noodles taste different from each other? Obviously, the vanilla did something to the noodles that were on the first plate, but what did it do to them? Well, vanilla extract is made by taking vanilla beans like those pictured on the left and crushing them. The crushed beans are then mixed with water and alcohol. The resulting solution is filtered and sold as vanilla extract. When you put the noodle directly on the vanilla-soaked napkin, the noodle absorbed some of that solution. As a result, you tasted the vanilla extract along with the taste of the noodle.

But why did the noodles that weren't touching the napkin also taste different from the plain noodles? Well, when you open a bottle of vanilla extract, you smell a strong odor. That's because the vanilla and the alcohol evaporate a bit from the solution, and those gases enter your nose. When you put the vanilla-soaked napkin under the bowl, the vanilla and alcohol continued to evaporate, but they were held under the bowl. Because of this, even the noodles that weren't touching the napkin were exposed to vanilla and alcohol, and they ended up absorbing some of the gases. As a result, they also had a bit of the flavor of vanilla.

What does this all have to do with Girolamo Fracastoro? In 1546, he wrote a book about how diseases spread. He suggested that there are tiny particles that cause certain diseases, and these particles can be spread in three ways. First, a person with the disease has those particles on his or her body, and by touching someone else, he can transfer the disease-causing particles. Second, the disease-causing particles can get into clothes, bed sheets, etc., and they can be transferred to a person who then touches them. Finally, they can even travel through the air to reach a new person.

In your experiment, the noodles represented people, and the vanilla extract represented infection-causing particles. When you poured the vanilla on the napkin, you put it in direct contact with the vanilla, and as a result, the vanilla went all over the napkin. The noodles represented people, and the noodle that you laid on the napkin represented someone who touched the clothes or bed sheets of a sick person. That noodle absorbed some of the vanilla extract, much like a person could get the disease-causing particles by touching the clothes or bed sheets of a sick person. The noodles that were not touching the napkin represented people who were close to but not touching a sick person. Those noodles also absorbed some vanilla extract, much like a person could get disease-causing particles by just being too close to a sick person.

Hopefully, you see how close Fracastoro was to the truth. He was the first person to put forth a reasonable explanation of how diseases spread from person to person. He didn't have all the facts right, of course. For example, only certain diseases can be spread from person-to-person, and even some of those require a lot more than just being near a sick person. Nevertheless, as a result of his insight, doctors could slow down the rate at which disease spread by keeping sick people away from healthy people, making sure healthy people didn't use the clothes or bed sheets of sick people, etc. It is important to note, however, that Fracastoro was not the very first to suggest this; the Bible was. In Leviticus 13, the Bible discusses determining whether or not someone has the disease of leprosy. If the person has the disease, verse 46 says that the person is to live away from everyone else. Of course, it's not surprising that the Bible was the first to mention such a practice, since it was inspired by the Greatest Physician of all!

LESSON REVIEW

Youngest students: Answer these questions:

1. What are you smelling when you open a bottle of vanilla?

2. Why should you avoid using the clothes or bed sheets of a sick person?

Older students: Write a short story about a particle that wants to make people sick. Have it plan the three different ways it can go from person to person to spread its disease, just as Fracastoro thought.

Oldest students: Do what the older students are doing. In addition, explain why doctors tell people to avoid shaking hands with others during flu season. Check your answer and correct it if it is wrong.

Lesson 17: Conrad Gesner (1516 – 1565)

This is a portrait of Conrad Gesner.

Even though we have been concentrating on human anatomy and medicine in the past several lessons, the scientific revolution brought advances in many other areas of science. In fact, one of the great natural philosophers of this time period was **Conrad Gesner**. Although he was trained as a medical doctor, he was fascinated by many aspects of the natural world, and as a result, he is an excellent example of a **naturalist**, which is someone who studies nature. Today, that term has picked up a second meaning, referring to someone who denies the existence of supernatural things, such as miracles. Of course, Gesner wasn't that kind of naturalist at all. He was a Christian, so he understood that miracles can happen.

In fact, Gesner was a Protestant, which is someone who is a part of a church that is separate from the Roman Catholic church. Since the Roman Catholic church had a lot of power during this time in world history, the fact that he was a Protestant caused him a bit of trouble. For example, some of his writing was put on the Roman Catholic church's *Index of Prohibited Works*, which was a list of books that no practicing Roman Catholic was allowed to read.

Because Gesner was fascinated by the natural world, he wrote on all sorts of topics, including **botany** (baht' uh nee – the study of plants), **zoology** (zoh awl' uh jee – the study of animals), **geology** (jee awl' uh jee – the study of rocks), and mathematics. Because he recognized God as the Creator of what he studied, he also wrote on **theology** (the study of the nature of God).

He wrote a book on geology, and the English translation of its title is *A Book on Fossil Objects, Chiefly Stones and Gems, their Shapes and Appearances*. To someone living today, the title is a bit confusing, because the word "fossil" meant something different in Gesner's day compared to what it means today. You see, the Latin word "fossus" means "to be dug up." In Gesner's day, then, "fossil" just meant "something that has been dug up." As a result, anything interesting that was pulled out of the soil was called a fossil. Today, of course, the term "fossil" means "the preserved remains of a once-living organism." So when we use that term, we are thinking about dinosaur bones or other preserved remains that tell us something of the plants and animals that lived in the past.

Now interestingly enough, Gesner did write about what we call fossils in his book. However, natural philosophers back then didn't recognize fossils as the remains of once-living organisms. Instead, they thought that these interestingly-shaped "rocks" were just another kind of stone or gem. So Gesner included fossils in his discussions of stones and gems. One thing that made this book revolutionary was that it included a lot of drawings. Books about geology prior to Gesner's merely tried to describe stones, gems, and fossils using words. Gesner recognized that this was not the best way to help students understand what was being discussed, so like Vesalius, he used woodcuts to illustrate all the things that he discussed.

One interesting aspect of Gesner's book on geology is that it included the first written description of a pencil! Most people in this time period used pen and ink to write, but sometimes people would use coal, lead or other kinds of rocks to make marks on paper. Gesner wrote about a substance that he called "plumbago" (plum bah' goh) which was found in the ground and was excellent at making marks on paper. However, it was messy to hold, and it was rather easy to break. As a result, the best way to use it was to hold the substance in something. He wrote about a hollowed-out shaft of wood in which a sharpened piece of plumbago could be inserted. A person could then hold on to the wooden shaft and use the sharp end of the plumbago to write on paper. This, of course, is what a pencil is – a wooden shaft that holds a black stick. When the black stick is sharpened, you can use it to write things on paper.

What do you call the black stick inside a pencil? Most people call it "pencil lead," because in Gesner's time, people thought it really was lead. When mined from the ground, lead is dark gray and shiny. So is the substance Gesner called plumbago. It also looked a lot like coal, but natural philosophers didn't think it was coal. Why? Perform the following experiment to see.

Coal and Graphite

What you will need:
- A small lump of charcoal
- A pencil "lead" (The easiest thing to do is get a piece of "lead" from a mechanical pencil. However, you can whittle down a pencil to get some of the "lead." The piece only needs to be about 2 centimeters – just under an inch – long.)
- A candle that can stand on its own or is in a holder
- A metal pie pan or other metal container that is bigger than the candle
- Metal tweezers
- A hammer
- Some paper
- A stove
- Matches or something else you can use to light the candle
- A winter glove
- A sink with running water
- An adult to help you

What you should do:
1. Hold the lump of charcoal in your hand and use the corner of it to write a short word (like "Hi") on the paper.
2. Gently hold the pencil "lead" and use it to write the same word on the paper. Be careful, because it is easy to break the pencil "lead."
3. Compare the two words.
4. Go outside and put the pie pan on a flat, hard surface. Put the charcoal inside it.
5. Use the hammer to break the charcoal. You want a small piece of charcoal that will fit in the tweezers.
6. Empty the pie pan of the remaining charcoal and take it back inside.
7. Put the pie pan on the stove and put the candle in the center of the pan. Don't turn on the stove. You are just using the stove as a safe place to burn things.
8. Have an adult help you light the candle.
9. Put a glove on the hand that you will use to hold the tweezers. This is to protect it in case the tweezers get hot in the next step.
10. Use the tweezers to hold the small piece of charcoal over the flame of the candle for 30 seconds.

11. Pull the small piece of charcoal out of the flame, look at it, and gently blow on it. What happens?
12. Put the small piece of charcoal under running water for a few seconds, and once it is totally wet, throw it away.
13. Repeat steps 10 and 11, but this time use the pencil "lead." What happens?
14. Clean up your mess. The tips of the tweezers will be blackened, but you should be able to wash the black off with some soap and a scouring pad.

What did you see in your experiment? When you wrote with it, the charcoal was crumbly, while the pencil "lead" was not, right? Also, while they both made marks on the paper, the marks made by the pencil "lead" were sharper and more distinct. When you put the coal in the candle flame, it probably started to glow red after a few seconds. When you took it out and blew on it, the red embers got brighter, right? That's because the charcoal was burning. That's why I had you put it under running water – to extinguish it.

Even though it is still called "pencil lead," we now know that the writing part of a pencil is made of a form of carbon called graphite.

But what happened with the pencil "lead?" It didn't burn at all, did it? This is what natural philosophers observed about the substance Gesner called plumbago. It looked a lot like coal, but while coal burned, plumbago didn't. Since it didn't burn, they thought that it couldn't be a form of coal, so they decided it had to be a form of lead, which it also resembled. So that's why people call it "pencil lead." When it was first used in pencils, it was thought to be lead.

However, we now know that it's not lead. It's actually a form of carbon called **graphite** (graf' eyet). Guess what? Coal contains a lot of carbon as well! So even though graphite doesn't burn well and doesn't have all the same properties of coal, it has the same main ingredient – carbon. The difference is that graphite is pure carbon, while coal has some other chemicals in it. So even though Gesner got the identity of the substance that makes up a pencil "lead" wrong, he at least gave us the first description of what a pencil is!

LESSON REVIEW

Youngest students: Answer these questions:

1. What do people mean when they say that Conrad Gesner was a naturalist?

2. What is the writing part of a pencil made of?

Older students: Draw a pencil in your notebook and point out the pencil "lead." Explain why it is called that, and also explain what it is really made of. In addition, explain what a naturalist is.

Oldest students: Do what the older students are doing. In addition, find out why Gesner chose the name "plumbago" for what he thought was a form of lead. Check your answer and correct it if it is wrong.

Lesson 18: Conrad Gesner and Plants

As I mentioned in the previous lesson, Gesner contributed to many fields of science, including botany, the study of plants. In fact, that's what he was best known for in his time. The first two books he published were on plants, and the first one (*Historia Plantarum*) ended up being very important, because it was small but at the same time full of information regarding the medical uses of many different plants. Remember, Gesner was trained as a medical doctor, so it makes sense that he would write about how botany applies to medicine. The compact book that he produced ended up being an excellent "handbook" for medical doctors during that time period.

One important contribution Gesner made to the study of plants was to suggest how scientists might be able to classify them. You may have already learned that scientists like to classify things so they can make sense of all the amazing things they study in God's creation. It took scientists a long time to come up with a useful system to do this, but Gesner helped when it came to plants because he suggested that the structure of a plant's flowers and seeds should be used. To see why this is a good idea, perform the following experiment.

Flowers and Seeds

What you will need:
- ☞ Two distinctly different flowers, such as a daisy and geranium (If you are doing this during a time of year when flowers are not in bloom, you can usually get flowers fairly cheaply from a supermarket. The flowers can be of any variety, as long as they are very different from one another in terms of the number of petals, whether or not there are stalks at the center of the flower, etc. If you simply don't have the time or money, pictures will work, as long as they show the flowers in some detail.)
- ☞ A dried bean
- ☞ A sunflower seed in its shell
- ☞ A peanut with the shell intact
- ☞ A pair of pliers
- ☞ Your notebook or, for younger students, a piece of paper

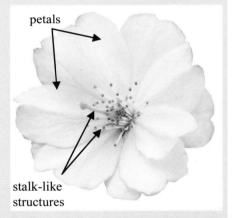

petals

stalk-like structures

What you should do:
1. Examine the first flower. Does it look similar to the flower pictured on the right?
2. Count the number of petals on the flower.
3. Are there stalk-like structures at the center of the flower?
4. Draw the flower.
5. Repeat steps 1-4 for the second flower.
6. Now write a summary of the differences between the flowers. Try to include as many differences as you can see.
7. Examine the uncracked shell of the peanut.
8. Crack open the shell and look at what it contains.
9. Pull out one of the peanuts.
10. Use your fingers to peel the thin, brown covering off the peanut. What does it feel like?
11. Look at the remains of the peanut once the thin, brown covering is removed.
12. Use the pliers to squeeze the peanut. Don't try to crush it; just gently squeeze the peanut. It should break into two halves.
13. Look at the two halves of the peanut. Are there differences between them?
14. Examine the dried bean.

15. Use the pliers like you did in step 12 to squeeze the bean. For best results, you should arrange the bean seed so that the thin edges are what the pliers touch, as shown in the picture on the left. Once again, squeeze just enough so that the bean splits into two halves.
16. Examine the two halves. Are there differences between them?
17. Look at one of the halves carefully. You should see that there is a thin covering on the outside of the bean. Use your fingers to try to peel off the thin covering. How easy is it to remove?
18. Examine the sunflower seed.
19. Crack open the seed. You can probably use your fingers to do this, but feel free to use the pliers if you want. If you decide to use the pliers, arrange the seed like you did the bean, with the thin sides of the seed touching the pliers.
20. Look at what you find inside the seed.
21. Try to split what you find inside in the same way that you split the peanut and the bean. Are you successful?
22. Write in your notebook a summary of the differences you see between the peanut, bean, and sunflower seed.
23. Clean up your mess and put everything away.

Plants produce such a wide variety of flowers that Gesner suggested a plant's flower should be used to help classify it.

What did you see in your experiment? The flowers were probably very different. For example, some flowers look like the one that I showed on the previous page – they have lots of petals and have stalk-like structures coming out of their centers. Others have fewer petals and don't seem to have stalk-like structures coming out of their centers. The pictures on the left give you an idea of the wide variety of flowers in creation. This is why Gesner thought that the structure of its flower should be used in classifying a plant. It makes sense that plants which make similar flowers are designed in a similar way. As a result, flower structure should be a good way to put plants into groups.

What did you find when it came to the bean, peanut, and sunflower seed? You should have seen *a lot* of differences. Let's start with the peanut. The hard, outer coating of a peanut is usually called the shell. However, a scientist calls it something else – a **pod**. The pod is made by the peanut plant as a protective covering for its seeds. A peanut pod usually holds two seeds, but sometimes it will hold only one. Others might hold three or four. So the part of the peanut that we eat is actually the peanut plant's seed. The shell is just the pod that the plant uses to protect its seeds.

What you might not know is that beans also come in a pod. You usually don't see the pod, because it is usually removed before the beans are packaged to be sold. If you grow your own beans, you know this, because you have to remove the pods yourself! However, a bean pod is a lot different from a peanut pod. It is usually a lot softer, and as you can see in the picture on the next page, there are usually a lot more seeds in a bean pod. So what you used in your experiment was the seed of the bean plant, which had already been removed from its pod.

There should have been a big difference between the bean seed and the peanut seed. First, the covering was really different, wasn't it? The peanut seed covering probably felt like thin paper and was easy to remove. The bean seed covering was thin, but it wasn't easy to remove. The sunflower seed's covering was even more different, because the shell of the sunflower seed was its covering. Unlike the peanut seed and bean seed, the sunflower seed doesn't come in a pod. It's just protected by its covering. You might have already learned that the covering of a seed is called its **testa**. So while the testa of a peanut seed is thin, papery and easy to remove, the testa of a bean seed is thin, a bit more sturdy and difficult to remove. In addition, the testa of a sunflower seed is thicker and very hard.

This picture shows bean seeds still in their pod.

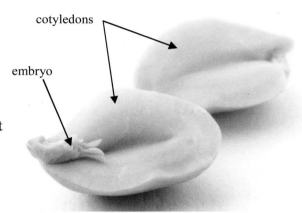

You were probably able to break all three seeds in half once you removed their testas. That's because each of the plants involved produce seeds with two **cotyledons** (kot' ul eed' unz). As you might have already learned, the cotyledons provide food for the developing baby plant, which is called the **embryo**. Most likely, the two halves of each seed looked different because one side held the embryo, while the other did not. It's possible one or more of your seeds didn't have embryos, because of when they were harvested

This picture shows the two halves of a peanut seed. They are different because of the embryo.

I hope you get an idea from just these three seeds about how different plant seeds are throughout creation. Once again, this is why Gesner thought it would be a great idea to classify plants based on their seeds. Plants that produce similar seeds should have similar designs. Scientists today recognize this fact, and they follow Gesner's advice, using a plants' seeds in its classification. In fact, they honor him by naming a group of plants (Gesneria) after him.

LESSON REVIEW

Youngest students: Answer these questions:

1. What two things did Gesner think should be used to help scientists classify plants?

2. What is a pod? Do all plants produce them?

Older students: After the drawings and summaries you made in your experiment, explain why it makes sense that scientists should use flowers and seeds to help them classify plants.

Oldest students: Do what the older students are doing. In addition, beans and peanuts are a part of the same family of plants. Find out the name of the family, and check to see if you got it correct.

Lesson 19: Conrad Gesner and Animals

So far, I have discussed Gesner's work in geology and botany, but nowadays he is best known for his work in zoology, the study of animals. In fact, Gesner is sometimes called the father of modern zoology, because he was the first in history to attempt to describe all of the animals that were known in his time. The book was called *Historiae Animalium*, which means "Histories of the Animals." It was composed of five separate volumes that took many, many years to complete.

This drawing of a rhinoceros can be found in Gesner's book on animals.

Like his book on "fossils," which you learned about in lesson 17, the book was filled with illustrations that were made from woodcuts. For example, the incredible drawing of the **rhinoceros** (rye nos' ur us) on the left was in his book. This was a major advance over most previous works that had been done on animals, and as a result, many people found the book incredibly interesting and useful. Some science historians say it was the most widely-read book on natural philosophy until the 1600s.

Now if you think about it, writing a book about all the known animals is really difficult! After all, what do you say about each individual animal? If you say too much, your book will be so thick that no one will publish it or read it. If you say too little, your book will not be very interesting or useful. See how difficult this is by doing the following experiment.

What to Say?

What you will need:
- Your notebook or, for younger students, a piece of paper
- At least one other person and his or her notebook (or some paper) – the more people you can include, the better
- A stopwatch or timer

What you should do:
1. Talk to the other person or people in the group and decide on an animal that everyone knows. If you have a pet, for example, choose that kind of animal. If not, choose a very common animal like a dog, cat, rabbit, duck, etc.
2. Once you have decided on an animal, have everyone spend three minutes (as determined by the stopwatch or timer) writing down as many facts as he or she can think of about that animal. Just write a list; don't worry about making it something that is easy to read. Also, don't share any of the things you are writing. This is supposed to be about what each individual thinks is important

about the animal. If you have students who are too young to write themselves, have everyone complete their list and then use another three minutes to take dictation from the younger students.

3. Once all lists are complete, have one person read off each fact on his or her list. Everyone else should listen, and if anyone else has something similar, the fact should be crossed off all lists. For example, if one person has "is covered with fur" and the other has "is hairy," those are pretty much the same, so everyone who has this fact should cross it off his or her list.

4. Have everyone look at his or her list and see how many things have been crossed off.

5. Repeat steps 3-4 for every person in the group, having that person read only the things that have not been crossed off his or her list.

6. Once everyone has had a turn, look at the lists to see if there are any facts that haven't been crossed off. Those are facts that were known about the animal and considered important to only one person in the group.

What did you find when it came to what the other people in the group knew about the animal and thought was important? I suspect that there were at least a few facts that were important to only one person in the group. Most likely, you crossed a lot off your list when the first person went, but only a few things for every person after that. What does that tell you? There are some facts about the animal that everyone in the group knew and thought were important. However, there were some facts that only a few people knew and thought were important.

Now you see one of the difficulties that Gesner faced in writing his book. He wanted to include a lot of known facts about each animal, but at the same time, he wanted to include what was important. How was he to do that, since everyone has different facts that they know, and everyone has different ideas about what facts are important? Well, he did something similar to what you just did – he ended up asking a lot of other natural philosophers. It turns out that Gesner developed friendships with many other natural philosophers, and he asked them to tell him the animals they knew about and what they thought was important about each! In addition, he read the works of older natural philosophers and included what they had written. As a result, while the book was authored by him, it was more of a "team effort."

Of course, the problem with such a team effort is that Gesner often had to rely on what other people said without being able to check the facts for himself. If what they said wasn't accurate, what Gesner wrote in his book wasn't accurate either. For example, consider the wonderful rhinoceros drawing on the previous page. Gesner had never seen one. In fact, he used a drawing that had been made by German artist Albrecht Dürer in 1515, who made it based on a sketch and a description of a rhinoceros that had just been sent from India to Spain as a gift from one monarch to another. It was the first rhino anyone in Europe had seen for over 1000 years, so the news traveled fast! Compare it to a photograph of a real Indian rhinoceros, such as the one shown on the right. Do you see the inaccuracies in the drawing?

This photograph shows you what an Indian rhinoceros really looks like. Notice the differences between it and the drawing on page 56.

The drawing makes it look like the rhinoceros is covered with armor, but as the photo shows, that's just the way its loose skin folds on itself. Also, notice that the real rhinoceros doesn't have the ridges along its back that are shown in the drawing, or the horn drawn behind the neck. So even though the drawing gets the basic shape of the rhinoceros correct, along with some of the details, it is wrong on many of the other details. Had Gesner seen a rhinoceros, he would have known that. However, had he limited his book to only those things he could see and verify for himself, it wouldn't have contained nearly as many animals, so it wouldn't have been nearly as useful.

The unicorn doesn't exist, but it is in Gesner's book about animals.

In addition to having many of the details wrong about specific animals, Gesner's book also contained some animals that simply don't exist. Look, for example, at the drawing on the left. That's a mythical animal known as a **unicorn**. Even though we know that no such animal ever existed on earth, it is in Gesner's book. Once again, this is because he relied on the works and reports of other people. There were those who said they had seen unicorns, and there were stories that mentioned them. As a result, even though they don't really exist, they made it into Gesner's book, and he writes about them as if they are real.

If Gesner's book had so many mistakes in it, why is he considered the father of modern zoology? Because even though his book wasn't perfect, there was a lot of very valuable information in it, which helped further our understanding of animals. This brings up an important point about science books: *most science books (even books written today) contain errors.* Please remember that. There is only one perfect book on the face of this earth, and that's the Bible. While you can hold fast to anything you read in the Bible, don't think the same is true of other books, even the one you are reading right now. All other books are the product of people, and people are imperfect. As a result, their work is also imperfect!

LESSON REVIEW

Youngest students: Answer these questions:

1. Why is Gesner sometimes called the father of modern zoology?

2. Why were there lots of errors in Gesner's book?

Older students: Explain in your notebook how Gesner was able to write about so many different animals and what that meant regarding the accuracy of his book.

Oldest students: Do what the older students are doing. Also, explain why Gesner can be called the father of modern zoology, even though his book had a lot of errors in it.

Lesson 20: Pierre Belon (1517 – 1564)

While Gesner tended to rely heavily on the words of others, another naturalist who lived at the same time took a completely different approach. The French natural philosopher **Pierre** (pee' air) **Belon** (bel' uhn) held several positions with some of the most important religious leaders of the day, and as a result, he traveled quite a lot. During his travels he studied and documented what he found in nature, and he wrote extensively about his findings. While he did discuss the works of others, he usually drew conclusions based only on what he had seen for himself. This meant that he wrote about fewer subjects than Gesner, but what he did write about came from his own personal experience. His first book, for example, was entitled *Observations of Several Curiosities and Memorable Things*, and it simply contained discussions about the interesting natural things he had seen in his travels. One rather special aspect of all Belon's books is that they were written in his native tongue – French. This is a bit unusual, as most works of natural philosophy were written in Latin.

This is a portrait of Pierre Belon.

As his studies continued, he eventually wrote a book called *The Natural History of Strange Marine Fish* in which he discussed the ocean creatures he had studied and dissected. Interestingly enough, even though the book was supposed to be about fishes, he included animals like the whale, dolphin, and hippopotamus! Even though he thought of whales and dolphins as fishes, he did make it clear that they had a lot in common with the animals on land, such as the fact that they breathe air with lungs and the mothers produce milk to feed their young.

Before I go on, I thought I might tell you the proper way to use the words "fish" and "fishes." The word "fish" can be its own plural, as long as we are talking about the same type of fish. So, for example, if you have three goldfish in a bowl, you have a bowl of *fish*. However, when you are talking about different types of fish, you have to use the word "fishes." That means an aquarium with one goldfish, one angelfish, and one betta fish would be an aquarium that contains *fishes*. Not everyone (not even every scientist) follows this rule, but technically, it's the way you are supposed to use those two words.

While Belon added greatly to our understanding of fishes, whales, dolphins, and other marine animals, he is best known for his study of birds. His book *The Natural History of Birds* is his best-known work. In it, he discusses both the anatomy of birds and their behaviors. He makes his admiration for birds clear in the 17th chapter of the book, where he says, "…it would be difficult to find a better example of the providence of nature and the wisdom of the all-powerful lord creator than by considering the nature of birds." [Pierre Belon, *The Natural History of Birds*, p. 50, translated by Jennifer Smyth of the Worth Library]

In his book, Belon has woodcuts of several birds that he collected himself, and it is thought to be the first book that deals with **comparative anatomy**. To give you an idea of what that means, do the following activity.

Anything Look Familiar?

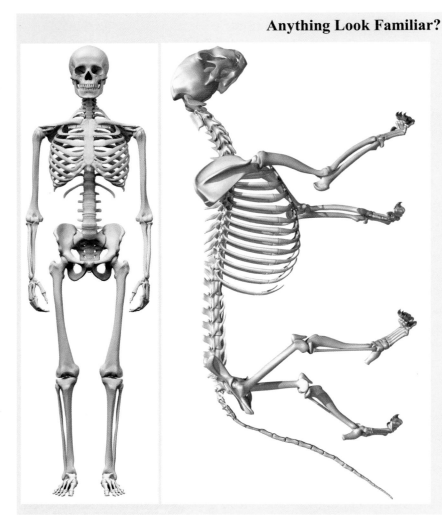

What you will need:
☞ Your notebook or, for younger students, a piece of paper

What you should do:
1. Look at the drawings on the left. The one on the far left is of a human skeleton, while the one that is closest to the text is of a cat's skeleton.
2. Title the page you will write on "Comparative Anatomy: Cats and People."
3. Write a list of all the things that you can see that are similar between the cat skeleton and the person's skeleton. You might want to go back to the drawing on page 18 so you can use the proper names of the bones.
4. Write a list of all the things you see that are different between the two skeletons.

Were you surprised by what you found? Cats and people are very different, but notice all the things they have in common! They each have a skull, a vertebral column, a ribcage, a scapula, and a pelvis. Sure, they are shaped differently, but their similarities are unmistakable. They each have a mandible attached to the skull, and they each have teeth in the mandible. Once again, the teeth and mandibles are a bit different from one another, but they are also very similar.

Now look at the legs and arms, which are called **limbs**. The arms of a person are composed of one upper bone (the humerus) and two lower bones (the radius and ulna). In between, there is a joint (the elbow). Now look at the front limbs of the cat. Do you see the same pattern? The elbow joint in the cat is rather different from that of the person, but the pattern is the same. A person's legs are made of one upper bone (the femur) and two lower bones (the tibia and fibula). In addition, the fibula is much thinner than the tibia. Do you see the same pattern in the cat? The person's hands are made of carpals, metacarpals, and phalanges. His feet are similarly made of tarsals, metatarsals, and phalanges. Notice the cat has the same pattern for its paws!

Now, of course, there are a lot of differences in the skeletons as well. As I already noted, while there are many similar bones, they are often shaped differently between the cat and human. Also, the human skeleton is made so you can walk using just your legs. The cat skeleton is made so that the cat must use all four limbs to walk. In addition, the cat has a tail, while the human doesn't.

This is what comparative anatomy is all about. We compare really different living things and look for their differences and similarities. Now, of course, lots of natural philosophers before Belon understood that living things share similarities. Indeed, Vesalius pointed out all sorts of mistakes made by Galen that were caused by Galen assuming humans and apes were nearly identical. What Belon did was produce the first really serious description of what birds and humans had in common when it came to their skeletons. He even used the names of the human bones (humerus, radius, ulna, etc.) to label the similar structures that he found in his bird specimens. That's why Pierre Belon is often called the father of comparative anatomy.

So what's the big deal about comparative anatomy? Well, it allows us to see how God used lots of the same designs throughout creation. Have you ever looked under the hood of a car? If you do, you will see lots of different parts that all work together to make the car go. What if you look under the hood of a different kind of car? What if you looked under the hood of a truck? What would you see? You would see that many of the engine parts are very similar. They may be shaped a bit differently, and there may be some things in the truck engine that are not in the car engine (or vice-versa), but overall, you would see a lot of similar things.

Why would you see so many similarities? Because all car engines have to do basically the same thing: convert the chemical energy of the gasoline into mechanical energy that turns the car's wheels. Since they have to do the same basic thing, they have a lot of very similar parts. However, some cars do things slightly differently from others. A racecar, for example, needs to go faster than a family car. Trucks have to haul more weight than a car. As a result, their engines are slightly different as well. By studying the similarities and differences among engines, you can learn what things the cars are doing the same, and what things they are doing differently.

The same can be said for living creatures. If we study their similarities and differences, we can learn what things God designed them to do similarly, and what things He designed them to do differently. That's why comparative anatomy is important, and we have Pierre Belon to thank for it! He might have made even more contributions to science, but unfortunately, his life was cut short when he was murdered. No one knows exactly why, but most historians think it was a political assassination.

LESSON REVIEW

Youngest students: Answer these questions:

1. If you see a bluegill (a type of fish) and a bass (another type of fish) swimming in a pond, would you refer to them as "fish" or "fishes?"

2. What is comparative anatomy?

Older students: Right under the list you made for your activity, explain what comparative anatomy is and why it is important in science.

Oldest students: Do what the older students are doing. Also, use your results to speculate on why there are so many similarities between a cat skeleton and a human skeleton.

NOTE: The next lesson has an experiment that needs to sit overnight. Start the experiment the day before you do the lesson.

Lesson 21: Michael Servetus (c. 1509 – 1553)

This is a stamp that Spain issued in honor of Michael Servetus (Miguel Servet in Spanish). The man is Servetus, and the diagram emphasizes the blood flow from the heart to the lungs and back, which he figured out.

Do you remember that despite all his work on human anatomy, Andreas Vesalius could not figure out how blood flowed in the heart? He thought that the heart somehow heated the blood so that the inside of the body stayed warm and that the job of the lungs was to prepare air and send it to the heart so the heart could use it to warm the blood. While that is definitely not right, his studies inspired a Spaniard named **Michael Servetus** (sur vee' tus) to learn more, and as a result, he was able to add a bit more to our understanding of the process.

In 1553, Servetus published a book entitled *The Restoration of Christianity*. He was well-educated in many fields of philosophy and theology, but he focused on studying the Bible in its original languages. In case you aren't aware, the Old Testament was originally written in Hebrew, and the New Testament was written mostly in Greek. Servetus thought that over the years, Christianity had been corrupted, and he wanted to correct that corruption by studying the Bible in its original languages so he could learn exactly what the inspired authors of the Bible wrote. Based on his studies, he thought a lot of what both the Roman Catholic church and the Protestants taught was wrong, and he wrote his book to try to make his case. Both the Protestants and the Roman Catholic church tried to execute him for writing the book, and unfortunately, the Protestants succeeded.

Why am I telling you about his book on theology and Christian beliefs? Because he included natural philosophy in it as well. You see, he was convinced that there was something special about blood. Deuteronomy 12:23 says, "Only be sure not to eat the blood, for the blood is the life, and you shall not eat the life with the flesh." Genesis 9:4 makes a similar statement. Servetus believed that since the Bible says "the blood is the life," then he should study blood to understand life.

While studying the blood of animals and the vessels through which it flows, he noticed two very important things. First, he noticed that the blood vessels which ran from the heart to the lungs and from the lungs to the heart were very big. Most natural philosophers of his day thought that the only reason blood ran to the lungs was to nourish them, just as blood nourishes all the other tissues. However, he said that the blood vessels are so large that they carried a lot of blood – much more than the lungs would need for nourishment. He didn't think God would design the blood vessels so large if they didn't need to be. As a result, he decided there must be some other reason for so much blood traveling from the heart to the lungs and then back again.

The other thing he noticed was that when blood went to the lungs, it was dark red. However, when it left the lungs, it was bright red. He decided that color change meant something important was happening to the blood while it was in the lungs. Why? Perform the following experiment to find out.

Oxygen Can Cause Color Changes

What you will need:

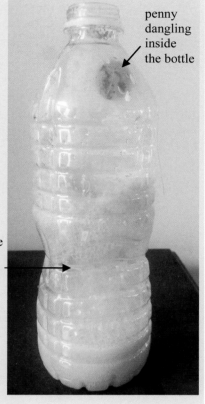

penny
dangling
inside
the bottle

suds from the
hydrogen
peroxide and
yeast

- Two shiny pennies (They should be really clean and shiny. If you can't find any shiny pennies, use a hard toothbrush and tomato ketchup to scrub them to the point where they are shiny.)
- White vinegar
- Salt
- Thread
- Scissors
- Tape
- Hydrogen peroxide (Drugstores carry it.)
- A ½-liter plastic bottle, like the kind water comes in
- Yeast (Grocery stores sell it for making bread.)
- Aluminum foil
- A ½-cup measuring cup
- A ¼-cup measuring cup
- A ¼-teaspoon measuring spoon
- A funnel
- A small glass

What you should do:

1. Cut the thread into two 10 centimeter (4 inch) lengths.
2. Tape the end of one length of thread so that it is securely held to the "heads" side of one penny. If there is a lot of excess tape, use scissors to cut the excess away.
3. Repeat step 2 for the other penny and other length of thread.
4. Add ¼ cup of vinegar to the small glass.
5. Add ¼ teaspoon of salt to the vinegar in the glass.
6. Swirl the glass so the vinegar and salt mix.
7. Use the ½-cup measuring cup and funnel to add ½ cup of hydrogen peroxide to the bottle.
8. Add ¼ teaspoon of yeast to the hydrogen peroxide in the bottle.
9. Swirl the bottle so the yeast and hydrogen peroxide mix. You should see lots of bubbles forming.
10. Hold one length of thread with your hand so the penny hangs down from it. Dip the penny in the vinegar/salt solution and hold it there for 10 seconds.
11. Pull the penny out of the solution and then put it in the opening of the bottle. Allow it to hang inside the bottle just a few centimeters from the top, as shown in the picture above. Make sure it doesn't touch the "suds" from the hydrogen peroxide and yeast.
12. Use tape to tape the rest of the string to the outside of the bottle so the penny dangles at the top of the bottle without you holding the string yourself.
13. Cover the opening of the bottle with a small amount of aluminum foil. Don't try to make the cover airtight; there just needs to be something covering the opening of the bottle.
14. Repeat step 10 with the other length of thread.
15. Pull that penny out of the solution and lay it next to the bottle so that the "tails" side is pointed up.
16. You now have one penny dangling inside the bottle and one penny sitting on the counter next to the bottle. Leave them there overnight.
17. Clean up everything except the bottle and the penny lying next to it.
18. In the morning, uncover the bottle and pull out the penny.
19. Compare the two pennies. Look at both the "heads" sides and the "tails" sides. What do you see?
20. Clean out the bottle, pull the thread off the pennies, and put everything away.

What did you see in the experiment? The penny that was dangling inside the bottle should have become really "dirty," while the penny that sat out next to the bottle wasn't nearly as "dirty." Why is that? Because there is oxygen in the air, and that oxygen chemically reacts with the copper in the penny. This reaction produces a new chemical that is not at all shiny. If enough of it formed, you might have even seen that it was green. This is what causes pennies to lose their shine. It takes a while, however, because there isn't a lot of oxygen in the air.

The penny that was inside the bottle wasn't exposed to air. Instead, it was exposed to nearly pure oxygen. That's because yeast causes hydrogen peroxide to break down into water and oxygen. The bubbles you saw forming in the experiment were made by the oxygen being formed. That oxygen filled up the bottle and overflowed into the room. By hanging the penny inside the bottle, then, you were exposing it to *a lot* more oxygen than it would have been exposed to had it just been sitting in the air. This caused the color change to happen a lot more quickly.

So what does the experiment tell you? Oxygen in the air can react with things to make a color change. When Servetus saw that blood changed from dark red to bright red when it passed through the

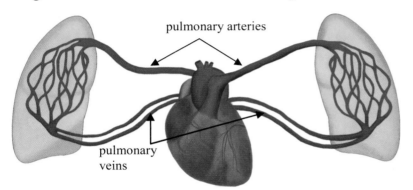

pulmonary arteries

pulmonary veins

lungs, he realized something in the air that the lungs held must be reacting with the blood, changing the blood. He didn't know it was oxygen – he just figured it had to be something in the air. As a result, he reasoned that blood must flow from the heart to the lungs. It then picks up the air in the lungs and comes back to the heart.

This very simplified drawing shows the heart with most of the major blood vessels removed. The vessels involved in pulmonary circulation are shown.

This route is called **pulmonary** (pull' muh nehr' ee) **circulation**, and it is an important part of how blood flows throughout the body. It also explains why the pulmonary arteries and pulmonary veins are so large – all the blood has to travel through them, because all the blood needs to get air from the lungs. So unlike what Vesalius thought, the lungs don't send air to the heart. The heart sends blood to the lungs to pick up the air, and then the blood flows back to the heart, filled with what it needs from the air.

LESSON REVIEW

Youngest students: Answer these questions:

1. Why was Michael Servetus so interested in blood?

2. What is pulmonary circulation?

Older students: Make a drawing like the one above in your notebook, and use it to explain pulmonary circulation. Be sure to use the term "pulmonary circulation" in your explanation.

Oldest students: Do what the older students are doing. Also, list the two things Servetus noticed that helped him figure out pulmonary circulation.

Lesson 22: Tycho Brahe (1546 – 1601)

Tycho (tee' koh) **Brahe** (brah' he), a Danish nobleman, had no plans to become a natural philosopher. In fact, he studied to be a statesman (a political leader) at the University of Copenhagen in Denmark. However, he was awed by a solar eclipse that happened in 1560. When he started doing some reading about astronomy, he was even more impressed that astronomers had predicted the event before it actually happened! This helped him become fascinated with astronomy, and as a result, he began studying the heavens in detail. Unlike most of the astronomers that came after him, Brahe did all of his observing without the benefit of telescopes. He used instruments to help him measure precisely where the stars were in the sky, but he didn't use anything other than his own eyes to actually view the stars.

This is a portrait of Tycho Brahe.

Because he was so detailed in his observations, he was able to see something rather remarkable in the year 1572. To get an idea of what he saw, perform the following experiment.

Simulating a Supernova

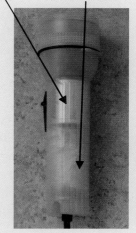

battery · foil where the other battery should be

What you will need:
- Aluminum foil
- A flashlight that uses two batteries (It is best to use a flashlight with a single bulb. Flashlights with LED lights will not give good results.)
- A white piece of paper
- A very bright room or a place outside where it is bright but is not exposed to direct sunlight. (Essentially, you want it to be so bright that light from the flashlight is hard to see when it is shone on the piece of paper.)
- Someone to help you

What you should do:
1. Unscrew the top of the flashlight and remove both batteries.
2. Make a wad of aluminum foil that is about the size of one of the batteries. Use a lot of foil so the wad is hard.
3. Put the wad of aluminum foil in the flashlight where the batteries go, and then put one battery in on top of the wad.
4. Screw the top of the flashlight back on. In the end, you should have a flashlight that has one battery and one battery-sized wad of aluminum foil, as shown in the picture above. In order for this to work, the wad of foil and the battery must be tightly held together in the flashlight. If your wad of aluminum foil really is about the size of a battery and is hard, it should work. If you put the flashlight back together and the wad of aluminum foil and battery can move around inside the flashlight, you need a bigger, harder wad of aluminum foil.
5. Turn on the flashlight. It should be a lot dimmer than usual.
6. Take the paper and flashlight into the bright area.
7. Have your helper hold the paper vertically.

8. Hold the flashlight very, very close to the paper and aim it at the center of the paper. You should be able to see a dim circle of light made by the flashlight on the paper. If you can't, you need to go to a more dimly-lit area.
9. Keeping the flashlight aimed at the paper, move the flashlight farther and farther from the paper. The circle of light should get dimmer and dimmer. Eventually, you should no longer be able to see the circle of light on the paper at all. If that doesn't happen, you need to go to a more brightly-lit area.
10. Once you can no longer see the circle of light on the paper, take one more step away from the paper so that you are just a bit farther away.
11. Without moving from where you are, turn off the flashlight, unscrew the top, and remove the battery and foil.
12. Put both batteries in the flashlight and screw on the lid.
13. Turn on the flashlight and make sure it works.
14. Without moving from where you were after you finished step 10, shine the flashlight at the paper your helper is holding. Do you see the circle of light again?
15. Put everything away.

The results of the experiment shouldn't have surprised you. When the flashlight had only one battery in it, it didn't have as much electrical energy to convert into radiant energy (light), so the flashlight was dimmer than usual. When you moved far enough away from the paper that the circle of light from the flashlight was no longer visible, that just meant the flashlight wasn't bright enough to make a visible reflection on the paper. However, when you put the second battery in, the light was much brighter, so you were able to see the circle of light again.

What does this have to do with Tycho Brahe? While studying the sky one night in 1572, he noticed a very bright star that had not been there the last time he had looked at that section of the sky. His observations were very detailed, and he was sure that he had not seen the star before. It seemed like a brand new star had just appeared in the night sky! This was a shock to him (and all astronomers who saw it), because almost all natural philosophers at the time still agreed with Aristotle's view of the heavens.

Remember, Aristotle (384 BC – 322 BC) thought that there were spheres that held the sun, each planet, and the stars, and that those spheres all revolved around the earth, which was at the center. In addition, he thought that everything in those spheres was **immutable** (ih myoo' tuh bul), which means that the spheres and whatever they contained could never change. In other words, anything beyond the moon was thought to be unchanging. However, Brahe saw with his own eyes that this simply wasn't the case. Prior to 1572, there was no star in that specific part of the night sky. After 1572, he could see a star there. Thus, something had changed!

Because so many other natural philosophers wanted to believe that Aristotle was right, they tried to argue that this new light that appeared in the night sky wasn't a star. Instead, it was some light that appeared between the earth and the moon. That way, a change had occurred, but it wasn't in any of the spheres beyond the moon. However, over the next few months, Brahe showed that the position of this new light in the night sky did not move in comparison to the stars. Since all the planets and the moon did move when compared to the stars, it became clear that this new light really was a new star.

Because of his observations, he wrote a short book called *The New Star*, in which he made his case that this bright light in the night sky was, indeed, a brand new star. This meant that Aristotle was wrong, and the heavenly spheres were not immutable. After all, the heavens changed, because a star that didn't exist before suddenly came into being. The book made a lot of people, even many church leaders, very uncomfortable, but it made Brahe famous among the powerful people in Denmark. As a result, King Frederick II of Denmark gave Brahe an island where he could build an **observatory**, which is a structure that is made for the purpose of making detailed astronomical observations. He also gave Brahe money so that he could support himself while he made those observations.

Now even though Brahe was correct about the fact that the heavens are not immutable, he was not 100% correct in his interpretation of what he saw. He did see a star, but it was not really a new star. The star had been there all along, but it was too dim for him to see with his eyes. However, the star exploded in 1572, and as a result of the explosion, it became very bright. That's why he was suddenly able to see it.

That's also why I had you do the experiment. While it was working on only one battery, the flashlight represented the star before 1572. When you moved it far from the paper, you could no longer see its light on the paper. Prior to 1572, the star was so dim that its light didn't reach the earth with enough intensity for it to be seen. However, when you put the second battery back in the

flashlight, it got brighter, and then you could see its light on the paper. In the same way, when the star exploded in 1572, it got a lot brighter, and as a result, Brahe could see it! Even though Brahe was wrong about it being a new star, we keep the name that Brahe gave it. Since Brahe wrote in Latin, he used the Latin word for "new," which is "nova," to describe the star. Scientists today call a star that explodes a **supernova**.

After about a year, Brahe's new star faded from view, because the explosion eventually died away. As a result, it could no longer be seen by anyone. However, if we turn our modern telescopes to that part of the sky now, we see what is called a **supernova remnant**, the remains of the awesome explosion that caused a dim star to be visible for a short time.

This image shows the remnant left over from the supernova that Tycho Brahe observed in 1572.

LESSON REVIEW

Youngest students: Answer these questions:

1. How did Tycho Brahe show that Aristotle's idea of the immutable heavens was wrong?

2. What do we call a star that explodes?

Older students: Explain what Tycho Brahe saw and how he was able to demonstrate that it was related to the stars and not the earth or moon. How did that show the heavens are not immutable?

Oldest students: Do what the older students are doing. In addition, explain why Brahe was wrong about the "new star" and give the name scientists use today for what he saw.

NOTE: The next lesson has an experiment that needs to sit long enough for water to freeze. Start it the night before you do the lesson, or plan your day so you can take a break as you let the water freeze.

68   The Scientific Revolution

Lesson 23: Tycho Brahe's View of the Universe

This is a picture of a comet that was visible in the Southern Hemisphere in 2004.

After a night of fishing, Tycho Brahe looked up in the sky to once again see something brand new. It wasn't a new star, like the one that brought him so much fame. Instead, this object was a **comet**, like the one pictured on the left. It had a bright spot in the front, and a long tail that extended from the bright spot. Comets were not unheard of in Brahe's day, but no one had studied them enough to really have an idea of what they were. Since Brahe had the wonderful observatory that he built with King Frederick II's money, he was able to observe the comet in detail. As a result, he learned some important things.

Before you find out what he learned, I want you to do an experiment that will help you understand what a comet is.

Simulating a Comet

What you will need:
- A Styrofoam cup
- Scissors
- Water
- Flour
- A measuring tablespoon
- A ¼-cup measuring cup
- Kitchen tongs
- A hand-held hair dryer
- An area where you can make a mess – It is best to take this outside starting in step 8, as long as you can find a way to keep the hair dryer plugged in.

What you should do:
1. Add one tablespoon of flour to the Styrofoam cup.
2. Add ¼ cup of water to the flour in the cup.
3. Mix the flour and water together. The flour won't dissolve in the water, and it will probably stick to the spoon in wet clumps. However, you need to thoroughly mix the two.
4. Put the cup in the freezer and let the mixture freeze.
5. Once the mixture is completely frozen, pull the cup out of the freezer.
6. Use the scissors to cut the cup and peel it away from the frozen water/flour mixture so that you have a nothing but a hunk of ice made from flour and water.
7. Use the kitchen tongs to hold the hunk of ice.
8. Take the tongs and ice outside or somewhere else you can make a mess. You need to have an outlet handy.
9. Plug the hair dryer in and turn it on the highest setting.

10. Point the hair dryer at the hunk of ice you are holding in the tongs. Watch what happens. It might take a little while to get started, but eventually you should see water and flour blowing away from the hunk of ice.
11. Move the angle at which the hair dryer is aimed at the hunk of ice. What happens to the flour and water blowing away from it?
12. When you are done, clean up your mess and put everything away.

What you made was actually a pretty good model of a comet. Astronomers often call comets "dirty snowballs," because they are a mixture of rocks, dust, frozen water, and frozen gases. When they are far from the sun, they can't be seen easily, because they are small and dim. However, as they get close to the sun, they start to heat up, and the frozen materials start to melt and evaporate. The gases that are made by this evaporation get hot and start to glow, which makes the comet easier to see.

In your experiment, then, the hunk of ice mixed with flour represented the comet before it got close to the sun. The hair dryer represented the sun. When the hair dryer blew on the hunk of ice, it started melting and blowing away the ice. This also exposed some flour, which blew off the hunk of ice as well. So the water and flour you saw streaming away from the hunk of ice represented the tail of the comet. As you changed the angle at which the hair dryer blew on the hunk of ice, what happened? The "tail" of your "comet" changed the way it was going – it always flew directly away from the hair dryer, right?

That's one of the things Tycho Brahe learned about the comet he studied. He watched the comet long enough to see that the direction its tail pointed changed over time. It always pointed directly away from the sun! This told Brahe that the sun was affecting the comet in a very important way. He didn't understand how the sun was doing it, but he could certainly see that it was!

Nowadays, we understand why the tail of a comet always points away from the sun. There is a constant stream of particles called **cosmic rays** coming from the sun. These particles make up a kind of "wind" that blows on the materials evaporating from the comet, just like the wind from the hair dryer blew on the water and flour in your experiment. Just as that stream of water and flour were blown directly away from the hair dryer, the gases coming off the comet are blown directly away from the sun. Most comets actually have two tails, because the dust coming from the comet is not as strongly affected by the sun as the gases are. As a result, the dust forms a second tail that bends in the direction of the comet's orbit.

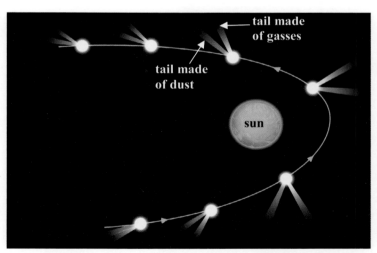

Most comets have two tails. The one made by gases points directly away from the sun because of the solar wind. The one made by dust is not as strongly affected by the solar wind, so it bends in the direction of the comet's orbit.

Because Brahe observed the comet in so much detail for so long, he discovered two other things. First, he discovered that the comet was well beyond the moon. Many natural philosophers (even some who came later in history) believed that comets were way up in the sky but still something that happened in the realm of the earth. At worst, they thought comets appeared somewhere between the earth and the moon. As he did with the new star he studied earlier, Brahe showed that this wasn't possible. Instead, the comet was way out in space.

The other thing he discovered was even more important. By tracking the comet for a long time, Brahe showed that it passed by Venus and Mercury. This was a real problem, because Aristotle's view of the universe (which was still the view held by most natural philosophers of the time) required that each planet be imbedded in a physical sphere. Those spheres rotated around the earth, carrying the planets with them. However, if the comet really was out in space, and if it really did pass by both Mercury and Venus, it would have to pass through the spheres. However, that wasn't possible according to Aristotle. He thought the spheres were like glass, and if something like a comet passed through them, they would break!

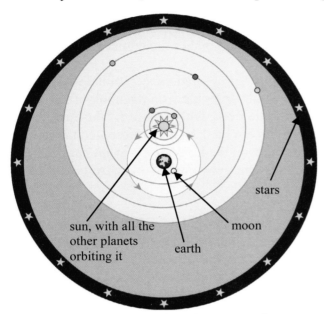

This drawing shows you the universe according to Tycho Brahe.

So Brahe used the comet to show that the universe couldn't be made of spheres like Aristotle thought. In addition, many of his observations showed that the planets really did orbit the sun, like Copernicus believed. Interestingly enough, however, Brahe didn't believe the sun is at the center of the universe. He thought that the earth was at the center because of the parallax problem you learned about in Lesson 3. As a result, he came up with what is probably the oddest view of the universe, which is shown in the drawing on the left. He thought the earth was at rest in the center of the universe, and the sun orbited it. However, he thought all the other planets orbited the sun while it orbited the earth.

As you can see, Brahe's idea is a mix between the geocentric view of the universe and the heliocentric view. While Brahe clung to this idea, it has even more problems than the geocentric view, so it was never believed by many natural philosophers other than Brahe. But even though Brahe was incredibly wrong when it came to his view of the universe, he at least moved science forward by destroying two of Aristotle's ideas that had been believed for thousands of years!

LESSON REVIEW

Youngest students: Answer these questions:

1. Why are comets sometimes called "dirty snowballs?"

2. Fill in the blank: Tycho Brahe used his observations of the comet to destroy Aristotle's idea that the universe was made of _____, each of which held a planet.

Older students: Explain what a comet is and how your experiment simulated one. In addition, explain why the tail of a comet always points away from the sun.

Oldest students: Do what the older students are doing. In addition, explain how Brahe was able to use the comet to destroy Aristotle's idea that the universe was made of spheres that each held a planet.

Lesson 24: Galileo Galilei (1564 – 1642)

It's now time to start discussing one of the most important figures in the history of **physics** (fiz' iks) and astronomy. You already know that astronomy is the study of planets, stars, and the like, but do you know what physics is? At one time, the word "physics" just meant "the study of the natural world," so all natural philosophers studied physics. Nowadays, however, it refers to the specific branch of science that tries to understand matter and energy and how the two of them work together. In fact, astronomy is considered a branch of physics, because astronomy studies the matter that we see in space (like planets, moons, and stars) and their energy (like the mechanical energy of their motion and the radiant energy of the light they emit or reflect).

Galileo (gal' uh lay' oh) **Galilei** (Gal' uh lay) was fascinated with the many different ways matter and energy related to one another, so he studied the motion of objects here on the surface of the earth as well as the motion of the objects in the sky. As a result, he taught us a lot about physics. In fact, some historians call him the father of modern physics. He actually wanted to be a priest, but his father urged him to go to a university to study medicine, so that's what he did. While he was studying medicine, however, he accidentally attended a class on mathematics. He was so fascinated by what he heard that he asked his father if he could study mathematics instead of medicine. His father reluctantly agreed, and as a result of his study of mathematics, Galileo became one of the most important natural philosophers of his day.

This is a statue of Galileo in Florence, Italy, which is near his hometown of Pisa.

One of Galileo's first contributions to our understanding of motion comes from an experiment he did with two **pendulums** (pen' duh lumz). I want you to recreate that experiment.

Pendulums and Time

What you will need:
- String
- Two washers or nuts
- Scissors
- Someone to help you

What you should do:
1. Cut the string into two 30-centimeter (1-foot) lengths
2. Tie a washer to one end of each string.
3. Have your helper hold one length of string so the washer hangs down and pulls the string tight.
4. Keeping the string tight, pull the washer several centimeters (a few inches) to one side of the position where it is hanging and then let go. What happens? The washer swings back and forth, right? You've just made a pendulum – a weight that hangs from a fixed point and swings back and forth.

5. Stop the washer and let it hang still again. Keeping the string tight, pull the washer to one side but not as far as you did before. Then let go. What happens? The washer swings back and forth again, but it doesn't swing as far to either side, does it?
6. Now have your helper hold the other string the same way in his other hand.
7. Have your helper bring his fingers together so that they are at exactly the same height, and then adjust the two washers so that the length of string from your helper's fingers to the washers is the same for both strings. See the picture on the left.

8. Have your helper pull his hands apart so the washers are now far from each other. However, he should not change how he is holding the string. The length of string from his fingers to each washer needs to stay the same.
9. Take one washer in each hand.
10. Keeping the string tight, pull one washer several centimeters to one side, as you did in step 4.
11. Keeping the string tight, pull the other washer to one side, but not as far, like you did in step 5.
12. In a moment, you are going to let go of both washers at the same time, but before you do, I want you to make a prediction about how long it will take each of them to swing from one side to the other. Will one swing faster than the other? If so, which one? Say your prediction out loud.
13. Let the washers go and watch them swing back and forth a few times. Did one swing faster than the other?
14. Clean up your mess and put everything away. If you are doing the "oldest student" review, you will want to wait until after you have done the review to do this.

Before you let both washers go, what did you predict? Most people predict that the washer pulled the farthest to one side will take longer to swing back and forth. After all, it travels farther in each swing, doesn't it? It makes sense, then, that it should take longer to swing back and forth than the washer that was pulled to one side by a shorter distance.

What you should have seen, however, is that the two washers swung back and forth in about the same amount of time. In fact, as you watched them both swing, they should have started out swinging in time with one another. After a while, one of them probably ended up getting out of time, but that's because of air resistance. Initially, they both swung together in perfect time, as long as you let them both go at the same time.

Before we go any further, I want to introduce three terms. The first is one you might have heard before: **hypothesis** (hy pah' thuh sis). When you made a prediction about what was going to happen when you let go of both washers at the same time, you were forming a hypothesis. You had observed a pendulum swinging back and forth, and based on what you observed, you made an educated guess about what would happen. That's a hypothesis. What did you do after you made your hypothesis? You tested it, right? You actually let both washers go and watched the result. Then you knew whether your hypothesis was right or wrong. Making a hypothesis and testing to see whether it is right or wrong are important parts of being a scientist.

The second term I want to introduce is **period**. That's a word you've heard before, but when scientists use the word, they often mean the time it takes for something to happen. For example, the time it took for the washer to swing over to one side and then back to the point where you released it is called the *period* of the pendulum that you made. In your experiment, you should have found that the period of each pendulum was the same, even though the washers had to travel different distances in order to get back to the side where they were released.

The third term I want to introduce is **displacement**. When you pulled the washer to one side, you were moving it from where it hung. The distance and direction that you moved it is called the displacement of the washer. When you pulled the washer several centimeters off to one side, it had a large displacement. When you pulled the washer a shorter distance to one side, it had a smaller displacement.

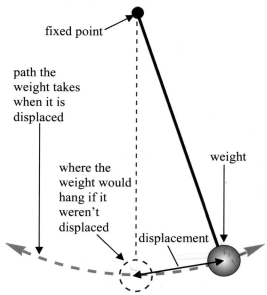

This is a sketch of a simple pendulum.

Galileo did several experiments like the one you did to show that a pendulum's period doesn't depend on its displacement. In other words, regardless of how far a given pendulum is pulled to one side, the time it takes to swing away and then come back to the place you released it is the same. Why is that? When you displace the pendulum a lot, it has to travel a long way to get back to where you released it. When you displace it only a little, it doesn't have to travel nearly as far. Why is the period the same regardless of how far it has to travel?

Well, the farther you pull it back, the faster it will swing. As things fall, they speed up. When a pendulum swings a short distance, it doesn't fall for very long, so it doesn't speed up very much. As a result, even though it doesn't have to travel very far to get back to where it was released, it makes that trip slowly. When a pendulum swings a longer distance, it falls longer and therefore speeds up more. So even though it has to travel a longer distance to get back to where it was released, it travels more quickly. For a pendulum, the increase in speed makes up for the increase in distance, so no matter how much a pendulum is displaced, its period will always be the same.

LESSON REVIEW

Youngest students: Answer these questions:

1. Fill in the blanks: A pendulum is a _____ that hangs from a fixed point and _____ back and forth.

2. What did Galileo show about the period of a pendulum?

Older students: Draw a picture like the one above, including the labels. In addition, define the period of a pendulum, and then state what Galileo showed about the period of a pendulum.

Oldest students: The period of a pendulum is not affected by its displacement, but it is affected by its length. Make a hypothesis as to which has a smaller period: a short pendulum or a long pendulum. Test your hypothesis with an experiment like you just did, but this time, make one pendulum shorter than the other.

Lesson 25: Galileo and Friction

Even though many of Aristotle's ideas were being questioned and shown to be wrong during this time of history, there were a lot of natural philosophers who followed his teachings without questioning them. One of his most important teachings is that everything in the world has a "natural" state – a situation it will attain if it is left alone. So, for example, a rock naturally wants to be on earth, because it is made out of things found in the earth. We can change that natural state, however, by forcing things to do what we want them to do. For example, we can force a rock to go away from earth by lifting it up, but as soon as we let go, it will fall back to its natural state – sitting on the earth.

Aristotle thought that the natural state of all objects that were made of things in the earth was to be at rest on the surface of the earth. If an object is left alone, then, it will simply sit there. We can make it move by pushing it, but as soon as we stop pushing it, the object will slow down and come to a halt. This, of course, is exactly what we see when we push things around. We can make them move as long as we are pushing them, but as soon as we stop, they slow down and eventually stop moving. Since Aristotle's idea is completely consistent with what we experience, most natural philosophers in Galileo's time believed it.

Galileo did experiments that told him no matter how much this idea made sense, it was wrong. I want you to perform an experiment similar to the ones Galileo did in order to learn what he learned.

A Rolling Ball Will Continue to Roll Until…

What you will need:
- 🖐 The cardboard tube from a roll of paper towels
- 🖐 A flat piece of cardboard that is at least 20 centimeters by 20 centimeters (8 inches by 8 inches)
- 🖐 Scissors
- 🖐 Tape
- 🖐 A piece of paper
- 🖐 A marble
- 🖐 Two large books
- 🖐 Someone to help you

What you should do:
1. Use the scissors to cut the cardboard tube in half lengthwise. You now have two troughs made from the cardboard tube.
2. Tape one end of each trough to the flat piece of cardboard so that the two troughs are about 2½ centimeters (1 inch) apart but lined up with one another.
3. Put a book under the other end of each trough. Your experiment should now look something like the picture below:

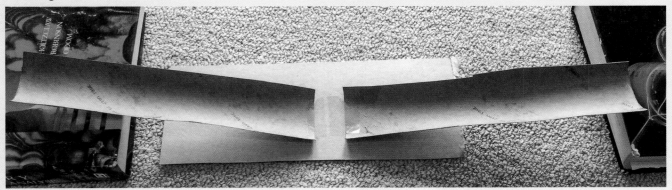

4. Adjust the position of the book on the left so the free end of the left trough is about 15 centimeters (6 inches) above the flat piece of cardboard. Don't worry about measuring the height and getting it exactly right – just estimate it.

5. Adjust the position of the book on the right so the free end of the right trough is noticeably lower than the left trough. The system in the picture on the previous page is set up that way.

6. Place the marble at the top of the left trough and let go. The marble should roll down the left trough, up the right trough, and if the right trough is low enough, it should roll off the trough and onto the book.

7. Move the right book slightly to the left so that the right trough rises just a bit. That way, its end is closer to the height of the left trough.

8. Repeat step 6.

9. Continue to repeat steps 7 and 8 until the right trough is high enough so that the marble rolls just to the top of the right trough but does not roll onto the book. Instead, it rolls back down the right trough and up the left trough.

10. Compare the heights of the two free ends of the troughs.
    Once you have the height just right, repeat step 6, and watch the marble roll until it comes to a complete stop. As you watch the marble, count the number of times it rolls back and forth.

11. Have your helper hold the flat piece of cardboard so that your experiment doesn't move when you do the next few steps.

12. Cut a piece of paper so that it is as wide as the troughs and is a bit longer than the distance between them.

13. Tape the piece of paper down so it makes a smooth surface connecting the two troughs, as shown below:

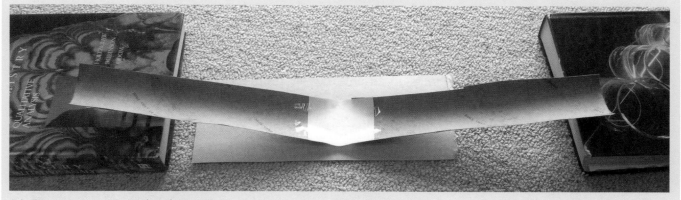

14. Repeat step 6. What happens?

15. Repeat steps 7 and 8 until once again, the marble rolls just to the top of the right trough but does not roll onto the book. Instead, it rolls back down the right trough and up the left trough.

16. Repeat step 6 and watch the marble roll until it comes to a complete stop. As you watch the marble, count the number of times it rolls back and forth.

17. Clean up your mess and put everything away, but save the troughs and cardboard. You will use them in the next lesson.

    What happened in your experiment? The free end of the right trough should have been almost (but not quite) as high as the free end of the left trough when the marble didn't roll onto the book. Once you got the height right, the marble should have rolled back and forth several times until it eventually came to a halt. However, when you put the paper in between the two troughs, the marble should have rolled off the right trough and onto the book, even though the height of the two troughs hadn't changed. In the end, you had to raise the right trough higher to keep the marble from falling off the trough and onto the book. Once you did that, you should have seen that the marble rolled back and forth more times before coming to a halt than it did without the piece of paper there.

What explains these results? The marble rolled down the left trough because gravity was pulling it down. Once it reached the bottom of the trough, it had been given a lot of mechanical energy. That energy allowed it to roll up the right trough. If the right trough wasn't too high, it had enough mechanical energy to roll past the top of the trough. However, as you raised the height of the right trough, the marble's mechanical energy was only enough to get it to the top of the right trough, but not past the top. As a result, it stopped and started rolling back down. Once again, when it got to the bottom, it had enough mechanical energy to roll up the left trough. However, it didn't roll nearly as high. This continued back and forth until the marble came to a rest.

When you added the paper, the marble could suddenly roll off the right trough and onto the book again. Why? Because it had more mechanical energy! Why? Because the paper formed a smoother surface, which reduced the **friction** (frik' shun) the ball was experiencing. As you have probably already learned, when two surfaces touch, they tend to "hold on" to each other a bit. That's friction, and friction works against motion, reducing the mechanical energy of a moving object. By adding the paper, you reduced friction, which means the marble could roll with more mechanical energy. When you adjusted the height of the right trough so that the marble couldn't roll off it, you also should have seen that the number of times the marble rolled back and forth was greater. Once again, that's because you reduced friction.

Do you see what this means? The marble came to a stop not because it has a natural state of being motionless. It came to a stop because *friction kept removing its energy.* If it hadn't been for friction, the ball would have kept rolling back and forth forever. It only stopped because friction removed the energy of its motion. By reducing friction, you increased how long it kept moving.

This told Galileo something very important: moving things don't come to rest because it's their natural state to be at rest. Moving things come to rest because friction works against their motion! If it weren't for friction, they would keep on moving. In the end, then, Aristotle was wrong. There is no "natural state" for objects; they tend to stay in whatever state they are in (moving, at rest, etc.) until they are acted on by a force. Objects in motion will stay in motion until something (like friction) stops them. Objects at rest will stay at rest until something (like a push or pull) causes them to move.

LESSON REVIEW

Youngest students: Answer these questions:

1. What is friction?

2. Why does a rolling ball eventually come to a stop, even though no one tries to stop it?

Older students: Make a drawing of your experiment, including the marble rolling down the troughs. Explain why the marble rolled back and forth but eventually came to a stop.

Oldest students: Suppose you could get rid of friction entirely in your experiment. How would the height of the two troughs compare when the marble just barely reached the top of the right trough without rolling off the trough and onto the book? Check your answer and correct it if it is wrong.

Lesson 26: Galileo and Falling Objects

Galileo not only showed that Aristotle was wrong when it came to why moving objects tend to stop; he also demonstrated that Aristotle was wrong when it came to how objects fall. If you studied Aristotle, you might remember that he thought heavy objects fell faster than light objects. Of course, this makes sense to some degree. After all, we know a feather falls very slowly, while a rock falls very quickly. However, many natural philosophers who lived after Aristotle found exceptions to his idea. For example, many had shown that lighter rocks didn't fall much (if any) faster than heavier rocks.

Galileo thought that most objects fell at a speed that did not depend on their weight at all. Interestingly enough, however, he didn't test this idea by dropping things! Instead, he tested the idea by rolling balls on ramps, much like the ones you used in the previous lesson. Technically, we call these ramps **inclined planes** because, in geometry, a plane is a flat surface. The ramps Galileo used were flat, and he tilted them so that balls could roll down them. Since another word for "tilted" is "inclined," you can see where we get the name. Perform an experiment similar to what Galileo did with inclined planes to see what he learned.

Rolling Down an Incline

What you will need:
- The two cardboard tube halves you used in the previous lesson
- Another cardboard tube from a roll of paper towels
- Scissors
- Tape
- A flat board that is at least a meter (39 inches) long
- A marble
- A book that is about 4 centimeters (1½ inches) thick
- A stopwatch that can read to hundredths of a second
- A marker

What you should do:
1. Cut the second cardboard tube in half lengthwise so that you now have four cardboard troughs.
2. Tape the four troughs together so they make one long trough.
3. Tape the long trough the board so it runs down the length of the board.
4. Put one end of the board on top of the book so it tilts. Your experiment should look something like this:

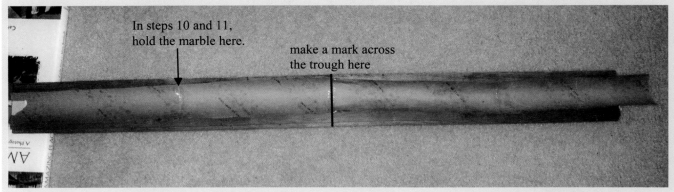

In steps 10 and 11, hold the marble here.

make a mark across the trough here

5. Use the marker to make a mark halfway down the cardboard trough, as shown in the picture above.
6. Hold the marble at the top of the trough.

7. Let go of the marble so it rolls down the trough. When the marble hits the mark you made, start the stopwatch. When it reaches the end of the trough and falls off, stop the stopwatch. Write down the time you measured.
8. Repeat steps 6 and 7 twice.
9. Add the three times you wrote down, and when you are done adding them, divide them by three. You just took an **average** of the three times you measured.
10. Hold the marble halfway between the top of the trough and the mark that you made. See the picture on the previous page.
11. Let go of the marble so it rolls down the trough. When the marble hits the mark you made, start the stopwatch. When it reaches the end of the trough and falls off, stop the stopwatch. Write down the time you measured.
12. Repeat steps 10 and 11 twice.
13. Add the three times you wrote down, and when you are done adding them, divide them by three.
14. Hold the marble at the mark you made.
15. Let go of the marble so it rolls down the trough. As soon as you let go, start the stopwatch. When it reaches the end of the trough and falls off, stop the stopwatch. Write down the time you measured.
16. Repeat steps 14 and 15 twice.
17. Add the three times you wrote down, and when you are done adding them, divide them by three.
18. Clean up your mess. Save the trough, as you will use one section of it in the next lesson.

Before I talk about the results of the experiment, let me explain why you made each measurement three times and then averaged the results together. Did you notice that each time you measured, the result was slightly different? That's because it is hard to start the stopwatch at exactly the right time and stop it at exactly the right time. As a result, each time you rolled the marble, you started and stopped the stopwatch differently. This is called **experimental error**. It's not that you did anything wrong. It's just that there is no way to do the experiment identically every time, so each time you did it, the results were slightly different.

When you added the three results together and then divided by three, you were averaging them together. This hopefully cancelled out some of the experimental error. After all, one time you might have started the stopwatch too early, making the time too long. The next time, you might have started it too late, making the time too short. In the end, by averaging the three measurements, you got a more accurate idea of how long it took the marble to roll from the mark to the end of the trough. If you repeated each experiment ten times and averaged the times, your result would probably have been even more accurate. However, it also would have been a lot more work. Scientists often repeat experiments many times and average the results specifically to reduce the effects of experimental error.

Compare the three averages you calculated. What do you see? The first average is the smallest, right? That means when you held the marble at the top of the trough and let go, the marble rolled from the mark to the end of the trough the fastest, right? The second average was larger, indicating that when the marble started lower on the trough, it rolled from the mark to the end of the trough more slowly. The last average should have been the largest, indicating that when the marble started even lower on the trough, it rolled from the mark to the end of the trough even more slowly.

Now, these results might not have been very surprising to you, but they illustrate something quite important: *The longer the marble rolled, the faster it moved.* When you let the marble go at the mark (the last set of measurements you made), it took a long time for the marble to travel the distance between the mark and the end of the trough, because it was moving slowly. When you released the marble from the top of the trough, by the time it got to the mark, it was already rolling pretty quickly. As a result, it traveled that same distance much more quickly.

When an object's speed changes, we say that it is experiencing **acceleration** (ak sel' uh ray' shun). So the marble experienced acceleration as it rolled down the ramp. Galileo thought that once an object (such as a ball) was heavy enough, the acceleration it would experience as it rolled down an inclined plane would be the same, regardless of its weight. So he did lots of experiments with balls rolling down inclined planes, and he measured the time it took those balls to roll a certain distance. He showed using mathematics that every ball did, indeed, accelerate the same, regardless of the weight of the ball.

Using these experiments, then, he concluded that objects that fall accelerate the same, regardless of their weight. As a result, a heavy rock and a light rock dropped from a tower would hit the ground pretty much at the same time, because they both experience the same acceleration the entire way down. But wait a minute. Galileo didn't drop things. He rolled things down a ramp. How did that allow him to make a conclusion about how things fall?

Well, Galileo understood that the same force which makes things fall (gravity) also makes balls roll down ramps. So even though he wasn't dropping things, he was using the same force. Why didn't he drop things? Because it was hard to measure time in Galileo's day (you will learn about that in a challenge lesson if you are doing those lessons). As a result, falling objects moved too quickly to be timed with any real precision. By using ramps, he was able to work with objects that moved more slowly, making it easier to time them. Some science books tell you that

Even though the Leaning Tower of Pisa was near Galileo's home, there is no evidence he used it in his experiments.

Galileo demonstrated that falling objects accelerate the same regardless of weight by dropping things off the Leaning Tower of Pisa, which was near his home. However, there is no evidence that he actually did that. Of course, he didn't need to; his experiments using inclined planes were enough.

LESSON REVIEW

Youngest students: Answer these questions:

1. What is acceleration?

2. Fill in the blank: Falling objects experience the same _____ regardless of their weight.

Older students: Define acceleration and use that word to describe the experiment you did and your results. Also, indicate whether or not the acceleration of a falling object depends on its weight.

Oldest students: Do what the older students are doing. In addition, explain what you did in your experiment to reduce experimental error.

Lesson 27: Galileo and Projectiles

Galileo's idea that an object in motion will continue with that motion until it is forced to do otherwise, as well as his idea of how objects fall, can be put together to describe the motion of a **projectile** (pruh jek' tyl). As you have probably already learned, a projectile is an object that is given some speed, but then it continues to travel through the air without anything else powering its motion. For example, if you shoot an arrow from a bow, the bowstring gives the arrow a push, but once the arrow leaves the bow, the bow can't push on it anymore. At that point, it flies through the air without anything else powering its motion.

If you studied the ancient natural philosophers that came before Galileo, you know that John Philoponus (c. AD 490 – AD 570) determined that the air through which a projectile travels actually fights against its motion. Jean Buridan (c. 1300 – c. 1360) then determined that a projectile moves according to its weight and the speed it was given when it was launched. Finally, Nicole Oresme (c. 1320 – 1382) showed that the motion of a projectile also depends on how it was moving the instant it was launched. If you shoot an arrow straight up in the air on a windless day, for example, it comes back to the earth at the same point from which you launched it, despite the fact that the earth is rotating. Because the arrow was rotating with the earth at the instant it was launched, it continues to rotate with the earth as it travels through the air.

Galileo brought all of these thoughts together by performing an experiment with projectiles. I want you to perform a similar experiment for yourself.

Projectile Motion

What you will need:
- The setup you used for the previous experiment
- A flat piece of cardboard like the one you used in Lesson 25
- The marble you used for the previous experiment
- A table
- Someone to help you

What you should do:
1. Remove the top section of cardboard trough from the previous experiment's setup. Disconnect it from the board as well.
2. Tape the middle of the flat piece of cardboard to one end of that trough.
3. Put the trough and cardboard on the table so the end of the cardboard is right at the edge, and prop the other end of the trough with one of the books so the top of the trough is on the very edge of the book, as shown in the picture below:

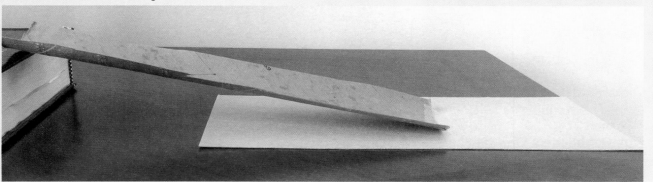

4. Have your helper kneel on the floor at the edge of the table. In a moment, you are going to have the marble roll down the trough, off the table, and onto the floor. Your helper should be positioned so he or she is not in the path of the marble but can easily mark where it hits the floor.
5. Put the marble at the top of the trough and let it roll down the trough and off the table.
6. Have your helper put his or her finger at the place the marble first hit the floor.
7. Go get the marble and bring it back to the table.
8. Move the book about 7.5 centimeters (3 inches) towards the edge of the table while keeping the trough and the cardboard right where they are. That way, the trough will have a steeper tilt.
9. Repeat step 5 while your helper still has a finger at the place it was in step 6.
10. Have your helper use a finger from his or her other hand to mark the spot where the marble first hits the floor this time.
11. Compare positions of your helper's two fingers. What do you see?
12. Repeat steps 7-11, but this time, have your helper move the finger he or she used in step 6 to the place where the marble first hits the ground, while leaving the other finger where it was in step 10.
13. Compare the positions of your helper's two fingers. What do you see?
14. Clean up your mess and put everything away.

The results of the experiment probably weren't very surprising. You should have seen that the steeper the tilt of the trough, the farther away from the table the marble traveled before hitting the floor. Galileo probably wasn't surprised by the results when he did a similar experiment. Nevertheless, he repeated it many different times, carefully marking where the ball landed each time. He also watched the ball as it fell, noticing that it moved in a curved path – falling down towards the floor, but also moving away from the table.

Why did the ball follow a curved path? Well, you know that as soon as the ball falls off the end of the table, it starts falling to the floor. However, even though it is being pulled down to the floor by gravity, it still has the motion it had before falling off the table. As Galileo had already determined, an object in motion will continue on with that motion until forced to do otherwise. Well, gravity forced the ball to start falling, but it did nothing to stop the motion the ball already had. As a result, that motion continued while the ball fell. The result was motion in two directions: down and away from the table. Those two motions resulted in the ball following a curved path.

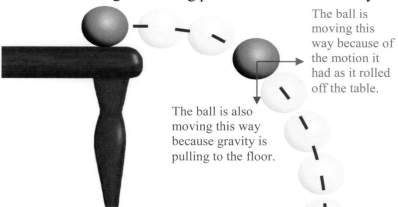

The ball is moving this way because of the motion it had as it rolled off the table.

The ball is also moving this way because gravity is pulling to the floor.

In your experiment (and Galileo's), the two different motions of the ball combined to make the ball follow a curved path.

None of this was new to Galileo. Natural philosophers had figured out by observation that projectiles moved along a curved path. What Galileo wanted to know was whether or not he could mathematically describe the curve. After all, if he could figure out the mathematics behind the curve, he could actually predict how a projectile would travel before it was launched! Well, it turns out that because Galileo repeated his experiment many different times in many different ways and made careful measurements each time, he was able to actually determine what kind of curved path a projectile follows. It is called a **parabolic** (pehr' uh bol' ik) path, and mathematicians had actually described such a curve long before the birth of Christ!

These are boats that are used to put out fires, but in this picture, they are using their sprayers to put on a show. Ignoring the effects of wind and air resistance, each jet follows a parabolic path, because the water is essentially a projectile being launched from the sprayers.

In some ways, this should surprise you. After all, in ancient times, mathematicians weren't worried about how projectiles travel through the air. They were worried about counting things, solving equations, describing the shapes and sizes of objects, etc. Why in the world would a projectile follow a path that could be described by something mathematicians had determined more than 1,500 years before Galileo did his experiments?

Well, it turns out that this is not very unusual. A lot of what scientists discover about creation can be described in terms of mathematical rules that were developed for reasons that had nothing to do with science. Why? Galileo himself had an answer to that question. He said that the universe "…cannot be read until we have learnt the language and become familiar with the characters in which it is written. It is written in mathematical language, and the letters are triangles, circles and other geometrical figures, without which means it is humanly impossible to comprehend a single word." [Stillman Drake and C. D. O'Malley, *The Controversy on the Comets of 1618*, University of Pennsylvania Press, 1960, pp. 183-184]

Why did Galileo believe this? Because he believed that God created everything that natural philosophers studied. As a result, the things being studied obeyed laws that God wrote into nature. The language in which He wrote those laws was mathematical, so those who studied mathematics discovered that language. To Galileo, then, it wasn't at all surprising that math which had been discovered centuries ago could be used to describe what he studied. In fact, he expected it! Galileo's discovery that projectiles follow parabolic motion was just the tip of the iceberg. As natural philosophers studied God's creation more and more, it became very clear that mathematics is absolutely necessary to fully understanding how creation works.

LESSON REVIEW

Youngest students: Answer these questions:

1. Fill in the blank: A projectile flies through the air without anything _____ its motion.

2. Fill in the blank: A projectile follows a _____ path.

Older students: Describe your experiment and then make a drawing like the one on the previous page. Explain why the ball was a projectile and why its path was curved once it fell off the table. Give the name that mathematicians use to describe the curve, and write down that all projectiles follow it.

Oldest students: Do what the older students are doing. In addition, explain why Galileo thought mathematics is capable of describing how creation works.

Lesson 28: How Galileo Measured Time

In Lesson 26, you measured the time it took for a ball to roll a certain distance down a ramp. You noticed that the longer the ball had been rolling down the ramp, the faster it went. It was an easy experiment to do because you were able to use a stopwatch. Galileo did similar experiments to show that all objects, regardless of mass, experienced the same acceleration when falling. However, it wasn't as easy for him, because back then, there weren't stopwatches. How did Galileo measure the time it took for balls to roll down his inclined plane?

Even though stopwatches weren't around in Galileo's time, there were clocks. Indeed, the first mechanical clock was probably invented in the late 1200s. However, they were notoriously inaccurate, even in Galileo's time. In fact, for a long time, mechanical clocks had to be corrected using sundials! In addition, most mechanical clocks in Galileo's time only measured the hour of the day. Tycho Brahe had a clock with a minute hand, but that was pretty rare in those days. Even if Galileo had such a clock, it wouldn't be able to measure seconds or fractions of a second, which was necessary in order to do an experiment like the one you did.

This clock was installed on the outside of a church in London in 1671, about 30 years after Galileo died. It was London's first public clock with a minute hand.

So how did Galileo measure time in his experiments? Do the following experiment to find out.

Using Water to Tell Time

What you will need:
- A large Styrofoam or paper cup
- A pen
- A sink with a water tap
- A stopwatch
- A ½-liter bottle, like the kind water comes in
- Paper towels
- A ¼-cup measuring cup (the kind usually used to measure solids)
- A ½-cup measuring cup (the kind usually used to measure solids)
- A 1-cup measuring cup (the kind usually used to measure solids)
- Someone to help you

What you should do:
1. Use the pen to poke a small hole in the bottom of the Styrofoam cup at the center.

2. Fill the cup with some water, and hold it over the sink. Look at the water leaking out of the bottom of the cup. It should be leaking out in a steady but small stream. If the water is dripping out slowly drop by drop, empty the cup and use the pen to make the hole a little wider.
3. Once you have the hole sized correctly, fill the bottle with water, and set it somewhere within reach.
4. Place a single paper towel on a counter by the sink, and put the 1-cup measuring cup in the center of the paper towel.
5. Give your helper the stopwatch.
6. Fill the Styrofoam cup full of water, but cover the hole with a finger so water doesn't leak out.
7. Making sure no water is leaking from the cup, hold it so the hole is directly over the 1-cup measuring cup.
8. Pull your finger away from the hole so the water starts filling the measuring cup. At the same instant, tell your helper to start the stopwatch.
9. Keeping the Styrofoam cup over the measuring cup so that the measuring cup fills with water, grab the water bottle with your other hand.
10. As the Styrofoam cup loses water, add more water to the cup from the bottle so that the cup stays pretty much full. Be sure not to let any of the water from the bottle spill into the measuring cup! The only water that goes into the measuring cup should be the water leaking out of the bottom of the Styrofoam cup.
11. Watch the measuring cup fill up. As soon as the very first bit of water spills over the top of the measuring cup, tell your helper to stop the stopwatch.
12. Write down the time. This is the time it took to fill the measuring cup until it overflowed with water.
13. Throw away the paper towel and dry the counter with another paper towel.
14. Repeat steps 4-13, but this time use the ½-cup measuring cup.
15. Repeat steps 4-13 again, but this time use the ¼-cup measuring cup.
16. Compare the three times you measured. Do you notice a pattern?
17. Clean up your mess and put everything away.

What did you see in the experiment? You should have noticed that the smaller the cup, the shorter the time it took to fill the cup. That makes sense, of course. However, you might have noticed something else. The ½-cup measuring cup should have taken about twice as many seconds to fill as the ¼-cup measuring cup. Now once again, that should make sense. A ½ cup is twice as much as a ¼ cup, so it makes sense that it would take twice as long to fill a cup that is twice as big. In the same way, it should have taken about twice as long to fill the 1-cup measuring cup as it did to fill the ½-cup measuring cup. What does that tell you? It tells you that when water is flowing in a steady stream, the amount of water that flows depends on the time: twice as much water takes twice as much time.

Believe it or not, this is very similar to how Galileo measured time in his experiments! He had a large container that he kept full of water. There was a small tube at the bottom that allowed water to leak out of the container and into a smaller container. When he wanted to start his timer, he allowed water to flow into the smaller container. When he wanted to stop the timer, he stopped the water. He realized that the amount of water in the smaller container was a measure of how much time had passed.

Now in your experiment, you measured the *volume* of water (¼ cup, ½ cup, 1 cup), because that was an easy thing for you to measure. Galileo didn't do that. Instead, he *weighed* the water to determine how much was there. The larger the weight, the longer the time that had passed. So Galileo measured time by weighing water! That's pretty clever, isn't it?

Of course, Galileo wasn't the first to realize that a steady stream of water filling up a container was a way to measure time. In fact, the first clocks that weren't sundials were probably water clocks. As far as historians can tell, water clocks have been around for more than 3,000 years. The basic design was simple: water dripped from one container into another container. The water level in the second container told the time – the higher the water, the later the time. The drawing on the right, for example, is of an ancient Egyptian water clock. As water dripped into the tube at the bottom of the clock, the float rose. This pushed a rod up, and the teeth on the rod turned a gear, which moved the hour hand of the clock.

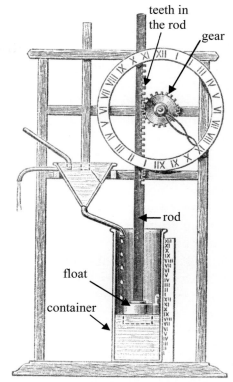

This is a drawing of an ancient Egyptian water clock.

Not all water clocks were that elaborate. Some just had a glass container with lines on it. You read the time by just looking at what line the water level was closest to. Of course, there are other timekeeping devices that use a similar principle. Have you ever seen an hourglass? It measures the passage of time by allowing sand to fall from the top of the hourglass to the bottom of the hourglass. Since the sand falls in a fairly steady stream, the height of the sand in the bottom of the hourglass is a measure of how much time has passed.

Think about what it takes to measure the passage of time. It takes something that happens at a steady pace. In your experiment, water leaked out of the Styrofoam cup at a steady pace. In a water clock, water drips into a container at a steady pace. In an hourglass, sand falls from the top of the hourglass to the bottom at a steady pace. If you have something that happens at a steady pace, you can measure the passage of time with it.

Even modern clocks still use this method for measuring time, but they don't use water or sand. Instead, most clocks you use these days use a small piece of **quartz** (kworts), which is a natural mineral. When electricity is passed through the quartz, it vibrates at a steady pace. The clock counts the number of vibrations, and the more vibrations, the more time has passed. So even though the technology has changed, the basic way in which time is measured is still the same as it was back in ancient times!

LESSON REVIEW

Youngest students: Answer these questions:

1. Back in Galileo's day, which was more accurate: a mechanical clock or a sundial?

2. Fill in the blank: Galileo measured time by _____ water that dripped into a container.

Older students: Explain how Galileo measured time and why he had to do it that way. Also, explain how most clocks today use the same principle with different materials.

Oldest students: Do what the older students are doing. In addition, come up with a reason why I had you keep the Styrofoam cup filled in your experiment. Check your answer and correct it if it is wrong.

Lesson 29: How Galileo Measured Temperature

How do you know what the temperature is? You probably look it up on the internet. But how do the people posting it on the internet measure the temperature? They use a thermometer. Back in Galileo's time, however, thermometers had not been invented. Nevertheless, Galileo really wanted to measure temperature, so he developed something called a **thermoscope**. Perform the following experiment to see the way his thermoscope worked.

Using Air and Water to Measure Temperature

What you will need:
- A ½-liter bottle, like the kind water comes in
- A large glass
- Food coloring
- A spoon
- A large pot for heating water
- A stove
- Kitchen tongs
- Water
- An adult to help you

What you should do:
1. Fill the pot with hot water and have an adult help you put it on the stove to heat it.
2. Fill the large glass nearly full of water and add a few drops of food coloring.

3. Stir the food coloring so the water in the glass is evenly colored.
4. If the lid is on the bottle, remove it.
5. Holding the bottle by its top with the kitchen tongs, have an adult help you push the bottom of the bottle into the water that is heating on the stove. **BE CAREFUL**. The stove and pan are hot! Don't touch them. Just push the bottom of the bottle into the water so about half of it is underwater. You are using the hot water in the pot to heat the air inside the bottle.
6. Continue to use the tongs to hold the bottle in the water that is being heated for five minutes or until the water starts to boil, whichever comes first.
7. Lift the bottle out of the water and quickly turn it upside down.
8. After it has been upside down for a few seconds, grab the bottle with your hand. It won't be hot enough to burn you.
9. Lower the top of the bottle into the glass of water until the opening of the bottle is about a centimeter (half an inch) under water, as shown in the picture on the left.
10. Hold it there for a couple of minutes, making sure that the opening of the bottle stays underwater the entire time.
11. Watch what happens.
12. Clean up your mess and put everything away.

What did you see in the experiment? When you put the upside-down water bottle into the colored water, you should have seen the colored water rise into the bottle. As time went on, more and more water should have risen into the bottle. Why did that happen?

You have probably already learned that when things heat up, they expand (get bigger). When things cool down, they contract (get smaller). This is true of pretty much everything, including air. As you heated the air inside the bottle, then, it started to expand. Since the bottle was open, the expanding air pushed its way out of the bottle and into the rest of the kitchen. When you turned the bottle over and put its opening under the water that was in the glass (at room temperature), the air inside the bottle started to cool. As it cooled, it contracted, leaving space in the bottle. There was no way for air to come in to take up that new space, so the contracting air pulled water into the bottle. The colder the bottle got, the more water it took in. If you had later warmed the bottle (with a hair dryer, for example), water would have been pushed out of the bottle and back into the glass.

So the height of the water in the bottle told you something about the temperature of the bottle. As the bottle cooled down, water rose higher. If the bottle warmed up, the water level in the bottle would go down. This was the basis of the thermoscope Galileo (with help from some other natural philosophers) developed. Of course, his thermoscope was a bit different from yours, but it worked using the same idea.

A replica of Galileo's thermoscope is shown on the right. The bottom container had water in it, but the tube and the top container just had air in them. When the surroundings got cooler, the contracting air would pull the water up the tube and towards the container on the top. When the surroundings got warmer, the expanding air would push the water back down into the bottom container. In the end, then, the level of water in the tube would tell you how warm or cold it was.

At this point in history, then, the best a thermoscope could do was tell you about the *change in temperature*. When water rose in the tube, the temperature was decreasing, and when water fell in the tube, the temperature was increasing. However, there was no standard scale for measuring temperature. That didn't come along for another 100 years or so. Nevertheless, just being able to have a visual measurement of the change in temperature was useful for natural philosophers, especially those who were trying to understand weather.

This is a model of Galileo's thermoscope.

The fact that things expand and contract when the temperature changes is still the basis of how temperature is measured. In fact, most thermometers we use today are based on a liquid (such as alcohol) expanding and contracting as the temperature changes. One of the more interesting uses of this idea is called the **Galileo thermometer**. Even though it bears Galileo's name, Galileo didn't have anything to do with its invention. Nevertheless, it demonstrates an important concept in science, so it is worth discussing.

You probably have already learned the term **density**. It is a measure of how much matter is packed into a certain volume. For example, think about a Styrofoam ball that is the same size as a baseball. Would the two balls weigh the same? No, they wouldn't. The Styrofoam ball would weigh less, even though it is exactly the same size as the baseball. Why? Because matter is not packed as tightly into the Styrofoam ball. As a result, it holds less matter than a baseball of the same size, and that makes it weigh less.

Now let's say you have exactly 1 pound of water. As you heat up the water, what will happen to it? It will expand, right? That means it will take up more space. In other words, its volume will increase. What will happen to its weight? Nothing. You aren't adding water or taking water away, so the weight is exactly the same. However, the volume has increased. What does that mean? It means the same amount of weight (or the same amount of matter) is packed into a *larger* volume. What does that tell you about its density? The same amount of weight is contained in a larger volume, so the water is *less dense* – its matter is packed more loosely.

Before we go on, let's make sure you really understand that. If I heat up a certain amount of water, the same amount of matter ends up occupying a larger space. As a result, the matter is packed more loosely. That means *as I warm water up, its density decreases*! If I cool down that water, the same amount of matter starts occupying a smaller amount of space. That means the matter is being packed more tightly. So, *as I cool water down, its density increases*!

Now think about why things float. An object floats if it weighs less than an equal volume of water. So let's suppose something just barely floats in water. That means it weighs just a little less

The number on this bulb indicates the temperature.

than an equal volume of water. Suppose while the thing is just barely floating, I heat up the water. What will happen to the water's density? It will decrease, right? That means an equal volume of water will weigh less! If I heat the water up enough, the density will decrease to the point where the thing that is floating is now *heavier* than an equal volume of water, and the thing will sink!

Now think about the opposite situation. Think of something that is just barely heavier than an equal volume of water. It will sink, but just barely. Suppose I cool down the water. The density of the water will increase, causing an equal volume of water to weigh more. If the water cools down enough, the thing that just barely sank will suddenly weigh less than an equal volume of water, and it will float!

That's the idea behind the Galileo thermometer in the picture. Each of the bulbs weighs just enough so that at a certain temperature (written on the bulb), it weighs exactly as much as an equal volume of water. As a result, it will not sink to the bottom or float to the top. It will sit near the middle of the tube. You can determine the temperature by looking at the bulb that is lowest in the tube, but not sitting on the bottom. The temperature written on the bulb is the temperature! Now even though Galileo didn't invent this kind of thermometer, it uses the idea that things expand and contract when the temperature changes, so in a way, Galileo was the inspiration for its design.

Even though he didn't invent it, this is called a Galileo thermometer.

LESSON REVIEW

Youngest students: Answer these questions:

1. Fill in the blank: Galileo measured temperature change with the level of _____ in a glass tube.

2. When water gets hotter, what happens to its density?

Older students: Draw a diagram of the thermoscope Galileo made and explain how it worked.

Oldest students: Do what the older students are doing. In addition, draw a diagram of a Galileo thermometer and explain how it works. Use the word "density" in your explanation.

Lesson 30: Galileo and the Telescope

In the next set of lessons, you will learn that Galileo made some very important discoveries about the heavens. Some of those discoveries were the result of his ability to see planets better than anyone else in his day. How did he get that ability? Perform the following experiment to see for yourself.

Making Your Own Telescope

What you will need:
- Weak reading glasses (A power of 1.50 is ideal.)
- A magnifying glass (It should have a larger power than the reading glasses.)
- A meterstick or yardstick
- Tape
- A window with a view of something interesting

What you should do:
1. Tape the side of one earpiece on the reading glasses to the meterstick so that the glasses are on the end of the meterstick, as shown in the picture on the right.
2. Put the meterstick on your shoulder so the glasses are in front of you but far from your eyes, as shown in the picture.
3. Hold the magnifying glass up against the eye that is farthest from the meterstick, and close your other eye.
4. Look through both the magnifying glass and the lens of the reading glasses that is farthest from the meterstick.

Use the magnifying glass to look through this lens.

5. Move the meterstick around until you see something interesting through the lens of the reading glasses. **DO NOT point it at the sky anywhere near the sun! Looking at the sun through this contraption will hurt your eyes!**
6. Move the meterstick back and forth, and you should see the focus change.
7. Play with moving the meterstick around and moving it back and forth to see how the image you are seeing through the reading glasses changes. Do you see that everything you are looking at is upside down? That makes it hard to move the glasses in the right way, doesn't it?
8. Besides being upside down, what is different about looking at something through both the magnifying glass and the reading glasses as opposed to just looking at it with your unaided eyes?
9. OPTIONAL: Save the setup for a clear night when the moon is out. See if you can look at the moon in the same way. How much difference do you see between looking at the moon with your naked eyes and looking at it through this contraption?
10. Clean up your mess and put everything away when you are done.

What did you see in the experiment? If all went well, what you saw through both the magnifying glass and the reading glasses should have been bigger than they appeared to your unaided

eyes. That's because you made a simple **telescope**, a device that makes distant objects appear to be nearer. Some telescopes use mirrors and a magnifying lens to get the job done, but the first telescopes that were made operated basically like yours did. There was a weak magnifying glass on the end of the telescope, and a stronger magnifying lens where you put your eye. When you looked at an object far away through both lenses, it made the object look closer.

How does this work? As you might have already learned, lenses bend light. The lenses that make up reading glasses and magnifying glasses bend it so that the light which hits the lens straight on is focused to a specific point, called the **focal point** of the lens. So the reading glasses in your experiment took the light coming from the objects you were looking at and bent it towards the focal point. When that light hit the lens of the magnifying glass, it was bent again. This sent the light to your eyes, making it look like the object you were looking at was much closer. Here's an illustration of how it worked:

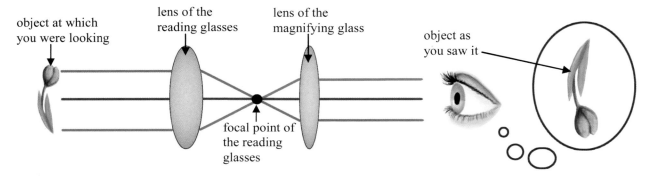

Do you now understand why the image you saw was upside down? Look at the red line coming from the flower. It represents light reflecting off the top of the flower and traveling to your telescope. When the lens of the reading glasses bends the light, it bends down. By the time that light hits the lens of the magnifying glass, it is at the bottom of the magnifying glass. As a result, you see the top of the flower at the bottom of the magnifying glass. On the other hand, the green line that comes from the flower represents light reflecting off the bottom of the flower. It is bent up, which causes it to hit the top of the magnifying glass. As a result, you see the bottom of the flower at the top of the magnifying glass.

By using two lenses together, then, a telescope can bend the light coming from distant objects to make them appear much closer than they actually are. As a result, you can see distant things much more clearly. Obviously, this is a very handy tool for someone trying to understand the heavenly bodies, since they are very far away. Galileo used his telescope to learn a great many things about planets, stars, moons, etc.

In a later lesson, you will learn some of the things that Galileo discovered with his telescope. For right now, however, I want to concentrate on the telescope itself. Many textbooks and websites tell you that Galileo invented the telescope. That's not really true.

Believe it or not, we don't really know who invented the telescope. There are at least three people who might have. Not surprisingly, all of them were people who made eyeglasses for a living. Back then, such people were called "spectacle makers," and they had a lot of experience with lenses. It's not surprising, then, that one of them figured out what would happen when you arranged two lenses properly.

A Dutch spectacle-maker named Zacharias Janssen claimed to have invented the telescope in 1608, but there is no strong historical evidence to support his claim. Another Dutch spectacle-maker named Jacob Metius actually applied for a **patent** in 1608. A patent is a legal document that affirms a person has invented something and allows that person to control how the invention is produced so that he can profit from the invention. By filing for a patent, then, Jacob Metius claimed to be the inventor of the telescope. However, a German spectacle-maker (who was living in the Netherlands) named Hans Lippershey also applied for a patent for the telescope, and his application was earlier than Jacob Metius's by a few weeks. As a result, he is generally given credit for inventing the telescope.

This is a portrait of Hans Lippershey, who has the strongest claim to inventing the telescope.

Why is Galileo often thought of as the telescope's inventor? Well, in 1609, he heard about a man who was in Padua, Italy, trying to sell an instrument that allowed distant objects to appear closer to you. At the time, Galileo was in Venice, Italy, but he immediately recognized how useful this instrument would be for his examination of the heavenly bodies. He rushed to Padua to find the man who was selling the instrument, but ironically, the man had left for Venice.

A friend of Galileo's in Venice ended up seeing the instrument. The government was interested in buying it for use in sailing and warfare, but Galileo's friend advised them against it, because he knew Galileo could make a better one. Once Galileo heard the details of the telescope, he made a significantly better one and turned it towards the sky. What he saw through that telescope would change the science of astronomy forever, as you will learn in a later lesson. So even though Galileo didn't actually invent the telescope, he was the first to publish how he made it and what he learned by using it.

LESSON REVIEW

Youngest students: Answer these questions:

1. Fill in the blanks: Because of the way the lenses bend light in a telescope, distant objects appear to be _____ than they actually are, and they appear _____ ____.

2. Did Galileo invent the telescope?

Older students: Draw a diagram like the one that appears on the previous page, and underneath, explain how it relates to the experiment you did. Also, use it to explain why the things you saw through your telescope appeared closer but upside down.

Oldest students: Do what the older students are doing. In addition, explain how we know that Galileo did not invent the telescope.

Section 3: The Revolution in the Early 17th Century

This is the Astronomer's Monument, which is at the Griffith Observatory in Los Angeles, California. It pays tribute to six great astronomers of the past, including Johannes Kepler.

Lessons 31-45: The Revolution in the Early 17th Century

Lesson 31: Galileo and Heliocentrism

Although Galileo made many different contributions to science, he is probably best remembered as a champion of the heliocentric view of the universe. While Copernicus's book did present some evidence in support of his heliocentric view, Galileo discovered many other pieces of evidence to support the view. One reason is that Galileo was the first to use a telescope for looking at heavenly bodies. This allowed him to see the heavenly bodies in a much more detailed way than anyone before him, and those observations provided strong evidence for the heliocentric system.

This is a telescope picture of Jupiter (the large, white disk in the center) and its four Galilean moons (the small dots).

For example, when Galileo studied Jupiter through his telescope, he was surprised to find *four moons* orbiting the planet. Today, we call them the **Galilean moons**, and they demonstrate that there are objects in the universe that do not orbit the earth. This went against the geocentric system, which said that all things in the universe orbited the earth. We now know that there are a lot more than four moons orbiting Jupiter (at least 67!), and we know that Mars, Saturn, Uranus, Neptune, and even Pluto also have moons orbiting them.

Galileo saw other things through the telescope that contradicted not only the geocentric view, but also Aristotle's ideas about the heavens. For example, Aristotle said that all the heavenly bodies (the sun, moon, stars, and planets) are perfect, because they are in the heavens above the earth. However, with his telescope, Galileo saw that the moon is not perfect. Instead, its surface is covered with craters and mountains. Since Aristotle's views were believed by most geocentrists, this ended up being an argument against geocentrism.

He also observed the sun with his telescope. He didn't spend a lot of time looking directly at the sun, but instead, allowed the telescope's eyepiece to shine its image on a piece of paper, and he looked at the piece of paper. If you did Lesson 59 in *Science in the Beginning* (a challenge lesson), you did something similar with binoculars. When he looked at the sun that way, he saw **sunspots**, which are dark patches on the sun. This indicated that, like the moon, the sun was not perfect, even though Aristotle thought it was. Also, as he observed the sunspots, they seemed to move across the face of the sun, which told Galileo that the sun rotates. He argued that if the sun could rotate, so could the earth, which is necessary in the heliocentric system in order for night to turn into day.

However, the observations Galileo made with his telescope that best supported the heliocentric view were of the planet Venus. By carefully studying Venus with a telescope night after night, he showed that, like the moon, Venus had **phases**. In his telescope, there were times the entire planet was lit up, but there were other times when only half of the planet was lit up. Just like the moon, there were even times when only a thin crescent of Venus was lit up. While this observation was easy to understand using the heliocentric view of the universe, it was impossible to understand using the geocentric view. To understand why, do the experiment on the next page.

The Phases of Venus

What you will need:
- 🖐 A flashlight
- 🖐 A baseball or some other hand-sized ball that is white or at least brightly colored
- 🖐 A dim room
- 🖐 Someone to help you

What you should do:
1. Stand at one end of the dim room.
2. Turn on the flashlight, hand it to your helper, and have him or her stand about a meter (3 feet or so) in front of you.
3. Hold the baseball so that your fingers and hand are below the ball.
4. Stretch out your arm so the ball is as far in front of you as it can be.
5. Hold the baseball up so it is at eye level.
6. Have your helper shine the flashlight directly at the ball. Since the ball is in front of your face, you shouldn't see the flashlight's light reflecting off the ball, as the flashlight should be shining on the part of the ball that is facing away from you.
7. Standing still, slowly move your arm so the ball travels in a horizontal circle that stays in front of your face the whole time. It should not move up and down at all. It should just move in a circle that is between you and the flashlight.
8. Have your helper continually adjust the flashlight so it is always aiming at the ball as it moves.
9. Notice how much of the ball is lit up by the light from the flashlight.
10. Repeat the circle until you have a good idea of how much of the ball gets lit up by the flashlight as it moves in the circle.
11. Put everything away.

Did you notice that not much of the ball was lit up by the light from the flashlight? When it started off directly in front of you, no part of the ball facing you was lit up, because the flashlight was shining on it from behind. As the ball started moving in a circle, part of it became lit up, but by the time the ball traveled through half of a circle, the flashlight was shining on it from behind again, so once again, no part of the ball that was facing you was lit up. As the ball completed its travel around the circle, part of it got lit up, but there was never a time when every part of the ball that was facing you was lit up by the flashlight.

How does this relate to the geocentric and heliocentric views? Remember that in order for the geocentric view to be consistent with the way ancient astronomers saw the planets moving in the sky, each planet had to travel in an epicycle, as shown in the drawing on the left. In your experiment, then, the baseball was Venus, you were the earth, the flashlight was the sun, and the circle in which the baseball moved was Venus's epicycle. Since you saw that not much of the baseball got lit up by the flashlight in this configuration, you know that in the geocentric system,

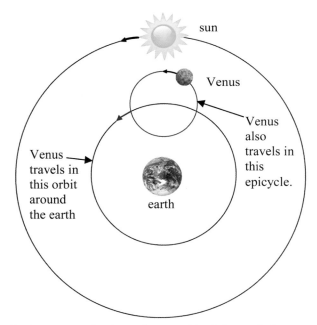

In the geocentric view, planets orbited the earth, but they also traveled in circles (called epicycles) along that orbit.

there are times when Venus goes through a series of phases in which none of them involve Venus being completely lit up by the sun.

That's not what Galileo saw! Instead, he saw that Venus passed through the same set of phases all the time. Just like the moon, Venus smoothly went from being fully lit up by the sun to being not lit up at all. While this was not expected in the geocentric system, it makes perfect sense in the heliocentric system. If you want to see for yourself, repeat the experiment, but this time, have your helper hold the baseball in one hand and the flashlight in the other. He should hold the flashlight near his body and hold the baseball far from his body. He should shine the flashlight at the baseball and then slowly spin in a circle while you watch. This simulates Venus orbiting around the sun. As you watch the ball, you will find that it goes through phases just like those of the moon.

All these observations led Galileo to believe in heliocentrism. He even wrote a book called *Dialogue Concerning the Two Chief World Systems* in which he compared the geocentric and heliocentric views to the evidence. While he didn't specifically state in the book that he believed in heliocentrism, it was clear that the heliocentric view was the only one consistent with the data.

Unfortunately, this got him in trouble with the Roman Catholic church, which was still convinced that the geocentric view was correct. In the end, the church put him on trial, and they convicted him of being "vehemently suspected" of **heresy**, which means they thought he believed and taught something (heliocentrism) that was against the official teachings of the church. He was forced to publicly recant his belief in heliocentrism, and he spent the rest of his life under house arrest. As you will see, however, Galileo was shown to be right in the end, and the Roman Catholic church (as well as the Protestant Reformers, who also believed strongly in geocentrism) were shown to be wrong.

This painting shows Galileo's trial as it was imagined by 19th-century artist Joseph-Nicolas Robert-Fleury.

LESSON REVIEW

Youngest students: Answer these questions:

1. How many moons did Galileo find orbiting Jupiter?

2. What did Galileo observe about Venus that provided a lot of evidence for heliocentrism?

Older students: Summarize the four things that Galileo observed with his telescope and how each provided evidence for heliocentrism (or against geocentrism and Aristotle's teachings).

Oldest students: Do what the older students are doing. In addition, explain how your experiment shows that the observed phases of Venus are evidence against geocentrism.

Lesson 32: Johannes Kepler (1571 – 1630)

This portrait of Johannes Kepler is by an unknown artist.

Another natural philosopher who greatly helped our understanding of the solar system was **Johannes** (yoh' han us) **Kepler**. He initially went to a university to study theology, hoping to become a minister. However, he demonstrated an amazing ability in mathematics, so he was offered a job as a mathematics teacher. While he still wanted to become a minister, he felt that God was leading him to take the teaching position. As time went on, he became more accomplished as a mathematician, and he was eventually hired by Tycho Brahe, who wanted his help in understanding the astronomical observations he had been making.

As Kepler continued to study astronomy, he also learned a lot about optics. This was partially due to the fact that he had read about the observations Galileo made with his telescope. He was a great admirer of Galileo's work, and he wanted to follow in the man's footsteps. As a result, he built his own telescope and began using it to study the heavens. Obviously, the process of building a telescope involved understanding how lenses focus light, and as a result, he was the first to provide a detailed explanation as to how telescopes actually work.

Kepler also extended his study of optics to the human eye, and as a result, he was the first to really explain how the eye forms the images we see. To understand more about this process, perform the following experiment.

Images in the Eye

What you will need:
- ✋ A flashlight that has a face which is at least 4 centimeters (1.5 inches) across
- ✋ A magnifying glass that is larger than the flashlight's face
- ✋ Black construction paper
- ✋ Scissors
- ✋ Clear tape (like cellophane tape)
- ✋ A blank sheet of white paper
- ✋ A dim room
- ✋ Someone to help you

What you should do:
1. You need to make a "smiley face" that will be taped onto the face of your flashlight. Use the scissors to cut two circles for the eyes and a larger, curved piece that will serve as the smiling mouth.
2. Tape your smiley face on the flashlight as shown in the picture above.

3. Have your helper stand at one end of the room, holding the flashlight and pointing it away from him or her. Your helper should be holding the flashlight so that the smiley face is "right-side up." In other words, the eyes should be at the top of the flashlight, while the mouth is at the bottom.

4. Use one hand to hold the magnifying glass about ½ a meter (1½ feet) away from the flashlight so that the light from the flashlight shines through the magnifying glass.

5. Hold the piece of paper right in front of the magnifying glass so the light from the flashlight shines through the magnifying glass and onto the paper.

6. Move the paper so that the distance between it and the magnifying glass increases. As you do, watch the paper to see what the light from the flashlight looks like.

7. At some point, you should see the smiley face appear on the paper. You should be able to adjust how sharp it appears on the paper by changing the distance between the paper and the magnifying glass.

8. Once you get a nice, sharp image of the smiley face on the paper, notice where the eyes are and where the mouth is. Compare that to the flashlight itself.

9. Move the paper slowly towards the magnifying glass. Notice what happens to the image of the smiley face.

10. Put the paper back where the image of the smiley face is sharp, and this time move the paper slowly away from the magnifying glass. Once again, notice what happens to the image of the smiley face.

11. Clean up your mess.

What did you see in the experiment? First, you should have noticed that the smiley face was upside down on the paper. Second, you should have noticed that if you moved the paper away from the place where the image of the smiley face was sharp, the image blurred. As you continued to move the paper, you should have gotten to a point where you couldn't even see a blurred image on the paper anymore. This was true when you moved the paper closer to the magnifying glass as well as when you moved it away from the magnifying glass.

Kepler showed us that this is how the eye deals with light. When light enters the eye, it passes through a lens that bends light to a single focal point, just like the lens of a magnifying glass. The light then hits the back of the eye, which is called the **retina** (ret' nuh). You actually see that image – the one focused on your retina. In your experiment, then, the smiley face represented what was being looked at, the magnifying glass represented the lens of the eye, and the white piece of paper represented the retina.

When you saw a sharp image of the smiley face, that told you the image of the flashlight's face on the paper was focused clearly on the retina. When you moved the paper from that position, however, the image of the smiley face became blurry. That's because the magnifying glass focused the image of the smiley face to a single point. When the paper was at that single point, you saw a nice, sharp image. When you moved the paper away from that point, the image got blurry, because the paper was not at the point where the image was being focused.

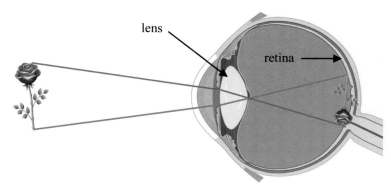

The lens of the eye focuses the image of what you are seeing onto your retina.

If you look at the drawing on the previous page, you will also see why the image on the paper was upside down. Because of the way the lens focuses light, the light coming from the top of the object will be on the bottom of the retina's image, and the light coming from the bottom of the object will be on top of the retina's image. So in reality, you see the world upside down! Of course, the world doesn't appear upside down to you because as an infant, you touch all the things that you see, and your brain figures out that the images you are seeing are upside down. As a result, your brain learns to flip the images so that what you see is consistent with what you are touching.

Now in your experiment, the magnifying glass had only one power. As a result, it focused light to only one point. Your eye's lens is better than that. It can adjust its shape so as to focus light to different places. That way, your eyes can adjust to see a sharp image of whatever object you want to examine.

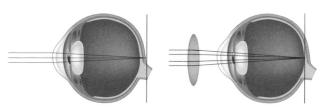

In farsightedness, the lens focuses light too weakly, putting the image behind the retina (left). This is corrected by a lens that focuses light before it hits the eye (right).

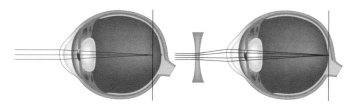

In nearsightedness, the lens focuses light too strongly, putting the image in front of the retina (left). This is corrected by a lens that defocuses light before it hits the eye (right).

Some people can't see things sharply, because their lenses don't focus images onto the retina. Some people can see things clearly when they are close, but they have a hard time seeing things that are far away. We say they are **nearsighted**. Others can see things clearly when they are far away, but they can't see things well when they are close. We say they are **farsighted**. Kepler explained that both problems were the result of light not being focused on the retina. The lenses in the eyes of a farsighted person focused the light *behind* the person's retinas. In other words, the lenses didn't bend light strongly enough in a farsighted person. This explained why glasses that focused the light before it reached the eye helped those people see. Nearsighted people had the opposite problem. Their lenses focused light too strongly, putting the image *in front of* their retinas. This explained why glasses with lenses that defocused the light before it reached the eye helped those people see. In each case, the right lens allowed the image to be focused on the retina, which produced sharp vision.

LESSON REVIEW

Youngest students: Answer these questions:

1. When an image forms on the retina of the eye, is it right-side up or upside down?

2. Fill in the blank: The eyes of farsighted people focus images _____ the retina.

Older students: Make a drawing like the one on the previous page, and use it to explain what the eye does to the light that enters it. Also explain why the images we see are upside down on our retinas. Finally, explain why we don't see the world upside down.

Oldest students: Do what the older students are doing. In addition, explain the difference between nearsightedness and farsightedness, and explain what the lenses that correct each problem actually do.

Lesson 33: Johannes Kepler and Astronomy

Kepler not only helped us understand lenses, light, and how the human eye sees; he also helped us understand **depth perception**. As you may have already learned, you can use your eyes to judge how far away things are from you. The reason you can do this so well is because you have two eyes that can both look at the same object. By judging the difference between how the light from that object hits each eye, your brain can get a really good idea of how far the object is from you. Kepler explained how that works.

In addition, Kepler was the first to give us an accurate idea of when Christ was actually born. The calendar marks Christ's birth with a switch from BC (before Christ) to AD (*Anno Domini*, Latin for "year of our Lord"). However, Kepler showed that this switch was made in the wrong year. Based on his calculations, Christ was actually born in 4 BC. Although most historians agree that Kepler was correct, the calendar has never been changed, because it had been used so much up to that point. To this day, then, the terms "BC" and "AD" are probably all off by 4 years!

Despite the fact that Kepler discovered many things, he is best known for his contributions to our understanding of the planets and the moon. Remember that he worked for Tycho Brahe, who had made many detailed measurements regarding the positions of the planets in the sky. Brahe came to distrust Kepler, so he wanted to give Kepler a problem that he thought couldn't be solved: the motion of the planet Mars. Brahe's observations of Mars produced many troubling results, and he honestly thought no one would be able to understand its motion. As a result, he gave Kepler the problem as a way to keep him busy while Brahe tried to figure out more easily-solved problems.

At the time, Kepler was a bit brash. He said he would solve the mystery of Mars's motion in eight days. It really took him at least five years! However, he was finally able to understand the planet's motion when he gave up an important assumption. You see, unlike Brahe, Kepler was convinced that Copernicus was right. He was convinced that the sun was at the center of the universe and that the planets orbited the sun. However, he clung to Copernicus's ideas a little too strongly.

Copernicus believed the planets orbited the sun in circles. Kepler believed that for a long time. However, he found that he could understand Mars's motion only if Mars's orbit was not circular. In order to understand all of Brahe's observations, he had to assume that Mars's orbit around the sun was **elliptical** (ih lip' tih kul). To see what I mean, do the following activity.

Ellipses

What you will need:
- A thick piece of cardboard or a table to which your parents will allow you to tape three pieces of paper
- Three blank sheets of paper
- A pencil
- String
- Scissors
- Tape
- A ruler

What you should do:
1. Cut a piece of string that is 20 cm (8 inches) long.
2. Tape a sheet of paper to the table or cardboard so that it does not move.

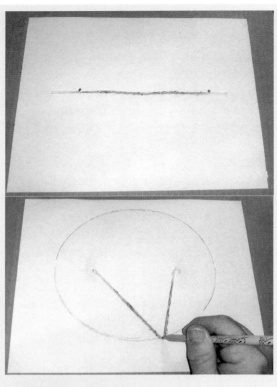

3. Lay the string down at the center of the paper, as shown in the picture on the top left.
4. Use the pencil to draw two dots, each of which is 2½ cm (1 in) from each end of the string, as shown in the picture on the top left.
5. Use the tape to attach one end of the string to the paper at one of those dots.
6. Use the tape to attach the other end of the string to the paper at the other dot.
7. Use the point of the pencil to stretch the string out so it is tight.
8. Keeping the string tight the entire time, move the pencil along the paper so that it marks where the string is, as shown in the picture on the bottom left. Do this both above and below the places where the string is taped to the paper, so that you have traced out a nearly complete oval.
9. Remove the string from the paper and remove the paper from the table or cardboard.
10. Repeat steps 2-9, but this time, make the dots 6½ cm (2½ inches) from each end of the string.
11. Repeat steps 2-9 one more time, but this time make the dots almost 10 cm (4 inches) from each end of the string. That way, they are almost touching one another.
12. Compare the three drawings you made. What do you see?
13. Clean up your mess, but keep the drawings handy.

What did you see in the experiment? The first drawing you made should have been the most oval in shape. The second drawing should have still been an oval, but it should have been more circular than the first drawing. The third drawing you made should be almost a perfect circle. What you actually drew were three **ellipses** (ih lip' sez). An ellipse is defined by two points, each of which is called a **focus**. It is a collection of points where the sum of the distances between the point and each focus is always the same. In your activity, the string was 20 cm (8 inches) long. As long as you kept it straight the entire time, the pencil swept out a line that contains all the points where the distances to each focus add to 20 cm (8 inches).

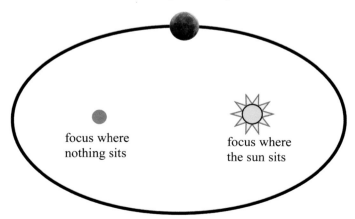

In order to understand Brahe's observations, Kepler had to assume that Mars orbited the sun in an ellipse, with the sun at one focus. The ellipse drawn here is exaggerated.

Kepler realized that if he allowed Mars's orbit around the sun to be an ellipse with the sun at one focus (and nothing at the other focus), he could understand all the observations that Brahe made over the years. As he looked at the observations of the other planets, he noticed that Brahe's observations of them were also best understood if each planet orbited the sun in an ellipse, with the sun at one focus. This became known as **Kepler's First Law**:

All planets orbit the sun in an ellipse, with the sun at one focus.

So rather than orbiting the sun in circles as Copernicus imagined, Kepler discovered that the planets orbit the sun in ellipses. Now it turns out that each planet's ellipse is different, and that was the reason I had you draw two more ellipses in your activity. The second ellipse you drew was less oval than the first one, and the third ellipse you drew was nearly a perfect circle. As you can see from your drawings, the closer the two foci (foh' ky, the plural of "focus") are to one another, the more circular and less oval the ellipse is.

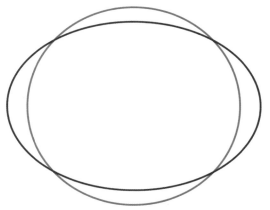

In order to describe how oval an ellipse is, we use the term **eccentricity** (ek' sen tris' uh tee). The larger an ellipse's eccentricity, the farther its foci are apart from one another, and therefore the more oval it is. If we look at all the planets, the orbit of Venus has the lowest eccentricity, which means its orbit is the most circular of all the planets. The eccentricity of the earth's orbit is also very low, which means its orbit is almost circular as well.

Both of these shapes are ellipses. The red one has a lower eccentricity, however, so it is less oval and more circular.

Well, Mars's orbit has the largest eccentricity of all the planets for which there was a lot of data available during Kepler's time. This means its orbit is more oval than the orbits of most other planets. That's why Brahe found his observations of Mars troubling. Since its orbit is so oval, its motion in the night sky is significantly more complicated than what anyone expected. Had Brahe not chosen to give the problem of Mars's motion to Kepler, he might never have figured out that the planets orbit the sun in ellipses, not circles! Now please keep in mind that even though Mars's orbit has a high eccentricity, it isn't as oval as the orbit drawn on the previous page. I exaggerated Mars's orbit to make the illustration easier to understand. Also, while Mars has a high eccentricity, it doesn't have the highest eccentricity of all the planets. Mercury has a more eccentric orbit than Mars, but there wasn't much data available for Mercury during Kepler's time.

Kepler produced two other laws regarding how the planets moved. Unfortunately, you don't know enough math to understand them right now. However, I can say that the laws indicate a planet's speed in its orbit is not constant. When the planet is nearer to the sun, it moves faster than when it is farther from the sun. That's another reason why planetary motion was hard to understand until Kepler came along. Everyone assumed that the speed of a planet was always the same. Kepler showed that it isn't.

LESSON REVIEW

Youngest students: Answer these questions:

1. What do we call the shape of each planet's orbit around the sun?

2. Fill in the blank: The lower the eccentricity of an ellipse, the more _____ its shape.

Older students: Write down Kepler's first law. Explain what an ellipse is and what eccentricity has to do with an ellipse. Name the planets whose orbits have the highest and lowest eccentricity.

Oldest students: Do what the older students are doing. In addition, make a drawing like the one on the bottom of the previous page, and indicate where the planet travels more quickly and where it travels more slowly.

Lesson 34: Johannes Kepler and Tides

Kepler made one more very important contribution to science. He was the first to offer the correct explanation for what causes the **tides**. Anyone who lives near the ocean knows that the water level near the shore changes throughout the day. In some regions of the world, the change is dramatic. For example, look at the two pictures below:

Both of them come from a place called Hopewell Cape on the Bay of Fundy, which is on the coast of Canada between the provinces of New Brunswick and Nova Scotia. Notice that in the photo on the left, people are walking around the interestingly-shaped rocks. The arrow in the picture on the left points out where I am in the picture. In the photo on the right, you see the same rock formations, but the water is so high, a large part of each rock formation is under water. I'm glad I wasn't standing near the rocks then!

What's the difference? Was there a lot of rain after the photo on the right was taken? No. The photo on the left shows the water level at the Bay of Fundy during **low tide**, and the photo on the right (which was taken about six hours after the photo on the left) shows the water level at the same location during **high tide**. Anyone who lives near the ocean is familiar with those two terms. At certain times during the day, the water level near the shore is very low; at other times during the day, it is very high. As the photos demonstrate, in some places the difference is amazing.

Now the Bay of Fundy is a rather dramatic illustration of the difference between high tide and low tide. While nearly every place that has an ocean shore experiences a difference between high tide and low tide, it is not often as big as what is seen at the Bay of Fundy (up to 15 meters, or 50 feet). Nevertheless, the fact that all ocean shores experience times when the water level is high (high tide) and times when the water level is low (low tide) has been well known throughout recorded history. As a result, natural philosophers had tried to explain it for some time. Kepler was the first to realize that the tides are caused by the moon. To see what I mean, do the following activity.

The Tides

What you will need:
- A ball that is about the size of a baseball or tennis ball
- A marker that can be used to make a mark on the ball
- A rubber band that can fit around the ball and still be stretched

What you should do:
1. Make a mark on the ball where it is easy to see.
2. Fit the rubber band so it goes around the ball.
3. Put your middle finger underneath the rubber band on one side of the ball and your thumb underneath the rubber band on the other side of the ball.
4. Use your finger and thumb to stretch the rubber band.
5. Move the ball around so the dot is right above the rubber band at a place where the rubber band is still right up against the ball. At this point, your activity should look like the picture above.
6. Think of the rubber band as illustrating the water level of the ocean. Where the rubber band is right up against the ball (like where the mark is now), the water level is low. Where the rubber band is stretched out away from the ball, the water level is high. At this point, then, the mark is at a spot that indicates a low water level (low tide).
7. Spin the ball so that the mark moves from left to right but stays above the rubber band at all times.
8. As the mark moves, think about how the water level (as represented by the rubber band) changes for the mark. As it moves to where the rubber band is stretched out, the water level rises. When it reaches the point where the rubber band is farthest from the ball, it experiences a very high water level (high tide).
9. Continue to spin the ball until the mark gets back to where it started. How many low tides did the mark go through? How many high tides did the mark go through?
10. Put everything away.

Your activity was a pretty good illustration of the tides. Kepler was the first to really understand that the reason a rock falls to the earth when it is dropped is because the rock is attracted to the earth and the earth is attracted to the rock. In other words, he understood that gravity is a force that causes objects to attract one another. As a result, he understood that the moon is attracted to the earth, and that the earth is attracted to the moon. This is what keeps the moon in orbit around the earth.

However, he also correctly understood that the moon doesn't just attract the earth, it attracts everything on the earth, including the water of the oceans. As a result, *the water in the oceans is pulled toward the moon*. Of course, that water doesn't travel to the moon, because the water in the oceans is also attracted to the earth. As a result, there is a "tug-of-war" that goes on between the moon and the earth when it comes to the oceans. The result of this "tug-of-war" is that the oceans bulge out in an oval that points towards the moon. In your activity, stretching two ends of the rubber band produced an oval around the earth, much like the oval of the water in the oceans.

When you spun the ball in your hands, you were simulating the earth's rotation, which takes 24 hours to complete. In the space of 24 hours, the moon doesn't change its position much, so in the end, the oval it makes of the oceans doesn't change much. However, as the earth rotates, any given part of the earth (like the mark on the baseball) passes through an area where the water level is low, an area where the water level is high, another area where the water level is low, and another area where the water level is high. In other words, any part of the earth experiences two high tides and two low tides every day.

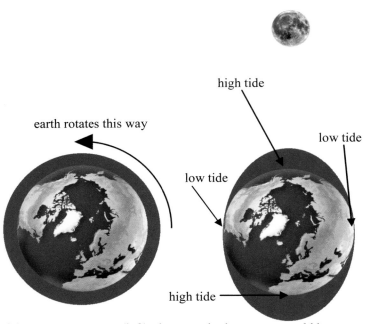

If there were no moon (left), the water in the oceans would be at the same level everywhere, and there would be no tides. Because the moon's gravity attracts the water (right), however, the water forms more of an oval, producing two high tides and two low tides each day.

So the change from high tide to low tide has nothing to do with the oceans emptying and filling with water. Instead, it is caused by the moon's gravity, which attracts the water in earth's oceans to it. This causes the oceans to form more of an oval than a sphere, and as the earth rotates, this causes any given part of the earth to pass through two areas where the oval is thin, producing a low tide. However, it also causes that same part of the earth to pass through two areas where the oval is thick, producing a high tide.

Before I finish discussing Kepler, you might remember that I told you he wanted to be a minister. However, he never became one. This actually troubled him for a long time, until he realized that he was actually glorifying God by studying His creation. As Kepler admitted, "For a long time I wanted to become a theologian; for a long time I was restless. Now, however, behold how through my effort God is being celebrated in astronomy." (O. Gingerich, "Johannes Kepler and the New Astronomy," *Quarterly Journal of the Royal Astronomical Society* 13, p. 346-372, 1972) Let that be a lesson to you: God can use you in *anything* that you do, as long as you are following Him!

LESSON REVIEW

Youngest students: Answer these questions:

1. What object in the night sky is responsible for the tides?

2. How many times each day does an ocean shore experience low tide? What about high tide?

Older students: Make a drawing like the one on the right side of the illustration above, showing the earth, moon, and the waters of the ocean. Use it to explain why each ocean shore experiences two high tides and two low tides every day.

Oldest students: Do what the older students are doing. In addition, do some research and explain the difference between **spring tides** and **neap tides**. Check your answer and correct it if it is wrong.

Lesson 35: Francis Bacon (1561 – 1626)

During this time in human history, there were several natural philosophers who realized that the way to understand the world around them was to observe it. They understood that collecting evidence was more important than relying on the authorities of the past. However, there were still many who thought that all natural philosophy needed to be done with reverence to the great thinkers of the past, such as Aristotle. This is why even though Galileo and Kepler collected all sorts of evidence to support heliocentrism, there were many natural philosophers who simply would not accept it. They were unwilling to consider the idea that the great thinkers of the past could be so wrong when it came to how the universe was ordered.

This is a portrait of Sir Francis Bacon.

Fortunately, there were men willing to fight against that mentality, and one of those men was **Sir Francis Bacon**, an English gentleman who spent most of his life in law and politics. His father was an important political figure, and Bacon decided to follow in his father's footsteps. He spent years studying and practicing law, and then he had a very successful career in politics. In fact, towards the end of his life, he was named Lord Chancellor, which was one of the highest political offices in England. Unfortunately, he eventually had to resign that position because he was convicted of accepting bribes.

Why am I talking about a lawyer and politician in this science course? Because while those professions occupied most of his time, Sir Francis Bacon also wrote about natural philosophy. In his main work, *Novum Organum Scientiarum* (*New Instrument of Science*), he argued that reverence for the great thinkers of the past was holding back our understanding of the world. In order to better understand the world, natural philosophers had to stop trying to understand things in terms of old ideas. They had to generate new ideas, and those ideas had to *start* with observations. After making observations, a natural philosopher could then begin trying to understand why the thing being observed behaved in the way that it did.

One reason Bacon argued so strongly for this method was that he knew that the world often behaved in a **counterintuitive** way. If you haven't heard that word before, it means going against what you expect. A natural philosopher might expect one result, but when he actually makes the observation, he might get a result that is quite different from what he expects. That's a counterintuitive result, and experiments often produce such results. Bacon believed that since the world can behave in a counterintuitive way, a natural philosopher shouldn't start with some ancient person's view of how the world should be. Instead, he should start with observations of how the world actually is. To give you an idea of what Bacon meant, perform the following experiment.

Oil, Water, and Salt

What you will need:

- ☝ Vegetable oil
- ☝ Water
- ☝ Salt in a saltshaker
- ☝ A glass that you can see through
- ☝ Your notebook or, for younger students, a piece of paper

What you should do:

1. Fill the glass halfway with water.
2. Add some vegetable oil to the water so that it forms a layer about 2 centimeters (1 inch) thick on top of the water.
3. In the next step, you are going to shake salt on top of the oil. Before you do that, however, I want you to predict what will happen as a result. If you are keeping a notebook, write a short description of what you have done and your prediction about what will happen when you shake the salt on the oil. If you are not keeping a notebook, tell someone what you think will happen.
4. Shake a lot of salt onto the top of the oil layer.
5. Observe what happens. You will want to observe for at least a few minutes. If you want to see the effect again, just shake more salt on the oil.
6. If you are keeping a notebook, write down what *actually* happened, and note whether or not your prediction was anywhere close to what you observed.
7. Clean up your mess and put everything away.

What happened in the experiment? You should have seen that once you added salt, small globs of oil sank to the bottom of the water, but then after a while, those same blobs rose back to the oil layer. Why did this happen? Remember that in order for something to float, it must weigh less than an equal volume of water. Oil floats because a given volume of oil weighs less than that same volume of water. A given volume of salt, however, weighs more than an equal volume of water. When you added salt to the oil, then, it added to the weight of the oil, causing it to sink.

Salt cannot dissolve in oil, but it does dissolve in water. When the glob of oil reached the bottom of the glass, the salt continued to sink until it completely passed through the glob of oil. At that point, the salt dissolved in the water. Once it had left the glob of oil, however, the oil became lighter than an equal volume of water, so it ended up floating back up to the top!

How did your prediction turn out? Don't worry. When someone told me about this experiment, I didn't make the correct prediction either. That's Sir Francis Bacon's point. I have been doing chemistry most of my adult life, and I have a PhD in the subject. Nevertheless, I couldn't predict what would happen in this situation, because the result is counterintuitive. This is why Bacon thought it was so important to start with observations. Since the world often behaves in a counterintuitive way, it doesn't make sense to attempt an understanding of it without first starting with experiments!

Because he promoted the idea that all knowledge of the world around us starts with experiments or observations, Sir Francis Bacon is often called a champion of **empiricism** (em pir' ih siz' uhm), the idea that the only way we can learn anything is through experiment or observation. However, that's not completely correct. Bacon thought that empiricism was the proper way to learn about the world around you, but he was also a Christian. As a result, he thought that the Bible was the best source of knowledge when it came to other issues, such as the meaning and purpose of life, how to be good, and what happens after you die.

Interestingly enough, while Bacon promoted the idea that the only way to properly learn about the world around you was by making observations and doing experiments, he is not actually remembered for any of the experiments he did or observations he made! This might be due, in part, to the fact that he spent a lot of time practicing law and dealing with politics. As a result, he didn't have a lot of time for experiments. Nevertheless, Bacon was in the interesting position of strongly arguing that experiments had to be an important part of natural philosophy, even though he didn't do any memorable experiments himself!

Despite the fact that Bacon produced no memorable experiments, he had a lasting impact on science. Remember, one reason many natural philosophers didn't want to believe in heliocentrism was because they held the great thinkers of the past in such high regard. Bacon's book was able to reduce the importance of the ancient thinkers and increase the importance of observations and experiments. As time went on, this allowed more natural philosophers to accept the heliocentric view of the universe, since there was so much evidence in its favor.

This illustration comes from Bacon's book. It shows a ship sailing through the "Pillars of Hercules," which mythology said marked the end of the well-charted ocean and the beginning of unknown waters. It symbolized the fact that he wanted natural philosophers to explore things that the ancient thinkers never dreamed of.

This brings me to another interesting point. While Bacon ended up making it easier for many natural philosophers to believe in heliocentrism, Bacon himself was a strong geocentrist! He believed that there was simply no way to make enough observations about the universe to understand its arrangement by observation. As a result, he believed what the Church of England taught at the time, which was geocentrism.

LESSON REVIEW

Youngest students: Answer these questions:

1. What is empiricism?

2. (Is this statement True or False?) Sir Francis Bacon believed in heliocentrism.

Older students: Explain why Bacon thought that natural philosophy should start with experiments. Also, define empiricism and explain where Bacon thought it should and should not be used.

Oldest students: Do what the older students are doing. In addition, explain why Bacon is so important to natural philosophy, despite the fact that he did no memorable experiments. Also, explain why he believed in geocentrism.

Lesson 36: Jan Baptist van Helmont (1580 – 1644)

This is a portrait of Jan Baptist van Helmont.

Jan (yahn) **Baptist** (bab teest') **van Helmont** was a restless young man. He was born in the Netherlands and was educated well. When he went to a university, however, he couldn't decide what to study, so he tried out many subjects. He finally settled on medicine, but he wasn't really happy with his decision. He even took a break from his studies to travel extensively, hoping he could find something in his travels to satisfy his curiosity. He didn't really find anything, so he eventually went back to a university, earned a degree in medicine, and started working as a physician. He married a woman from a wealthy family, however, so when his wife inherited a lot of money, he retired early and started studying whatever interested him.

Once he retired, he became fascinated with the subject of **alchemy** (al' kuh me), which was an attempt to turn cheap metals (like lead) into precious metals (like gold). There were other goals of alchemy as well, such as finding a potion that would keep people from dying. It was an odd mix of experiments and attempts at magic. While van Helmont seemed to believe in a lot of the magical aspects of alchemy (which aren't true), he was also very serious about doing experiments and observing their results. This allowed him to learn some things about science, despite the fact that he was trying to do magic. Perform the following experiment to see one of the things van Helmont learned.

Acid and Antacid

What you will need:
- Apple cider vinegar (You can use clear vinegar if you like, but the experiment will be slightly more disgusting as a result.)
- Water
- Antacid tablets (Any brand will do. Unflavored tablets would be ideal, but they are hard to find.)
- An aluminum pie pan (or a shallow dish that will not break when repeatedly hit by a hammer)
- Paper towels
- A hammer
- Three small glasses
- Two spoons for stirring
- A ¼-cup measuring cup
- Water

What you should do:
1. Put several (at least six) antacid tablets in the pie pan.

2. Take the pie pan, paper towels, and hammer to a workbench, table, or other surface that your parents say you can hit with a hammer.
3. Cover the pie pan with paper towels. This is to keep the pieces of antacid from flying around when you do the next step.
4. Use the hammer to crush the antacid tablets into tiny pieces. You won't be able to see them because of the paper towels, but that's okay. Just pound the hammer around where you think the antacid tablets are. Then you can lift the paper towels and see how you did. Repeat this process until the tablets have all been crushed into tiny pieces.
5. Bring the pie pan that holds the crushed antacid to where you will do the rest of the experiment.
6. Add ¼ cup of water to one of the small glasses.
7. Add ¼ cup of apple cider vinegar to another one of the glasses.
8. Add a small amount of apple cider vinegar to the third glass.
9. Scoop up some of the pieces of antacid into one of the spoons and dump them into the water. What happens? Stir them around a bit. What happens? Not very exciting, was it?
10. Scoop up some of the pieces of antacid into the other spoon and dump them in the glass that has ¼ cup of vinegar in it. What happens?
11. Once the bubbling slows down, stir the antacid and vinegar solution.
12. Add more antacid pieces to the same glass and stir again. Continue to do so until very few bubbles are made.
13. Dip a finger into the vinegar that is in the small glass (the one that has no antacid in it), pull your finger out, and lick it so you can taste the vinegar. **NOTE: You should NEVER eat or drink anything in an experiment unless someone who knows A LOT about chemistry tells you to do so. It can be very dangerous to eat or drink things from an experiment!**
14. Think about how the vinegar tasted.
15. Take a drink of the vinegar-antacid mixture. What's the difference?
16. Clean up your mess.

What happened in your experiment? When you added the pieces of antacid to the water, nothing exciting happened. However, when you added them to the vinegar, it began bubbling and frothing. Once you added enough, the bubbling pretty much stopped. Once all that was over, how did the taste of pure vinegar compare to the taste of the vinegar-antacid mixture? The mixture was a lot less disgusting, wasn't it? Why? Did the flavoring of the antacid cover up the vile taste of the vinegar? No. If you happened to find unflavored antacid, the mixture would still be a lot less disgusting.

Vinegar tastes sour because it has an **acid** in it, and acids taste sour. Not all things with acid in them taste as bad as vinegar, because they usually have other things that help cover the taste. Apple cider vinegar, for example, is a bit less vile than clear vinegar, because the apple cider vinegar at least has some apple flavor to help cut the terrible sourness that comes from the acid. When you added antacid to the vinegar, it destroyed the acid. That's why it is called an **ant**acid – it works against acids. When you added enough antacid to destroy the acid in the vinegar, it got rid of the extreme sourness, making the resulting solution less disgusting to drink. Using scientific terms, we would say that the antacid is an **alkaline** (al' kuh lin) substance, which is the opposite of an acid. It **neutralized** the acid.

Jan Baptist van Helmont spent a lot of time mixing things with acid. He understood that acid could make lots of things disappear. For example, if he added acid to a mineral known as calcite, the calcite would bubble and slowly disappear. He assumed that this meant the acid was transforming the calcite into something that easily dissolved. Of course, he was correct. He also realized that the bubbles coming off the calcite (like the bubbles that came from the vinegar once you added the antacid) were formed because a gas was also being made. In fact, he was the natural philosopher who first used the word "gas." He thought gases were chaotic, and so he chose to describe them with the Greek word "chaos." It turns out that "gas" is how a Dutchman would pronounce the Greek word for "chaos," and that's where the word comes from.

Because he had so much experience with acids "eating away" at different kinds of solids, he realized that acids must be one of the keys to how people digest their food. During this time in history, people understood that solid foods must be transformed in the digestive system of the body, but they didn't really know how. Many natural philosophers thought that the heat of a person's body transformed the food he ate, much like a stove can transform a mixture of ingredients into something like a cake. Van Helmont realized that this probably wasn't correct, and he figured that the body had some chemical means by which this was done.

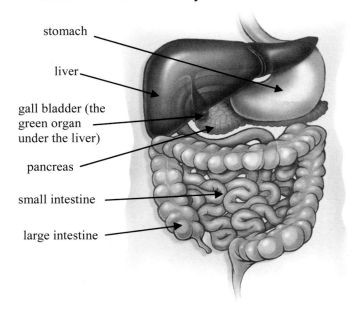

stomach

liver

gall bladder (the green organ under the liver)

pancreas

small intestine

large intestine

While van Helmont thought the gall bladder made a liquid that neutralizes stomach acid, we now know it is the pancreas that does that job.

As a result, he thought that the stomach must be full of acid. However, he realized there must be more to it than just acid, because he mixed various foods with acid and realized that while it did transform some food like it transformed calcite, there were some foods that it didn't seem to affect much at all. Of course, he was right on both points. We now know that the stomach contains acid (called **stomach acid**), but it is also contains other chemicals. The mixture of acid and other chemicals in the stomach is now known as **gastric** (gas' trik) **juice**, and Jan Baptist van Helmont was the first to understand its nature. In addition, van Helmont understood that the acid in the stomach eventually had to be neutralized, so he suggested that the gall bladder made a liquid that neutralized the acid once food passed into the small intestine. It turns out that's not correct. It is done by another organ, which is called the **pancreas**.

LESSON REVIEW

Youngest students: Answer these questions:

1. What is in your stomach – an alkaline solution or an acid?

2. What does an alkaline substance do to an acid?

Older students: Explain what happened to the vinegar in your experiment, being sure to use the terms "alkaline," "acid," and "neutralize." Explain how this is similar to what happens when the pancreas adds a liquid to what is coming out of the stomach and into the small intestine.

Oldest students: Do what the older students are doing. In addition, find out the word that chemists typically use for alkaline substances today. Check your answer and correct it if it is wrong.

Lesson 37: Jan Baptist van Helmont and Carbon Dioxide

In the previous lesson, you learned that Jan Baptist van Helmont was the first natural philosopher to use the word "gas." It turns out that he was fascinated by gases and found out that he could make them in his experiments. In fact, he was really the first natural philosopher to understand that air isn't the only kind of gas in nature. He knew that some of the gases he made in his experiments had to be different from air, because they behaved differently from air. To see what I mean, perform the following experiment.

Carbon Dioxide and Fire

What you will need:
- A tall glass that is easy to see through
- Two candles, one of which needs to be able to stand on its own or be put in a holder
- Matches or something else to light the candles
- A small glass, like a juice glass
- Vinegar (any kind)
- Baking soda
- A spoon for stirring
- A counter that is above a floor you can make a mess on
- Some newspapers or old towels
- An adult to help you

What you should do:
1. Put the candle that can stand on its own at the edge of the counter.
2. Have an adult help you light the candle.
3. Turn the glass upside down and put it over the candle, but hold it so that a large part of the glass's opening hangs off the edge of the counter. That way, there is an open space through which air can get into the glass. See the picture above to understand what I mean. Don't use the second candle yet. That's the next part of the experiment.
4. Watch the candle for a while. Does it go out? It probably will eventually, but it should take some time. If you get bored, you don't have to watch it until it goes out.
5. Pull the glass off the candle.
6. If the candle went out, have the adult help you light it again.
7. Have an adult help you light the second candle and hold it in your hand carefully.
8. Have the adult cover the candle again like you did in step 3, and this time, hold the candle in your hand right underneath the opening of the glass that hangs off the edge of the counter. Your experiment should now look like the picture above.
9. Watch what happens to the candle that is inside the glass.
10. Pull the glass off the candle again.
11. Fill the small glass about $\frac{1}{3}$ of the way with vinegar.
12. Scoop up some baking soda with a spoon.
13. This next part can get a bit messy, so put some newspapers or old towels on the floor right below where you have been doing your experiment.
14. Have an adult help you light the candle on the counter one more time.
15. Have the adult cover the candle again, as you did in step 3.

16. Put the glass of vinegar directly underneath the opening of the glass that hangs off the edge of the counter.
17. Shake *some* of the baking soda into the vinegar. The mixture should bubble quite a bit, which will probably lead to some spilling.
18. Repeat step 17 until the candle goes out again.
19. Clean up your mess.

What did you see in the experiment? In the first part, you probably saw the candle go out after a while. Why? Most people know that fire needs oxygen in order to burn. So most people will say the candle burned out because it used up all the oxygen in the glass, but that's not really true. There was a way for more oxygen to get into the glass (through the part of the opening that was hanging off the edge of the counter). There must be another reason why the candle went out.

Now before we move on, you have to understand that at this point in history, natural philosophers didn't understand that fire needs oxygen in order to burn. In fact, they didn't even know that there was a gas called "oxygen." Because of an experiment by Roger Bacon (c. 1214 – 1294), natural philosophers knew that fire needed air, and because of what Leonardo da Vinci added to that experiment, they knew that fire used only a portion of what is in the air, but that's all they knew up to this point in history.

In the second part of the experiment, you noticed that the candle under the glass went out much more quickly when a second candle burned underneath the opening of the glass. Why is that? Once again, you could say it's because the candle that burned underneath the opening used up the oxygen that was moving into the glass, but that's not really true either.

The third part of the experiment should have been the real indicator of what was going on. When you mixed baking soda and vinegar in a glass and held it underneath the opening, the candle also went out. The baking soda and vinegar were not using up oxygen, so why did holding it under the glass make the candle go out?

The real reason the candle went out in all three cases is because of another gas called **carbon dioxide**. As the candle burned by itself underneath the glass, it was using the oxygen in the air, but it was also making carbon dioxide. The carbon dioxide began filling the glass, and eventually, it filled the glass so much that it pushed out the bottom. That caused the candle to go out, because the carbon dioxide had pushed the air (including the oxygen) out of the glass.

When you put a second candle underneath the opening of the glass, it was making carbon dioxide as well. Most of that carbon dioxide rose and got trapped in the glass. As a result, it sped up the process of pushing the air out of the glass, and once again, the candle under the glass went out. Now, of course, the candle under the opening did use up oxygen as well, so that also contributed to the speed at which the candle under the glass went out.

That's why you did the third part of the experiment. The vinegar and baking soda were not using up oxygen, but they were making carbon dioxide. That's a product of the chemical reaction between those two chemicals. That carbon dioxide rose out of the small glass, got trapped in the large glass, and eventually helped the carbon dioxide made by the candle to push all the air out of the glass, extinguishing the candle.

Jan Baptist van Helmont noticed that he could make a gas by burning charcoal. He didn't know what that gas was, so he called it "gas sylvestre," which means "wood gas," since charcoal is made from wood. However, he also noticed that when wine is being made it produces a gas. When he did experiments on both gases, he found that they behaved the same. As a result, he assumed that they were the same gas, even though they were produced in two very different ways. Of course, he was right. Burning wood and fermenting wine both produce carbon dioxide, as do many other chemical reactions, such as mixing baking soda with vinegar.

Van Helmont went on to discover other gases as well, such as chlorine gas and sulfur dioxide. He didn't know what they were at the time, but he knew they were quite different from the "wood gas" that he had made by burning charcoal.

He also did several other interesting experiments. You might have learned about Nicholas of Cusa, who lived about 200 years before van Helmont. Nicholas described an experiment in which you weighed a pot of soil, planted a tree seed, and then weighed the water you added as the tree grew. He said you would find that the soil barely changes in weight, even though the seed develops into a very heavy tree. He used that to conclude that plants don't use anything from the soil. Instead, they get what they need from water. He was only partly right. Plants do take a small amount from the soil, and they also use carbon dioxide from the air.

Wine is being made in this barrel. Right now, it is fermenting, which turns the sugar in the grapes into alcohol. That makes carbon dioxide, which causes the bubbles you see in the picture.

Van Helmont actually did that experiment to see if Nicholas of Cusa was right. Why would he repeat an experiment that Nicholas described 200 years earlier? Because it is important for one scientist to check another scientist's work. It could be that Nicholas performed the experiment poorly or missed something in his analysis of the experiment. By checking his work, van Helmont was able to confirm Nicholas's conclusions. This is a very important part of the scientific process.

LESSON REVIEW

Youngest students: Answer these questions:

1. What is the gas that is made by burning charcoal as well as by mixing vinegar with baking soda?

2. Why did van Helmont repeat the experiment described by Nicholas of Cusa?

Older students: Describe your experiment in your notebook and explain why the flame went out in all three cases. Give an example of how carbon dioxide is made that doesn't involve burning or mixing vinegar and baking soda.

Oldest students: Do what the older students are doing. In addition, explain the value of repeating an experiment that was described 200 years earlier by Nicholas of Cusa.

Lesson 38: William Harvey (1578 – 1657)

This is a portrait of William Harvey.

Do you remember that Vesalius didn't really understand how blood flows in the body? He thought that the veins and arteries were two completely different systems, and that the heart's purpose was to warm the blood. An English physician who was trained in Italy, **William Harvey**, was finally able to do what Vesalius couldn't: He figured out how blood flows in the body and what the heart actually does.

How was he able to figure this out? Well, he did dissections of humans to study human hearts and human blood vessels. He also studied how the blood, heart, and lungs of live animals work. Do you remember Michael Servetus? He saw that the blood in the veins was a different shade of red than the blood in the arteries, and that allowed him to figure out that blood flows from the heart to the lungs, where it receives air. It then flows back to the heart and goes out to the rest of the tissues. Harvey made the same kinds of observations, but he also used math. How did math help Harvey figure out the way blood flows in the body? Do the following activity to find out.

How Much Water Can You Move?

What you will need:
- A large bowl
- A ¼-cup measuring cup
- A measuring glass that can measure at least 2 cups
- Water
- A stopwatch
- Someone to help you

What you should do:
1. Put the bowl in the sink and fill it pretty much full of water.
2. Leave the bowl in the sink and put the measuring glass on the counter next to the sink.
3. In a moment, you are going to dunk the ¼ measuring cup into the water so that it gets completely full and then dump it into the measuring glass that is on the counter. You want to do this smoothly and easily so that no water is spilled. You will do it four times, and your helper will time how quickly you can do it without spilling any water.
4. Have your helper hold the stopwatch. Have him or her start it and tell you to go at the same time.
5. When your helper tells you to go, do what I described in step 3. Have your helper stop the stopwatch when you have finished pouring water in the measuring glass for the fourth time.
6. Look at the volume in the measuring glass. If you didn't spill any water, it should say that there is one cup of water there, because four ¼-cups of water equal one full cup of water.
7. Look at how long it took you to put one cup of water into the measuring glass. Assuming you did things exactly the same as before, can you predict how long it would take you to get two cups of water into the measuring glass? Since two cups of water are twice as much as one cup of water, it

should take you twice as much time. So if it took you 10 seconds to put one cup of water into the measuring glass, it should take you 20 seconds to put two cups in the measuring glass.
8. I want you to test your prediction. Empty the measuring glass so there is no water in it.
9. Put more water in the bowl.
10. Repeat steps 4 and 5, but this time, fill the ¼-cup measuring cup and dump it in the measuring glass a total of eight times. Try to do it the same as before, and once again, don't spill any water.
11. How long did it take you? If you went at the same pace as before, it should have taken you about twice as long as it did the first time.
12. I won't have you test this prediction (thankfully), but predict how long it would take you to move 10 cups of water this way. To do that, take the time it took you to move one cup of water and multiply by 10.
13. Clean up your mess and put everything away.

What was the point of that activity? You measured the amount of time it took you to do a small task, and you used math to determine how much time it would take you to complete a larger version of that same task. You should have seen that this works fairly well. Believe it or not, William Harvey used a very similar mathematical technique to show that the prevailing view of blood in the body couldn't possibly be right.

At this time in human history, there were different ideas about how blood worked in the body, but one of the most popular views was that the body continually made blood. It was thought that the body took the food someone ate and converted it into blood, and when that blood came to the tissues, the tissues would use it up. As a result, most natural philosophers thought that blood was being constantly made and used in the body.

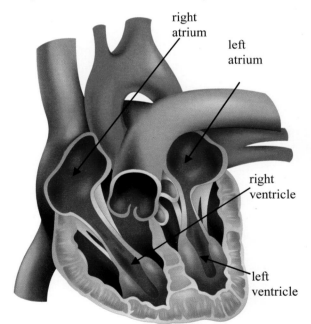

Harvey used math similar to what you used in your activity to show that this couldn't possibly be the case. He measured the amount of blood that could be held in a ventricle (one of the two bottom chambers) of the typical human heart. In animals, he saw that each ventricle was completely emptied in one beat, and he assumed that this was also true for humans. As a result, he realized that he could calculate the amount of blood that goes through the heart every day. He counted the number of times a person's heart beat each minute and then multiplied by 60. That told him the number of beats that happened every hour. Since there are 24 hours in a day, he multiplied that result by 24 to get the number of heartbeats a person has every day. He then multiplied that by the amount of blood that the two ventricles could hold.

This longitudinal section of the human heart shows its four chambers. Harvey looked at the volume of one ventricle.

What did he discover? He found that *several thousands of liters* (more than 1,500 gallons) passed through the heart every day! Now remember, all that blood was supposed to be made by the body from the food that a person eats. Obviously, there would just be no way a person could eat enough food to make several thousand liters of blood every day. As a result, he realized that blood couldn't be made and destroyed in the body. Instead, it had to be recycled. That told him blood traveled from the heart and to the tissues in the arteries, and it then flowed back to the heart in the veins.

He bolstered this argument with several other pieces of evidence. For example, he noted that if he pulled the heart from a living animal that was being operated on, the heart would continue to beat for a while. This indicated that the heart's main purpose was not heating, but beating. In the end, this helped him to understand that the heart is a pump that pushes blood out into the arteries. The pulse, then, was not the result of arteries expanding to suck blood out of the heart, as was thought at the time. Instead, the pulse was a result of the arteries being filled with blood by the pumping action of the heart.

The veins have valves that open when the blood is flowing towards the heart (left) and close when blood is flowing away from the heart (right).

There was one other important piece of evidence to support Harvey's view. His teacher, Hieronymus (hi ron' ih mus) Fabricius (fuh bree' see us) had discovered that veins are full of valves, such as the one shown in the drawing on the left. However, arteries do not have such valves. He wondered why God would put all those valves in the veins but not the arteries. He eventually figured it out. When blood is pumped through the arteries by the heart, the blood will always travel in the right direction because of the force the heart is using to push it. In the veins, however, the force is much lower. As a result, it would be possible for the blood to move in the wrong direction, because there isn't a lot of force pushing on it. The valves would keep that from happening, because they are designed to open if blood is flowing towards the heart, but close if the blood is moving away from the heart.

So Harvey used a combination of observations, mathematics, and a belief that God designed the body wisely to figure out what Vesalius could not. As a result, we now understand that blood circulates through the body, going from the heart to the lungs to pick up oxygen, going back to the heart so it can be pumped to the rest of the body, and then returning back to the heart.

LESSON REVIEW

Youngest students: Answer these questions:

1. What calculation did William Harvey do to indicate that blood must be recycled in the body?

2. Why are there valves in the veins?

Older students: Explain how William Harvey used math to help him understand that blood must circulate in the body. Explain two other pieces of evidence Harvey used to support that fact.

Oldest students: Do what the older students are doing. In addition, try to reproduce Harvey's calculation. Use the fact that a typical adult ventricle holds 60 milliliters (2 ounces) of blood and that a typical adult's heart beats 70 times each minute.

NOTE: The experiment in the next lesson requires the students to talk to a few adults. You might want to read the experiment and start trying to contact them now.

Lesson 39: James Ussher (1581 – 1656)

At roughly the same time William Harvey was studying blood flow in the human body, **James Ussher** was the head of the church of Ireland. For that reason, he is often referred to as "Bishop Ussher." While he focused most of his attention on church matters, he did spend some time researching and writing about history and theology. For example, he wrote a book about the Irish church and how it differed from the Roman Catholic church, and he also wrote a book on the history of Christianity in the British Empire that is considered to be one of the most important books written on the subject at the time.

In 1641, a large number of Irish people tried to rebel against England, which governed Ireland at the time. It is often called the "Irish uprising," and it changed Ussher's life. He was in England at the

This is a portrait of James Ussher painted by Sir Peter Lely.

time, and he could not get back to Ireland. He ended up losing his home and his job, but the English government gave him money and lands so that he could live there.

During that part of his life, he wrote the book for which he is most famous. Like many scholarly books of the time, it was written in Latin, but its English title is *Annals of the Old Testament, Deduced From the First Origins of the World*. The book is famous because it presented a long and detailed argument which attempted to calculate the date when God created the world. According to Ussher, creation began on the nightfall prior to October 23, 4004 BC. How did Ussher determine this date? Before I tell you, I want you to do a little experiment.

How Did Ussher Do It?
What you will need:
- ☞ The phone numbers or email addresses of your pastor and at least three other adults in your church (It is best to contact people who are knowledgeable about the Bible and matters that relate to the creation account as given in the book of Genesis.)

What you should do:
1. Ask your parents how Bishop Ussher calculated the date of creation.
2. Contact your pastor and ask him the same question.
3. Contact at least three other adults in your church and ask them the same question.
4. Compare the answers. Are they different from each other?

I wanted you to do that exercise for a very important reason. Most Christians who have studied the creation account as given in Genesis in a serious way know who James Ussher is and that he calculated the date of creation. However, most of them don't really understand how he did it. I am going to explain what Ussher did now, and I want you to think about how close the explanations you heard from the adults you contacted are to the actual way in which Ussher made his calculation.

Many Christians know that Genesis 5 gives a list of Adam's children, their children, and so on. A list like that is called a **genealogy** (jee' nee ol' uh jee), and this particular genealogy gives the ages

of each father when he had a son. Because the fathers' ages are given, Ussher could just count the years to see how time passed. For example, the genealogy says that Adam was 130 years old when he had Seth (Genesis 5:3). Then Seth was 105 years old when he had Enosh (Genesis 5:6). This means that $130 + 105 = 235$ years passed from when Adam was created until Enosh was born. Since Adam was created on the sixth day, that means Enosh was born 235 years and six days after God started creation. Ussher added ages like that through the entire genealogy, which ends with Shem, Ham, and Japheth, the sons of Noah.

Genesis 11 gives another genealogy, starting with Shem. That genealogy also lists the ages of the fathers when they had a son, so Ussher could continue adding ages until the birth of Abram (whom God later renamed Abraham). After that, however, there isn't another genealogy that lists the ages of the fathers. However, if you search the Bible enough, you can find the age of each father at the time when his first son was born from Abraham all the way to Solomon.

This is how artist Gustave Dore' imagined King Solomon. After Solomon, it became very difficult for Ussher to use only the Bible in his determination of when creation occurred.

Now here's the real problem: After Solomon, the Bible doesn't list the age of the fathers when the children were born. It does list the kings who reigned over Israel, and it lists how long their reigns lasted, but there were times when Israel didn't really have a king. Instead, there were temporary rulers, called "regents," and how long those regents ruled is not always given. As a result, there was no way that Ussher could just keep adding numbers together based on fathers and their sons, as he did up until the birth of Solomon.

There is also another problem. The Old Testament ends long before the New Testament begins. There is no discussion in the Bible about how many years passed during that time, so once again, there are no numbers to add together. Now once the New Testament begins, there is no problem in tracking time. Even back in Ussher's day, it was known that Christ was born in 4 BC. Since Ussher knew how many years passed between Adam and Solomon, if he could only figure out how many years passed between Solomon and Christ, he would know how long ago the creation week began.

How did he do it? Well, Ussher had studied *a lot* of history, and there are many people that are mentioned in both the Bible and other histories. In addition, there are events that are mentioned in both the Bible and other histories. So Ussher tried to take events in history for which their dates were known and find them in the Bible. Using those dates, he was able to estimate how much time passed between the birth of Solomon and the birth of Christ. Had Ussher not been such a dedicated student of history, he wouldn't have been able to complete his study!

Now how does the actual explanation of Ussher's work compare to the descriptions of the people you asked? Probably not very well. Most people who know about Bishop Ussher think he got all of his information from the Bible. They think that he just looked at all the genealogies in the Bible, used ages when he had them, and assumed ages when he didn't have them. But that's not how he did it at all. His analysis was a lot more complicated than that. He used the genealogies in Scripture when he could, but in order to complete his task, he had to use a lot of information from historical accounts that are not in the Bible.

There is one further complication to the story. The genealogies in Genesis 5 and 11 list the ages of the fathers when their son was born, but not all versions of the Old Testament give the same ages. The Hebrew Bible, which is the version that Ussher used, is thought by many to be the most reliable version of the Old Testament. However, some versions of the Old Testament, such as the Septuagint (sep too' uh jint'), have different ages than the Hebrew Bible, which results in a different date for creation. The people who use the ages listed in the Septuagint tend to date creation at roughly 5,500 BC instead.

How reliable is Ussher's date for creation? It's hard to say. His analysis was detailed, and he took great pains to be as accurate as he possibly could. Others had tried to do what he did, but they weren't nearly as careful and thorough as he was. Despite this, his analysis does depend a lot on what was known about history in his time. As we have learned more about history, others have tried to improve on his analysis. They have come to conclusions that are similar to his, but not exactly the same. Also, Ussher's analysis depends on the creation days being standard, 24-hour days. There have always been some Christians (even in Ussher's time and before) who didn't think that's the right interpretation of the Genesis days, so they would say that Ussher's analysis is wrong for that reason.

In the end, the Bible doesn't tell us exactly how long ago God created the earth. Ussher did an incredible job of using the Bible and history to come up with an estimate of when that happened, but it did involve him making assumptions. The accuracy of his date for creation depends on how good his assumptions were. Since we will probably never know exactly how good they were, we will probably never be able to say exactly how accurate his date is. I think it's a pretty good estimate, but there are many who disagree with me on that!

LESSON REVIEW

Youngest students: Answer these questions:

1. What do we call the lists in Genesis 5 and Genesis 11?

2. Did James Ussher use only the Bible in his calculation of when God created the earth?

Older students: Explain how Ussher calculated his date for creation, including both his use of genealogies and his use of history.

Oldest students: Do what the older students are doing. In addition, explain the problem the Septuagint poses to Ussher's method.

NOTE: The experiment in Lesson 41 (pp. 123-124) involves observation over a few days. Consider starting the experiment tomorrow and observing it until you reach Lesson 41.

Lesson 40: Joachim Jungius (1587 – 1657)

This stamp, issued by Germany, has Joachim Jungius's portrait on it.

While Galileo was making discoveries about the universe and Harvey was making discoveries about the human body, a German natural philosopher named **Joachim** (yoh' ak heem) **Jungius** (yoong' ee us) was making discoveries in mathematics, logic, botany, and chemistry. Have you ever heard the term "Renaissance Man?" It means someone who knows a lot of things about a lot of different subjects. Leonardo da Vinci was probably the best example of a Renaissance Man, but Joachim Jungius might be a close second. He started his career as a professor of mathematics, but later on studied medicine and became a doctor and a professor of medicine. He then became a professor of natural science. Later on, he became convinced that Germany was not educating its children well, so he became the head of a school that focused on getting young men ready to study at a university.

During his career, he studied nature constantly, trying to learn everything he could about the world around him. He developed a detailed classification system of plants based on their appearance. He made several discoveries related to mathematics, and he was convinced that mathematics was the basis of all science. Probably his most important contribution to science was his ideas related to chemical **elements**. If you studied Aristotle, you probably have heard the term "elements" before. However, Jungius's idea was much different from (and much closer to the truth than) Aristotle's.

Aristotle believed that there were five basic elements, (earth, air, fire, water, and ether [ee' thur]) and that all things were made of combinations of those five elements. Jungius realized that this couldn't possibly be right, but he did think that Aristotle's basic idea was right. Consider, for example, a flat, blank sheet of paper. It looks really smooth, right? However, if you look at it with a strong magnifying glass, you will see that it isn't smooth. Instead, it is made of fibers that twist around one another. So even though the paper appears to be the same everywhere, when you magnify it, you can see that it isn't. There are bundles of fiber that are thinner in some places and thicker in others.

In science, we have two important words that will help with this discussion: **homogeneous** (ho' muh jee' nee us) and **heterogeneous** (het' uh ruh jee' nee us). When something is the same throughout, we say it is homogenous, because the prefix "homo" means "same." When the makeup of something changes in different parts of the sample, we say it is heterogeneous, because the prefix "hetero" means "different." The water in a bottle of water, for example, appears the same everywhere, so it looks homogeneous. A bottle of Italian salad dressing, however, looks different depending on where you look in the bottle. In some parts of the bottle, there is mostly liquid with only a few spices floating in it. In other parts of the bottle, there are a lot of spices floating in only a small amount of liquid. As a result, we say that Italian salad dressing is heterogeneous. See the pictures on the next page for an illustration of the difference between homogeneous and heterogeneous.

Joachim Jungius said that most things which appear homogeneous really are not. Consider, for example, the blank piece of paper I mentioned earlier. If you look at it with the unaided eye, it looks homogeneous. With a good magnifying glass, however, you can see that it is made of bundles of fibers, and the makeup of those bundles is different depending on where you look on the paper. As a result, even though the paper appears to be homogeneous, it is actually heterogeneous. At the same time, however, he thought that there had to be some things that are truly homogeneous – no matter how much you magnified them, you would see that they are the same throughout. He called those things elements.

Jungius thought that all things we see are either elements or combinations of elements. If a substance was truly homogeneous, it must be an element. If not, it must be a combination of elements. To get an idea of what Jungius was thinking, perform the following experiment.

The water in the bottle on the left is the same throughout. It is homogeneous. The Italian salad dressing on the right is not the same throughout. It is heterogeneous.

Elements and Non-Elements

What you will need:
- ☞ Root Kill (It is found in the plumbing section of a hardware store. The ingredients list should have "copper sulfate" or "copper sulfate pentahydrate" as the main ingredient. If you can look inside the package, it should be full of blue crystals.)
- ☞ Steel wool
- ☞ A measuring teaspoon
- ☞ A measuring cup
- ☞ A spoon for stirring
- ☞ Two glasses that you can see through

What you should do:
1. Put a teaspoon of root kill in each glass.
2. Add a cup of water to each glass.
3. Stir the contents of each glass so that the blue crystals of Root Kill are pretty much gone. You might not get them all to dissolve, but most of them should.
4. Pull a small clump of steel wool about the size of your thumb from the rest of the steel wool.
5. Put the small clump of steel wool into one of the glasses. If it doesn't sink, push it to the bottom of the glass with the spoon you used for stirring.
6. Look through the glass at the steel wool. Do you see anything happening?
7. Wait for about five minutes.
8. Pull the steel wool out of the glass with your fingers. Compare it to the original clump of steel wool. What's the difference? Compare the solution in the glass with the steel wool to the solution in the other glass. What's the difference?
9. Clean up your mess and put everything away.

What happened in the experiment? You should have seen that the color of the solution that had the steel wool in it had changed. It wasn't the pale blue of the solution in the glass that had no steel wool in it. Also, you should have seen that the "steel wool" you pulled out of the solution was really different from the steel wool that hadn't been put in the solution. While steel wool is gray, the "steel wool" you pulled out of the solution was coppery-colored.

There's a reason the steel wool turned a coppery color in your experiment. The iron in the steel wool was replaced with copper! Where did the copper come from? It came from the Root Kill, which is made of a chemical called "copper sulfate." Where did the iron go? It became a part of the solute

(the stuff dissolved in the solution), which changed from copper sulfate to iron sulfate. So the liquid in the glass changed from a solution of copper sulfate to a solution of iron sulfate.

Joachim Jungius thought that copper and iron were both elements. No matter how much you magnified them, they would be homogeneous – their chemical composition would be the same everywhere. However, he also knew that copper could become a part of other things that weren't elements, such as copper sulfate. Of course, if you did the right kind of chemistry, you could pull the element of copper out of the copper sulfate. You did that in your experiment by adding the element iron. The element iron became a part of the new solute (iron sulfate), and as a result, the element

The wires on the left are made of the element copper. No matter where you look in the wires, you will find only one thing: copper. The copper sulfate on the right is not an element. Instead, it is a compound made up of three different elements: copper, sulfur, and oxygen.

copper was removed from the copper sulfate. Modern chemistry recognizes that Jungius was right. All substances can be classified as being either elements or **compounds**. An element represents the simplest substance, while a compound is made up of at least two different elements.

LESSON REVIEW

Youngest students: Answer these questions:

1. (Fill in the blank) When something is the same throughout, we say it is _____.

2. (Fill in the blank) The simplest substances are elements, and _____ are made up of at least two different elements.

Older students: Make an illustration that explains the difference between homogeneous substances and heterogeneous substances. Explain which of those words Joachim Jungius would apply to elements. Explain what a compound is and which word Jungius would apply to a compound.

Oldest students: Do what the older students are doing. In addition, explain your experiment in your own words, noting what you started with and what you ended up with.

Lesson 41: Evangelista Torricelli (1608 – 1647)

Italian natural philosopher **Evangelista** (ih van' juh lee' stuh) **Torricelli** (tor' uh chel' ee) was studying mathematics and philosophy while Galileo and Kepler were making their discoveries. He even wrote a letter to Galileo saying that he was delighted when he read *Dialogue Concerning the Two Chief World Systems* (Galileo's book about the arrangement of the universe) and was convinced that heliocentrism was correct. While Torricelli did study astronomy and even made improvements to the telescope, he is best remembered for his discoveries that Aristotle was wrong when it came to the nature of the air that is all around us.

This statue of Evangelista Torricelli is in his hometown of Faenza, Italy. It depicts him studying a barometer.

Aristotle taught that air had no weight. Despite the fact that many of Aristotle's ideas had been shown to be wrong, this one was still thought to be correct during this period in history. He also taught that it would be impossible to completely remove all the air from a container. He said you can't have a region of space that is completely empty of everything. That's called a **vacuum**, and according to Aristotle, nature fights so strongly against such a thing that it could never exist. Torricelli didn't think Aristotle was correct on either of those two points, and he did some experiments that showed he was right. The following experiment is similar to one that he did.

A Barometer

What you will need:
- A small glass, like a juice glass
- Blue food coloring (any dark color will work)
- A straw
- Tape
- A spoon for stirring
- A marker
- Someone to help you

What you should do:
1. Add several drops of food coloring to the glass.
2. Fill the glass about halfway with water.
3. Stir the water and food coloring together. If the resulting color isn't a dark blue, add more food coloring and stir until the color is dark.
4. Put the straw in the water and suck on the straw so it fills with water. Food coloring is safe to eat, so you can get some in your mouth.
5. While your mouth is still on the straw, push the bottom of the straw against the bottom of the glass.
6. Quickly remove your mouth and bend the top of the straw to form an airtight seal. This will trap some water in the straw. Ideally, the water should be about halfway up the straw, but that's not completely necessary. Just make sure there is a lot of water in the straw and some space at the top

Make the mark here.

airtight bend in the straw

tape holding the straw to the inside of the glass

that has only air in it. If you have a lot of water in the straw, relax your grip on the bend to allow some air in. That will allow some water to flow out of the straw.

7. Have your helper get a strip of tape and help you secure the bend in the straw so it stays airtight.

8. Lift the straw so that there is about 2 centimeters (about an inch) of space between the bottom of the glass and the bottom of the straw. The bottom of the straw should still be under water, but there should be space between it and the bottom of the glass.

9. Have your helper get another strip of tape and help you tape the straw to the inside of the glass so it remains in that position: underneath the water but with space between it and the bottom of the glass. At this point, your experiment should look something like the picture on the left.

10. Use the marker to mark the water level in the straw.

11. Put the glass and straw setup in a place where it won't be disturbed for a few days but can be seen easily.

12. Clean up any mess you made.

13. Check the water level in the straw twice each day and compare it to the mark you made in step 10.

After checking on the experiment for a few days, what have you noticed? Most likely, you should have seen that the water level in the straw changed. It might have gone above the line, it might have gone below the line. Depending on the weather over the days while you were checking, it might have done both. That's because the device you made is sensitive to **air pressure**.

You probably already know that the air around you presses on everything it touches. The device you made is sensitive to that. Why? Well think about what you did when you bent the straw to make an airtight seal. You trapped some air in the straw above the liquid. That amount of air can't change, because there is no way to get air into or out of the straw. However, the air that is pressing down on the water in the glass can change, because the glass is open. If more air gets into the room, it will press down harder on the water in the glass. That will force more water up into the straw. If air leaves the room, the remaining air won't be able to press down as hard on the water in the glass. At that point, the weight of the water in the straw is stronger, so the water level in the straw goes down.

Now what would bring more air into the room or cause air to leave the room? The answer is weather. Different kinds of weather bring in different amounts of air. As a general rule of thumb, days that are sunny have higher air pressure, while days that are rainy have lower air pressure. So when the water level rose in the straw, the weather was probably sunnier, because that meant higher air pressure. When the water level fell in the straw, the weather was probably cloudier or rainy, because that meant lower air pressure.

The device that measures air pressure is called a **barometer** (buh rah' muh tur), and you made a version of that in your experiment. Torricelli is credited with inventing it. He didn't use water, however. Instead, he used mercury, which is a very heavy liquid, roughly 14 times heavier than water. He took a glass tube that was about one meter (3 feet) tall and closed at the bottom. He filled it with mercury and then turned it over into a bowl of mercury. When he did that, the mercury in the tube fell, but only a little bit. In the end, a column of mercury about 76 centimeters (about 2½ feet) remained in the tube. However, like your experiment, the height of the mercury varied with the weather.

Torricelli decided that when the mercury fell down the tube, the top of the tube had truly nothing in it. It didn't have mercury in it, and since there was no way for air to get in the tube, it didn't even have air in it. Instead, it was completely empty. In other words, it was a vacuum. This, he said, showed that Aristotle was wrong. If you do it the right way, you can make a vacuum. Of course, today we know that Torricelli was right. He did, indeed, create a vacuum in his barometer, and since then scientists have developed other ways to produce a vacuum.

Of course, the other question he had to answer was why mercury remained in the tube at all. What was holding up the 76 centimeters of mercury in the tube? The answer, according to Torricelli, was the weight of the air outside the bowl of mercury. That weight was pushing down on the mercury in the bowl, and that push balanced out the weight of the mercury in the tube. When changing weather brought in more air, the air could push down harder on the mercury in the bowl. This forced mercury up the tube until the weight of the mercury in the tube increased enough to equal the force with which air was pushing down on the mercury in the bowl. When changing weather took air away, the weight of the mercury in the tube was greater than the push of air against the mercury in the bowl. As a result, the level of mercury in the tube lowered until the weight of the mercury in the tube decreased to equal the push of the air against the mercury in the bowl.

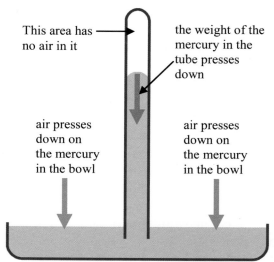

In Torricelli's barometer, the height of the mercury in the glass tube is determined by the point at which the weight of the mercury in the tube equals the force with which air is pushing on the mercury in the bowl.

Of course, the air pushes down on the mercury because it is heavy. So not only did Torricelli demonstrate that Aristotle was wrong about the existence of a vacuum, he also showed that Aristotle was wrong about air being weightless. In fact, air has weight, which is why a barometer works. Of course, had the natural philosophers of his day taken Job 28:25 seriously, they would have already known that Aristotle was wrong, because that verse clearly tells us that wind has weight!

LESSON REVIEW

Youngest students: Answer these questions:

1. What does a barometer measure?

2. On what two ideas did Torricelli demonstrate Aristotle to be incorrect?

Older students: Make a drawing like the one above, and use it to help explain how Torricelli's barometer works and what it measures. Also explain which two of Aristotle's ideas were shown to be wrong by this device.

Oldest students: Do what the older students are doing. In addition, answer the following question: Air pressure is usually measured in inches or millimeters of mercury. What do those inches or millimeters refer to? Check your answer and correct it if it is wrong.

Lesson 42: René Descartes (1596 – 1650)

Do you remember from Lesson 32 that Johannes Kepler explained many of the details associated with how we see things? He showed that light reflects off an object, enters the eye, is focused by the eye's lens, and hits the retina. Because of this process, an upside-down image forms on our retina, and that's how we see things. This explanation was very important to a French natural philosopher named **René** (ren nay') **Descartes** (day kart'). He wanted to believe that the human body (and the bodies of all animals) worked like machines – they simply followed the rules of nature, and everything they did could be explained in that way. In other words, people and animals didn't need supernatural help in order to live from day to day.

Now, don't think Descartes didn't believe in the supernatural at all! He was a devout Roman Catholic who wrote extensively about God and even tried to use philosophy to prove that He exists. However, Descartes believed that God is so powerful that He designed the world to operate on its own. Consider, for example, an inventor who makes a machine that can perform a necessary task. If the inventor has to constantly "hover" over his machine, fixing it over and over again because it constantly breaks down, the inventor would be praised for his machine, but people would want to improve it so that it could work on its own. If the inventor could make the machine do the task without ever needing to be fixed, he would not only be praised for the machine, but he would also be admired for how well he crafted it.

Descartes thought God was such a mighty Creator that He could produce a world which worked on its own, with no need for God to help it along from day to day. So he wanted to view people, animals, and all of nature as well-designed machines that worked according to known laws. When Kepler showed that vision was simply a consequence of several known laws, Descartes thought he could extend that to all of the human body. As a result, Descartes tried to explain human bodies (and animal bodies) as physical machines that simply worked according to the laws that natural philosophers had been discovering.

At the same time, however, Descartes realized that there is more to a human being than just his or her body. He knew that humans have souls, and he thought that animals did not. So while animals were nothing more than well-designed machines that ran according to known laws, people were something more. Their bodies were machines, but their *minds and souls* were a part of the image of God that their supernatural Creator had given them, as discussed in Genesis 1:26-27. This led to a view known as **dualism**: the belief that people have a dual nature – they are physical because they have physical bodies, but they are also spiritual, because they have minds and souls. To get an idea of what Descartes thought, do the following activity.

The Senses and the Mind
What you will need:
- Two chairs
- Two people to help you (One of them should be the parent/teacher.)
- Your notebook or, for younger students, a piece of paper
- A pencil
- The picture on page A2 of the Appendix in your parent/teacher's *Helps and Hints* book (**Only you and your parent/teacher should see this picture. Your other helper cannot be allowed to see it!**)

What you should do:
1. Arrange the chairs so they are back-to-back.
2. Sit in one of the chairs.
3. Have your helper (the one who is not your parent/teacher) sit in the other chair so that his or her back is to you. That way, your helper cannot see what you are seeing.
4. Have your helper take the notebook or paper and the pencil.
5. Have your parent/teacher show you the picture that is on page A2 of the *Helps and Hints* book.
6. Describe the picture you are seeing out loud, so your helper can hear you.
7. Have your helper draw the picture you are describing without ever looking at it. Your helper can ask you questions, and you can be as descriptive as you want, but he or she *cannot* see the picture.
8. Compare the picture to your helper's drawing.

How does your helper's drawing compare to the picture you saw? Obviously, it isn't exactly the same, but there are a lot of similarities, aren't there? If you do this exercise with several different people (none of whom have ever seen the drawing), you will find that you will get better at describing the picture, and as a result, the drawings will tend to get more and more similar to the picture.

Now, how did you know what to describe to your helper? You *saw* the picture. Descartes would say that the process by which you saw the picture was purely physical. It obeys the laws of nature. However, in order to describe it to your helper so he or she could draw it, you had to use your *mind*. You had to think about the picture and how to turn what you had seen into words. According to Descartes, that process is not physical. It does not follow the laws of nature. It uses the "extra," spiritual part of you.

According to Descartes, you have a dual nature. Your body allows you to experience things through your *physical* senses, which are from the physical part of you. When you think about what you have experienced, however, you are using your mind, which is from the *spiritual* part of you.

Now, of course, the physical part of you (your senses, for example) is not completely separate from the spiritual part of you (your mind). We know this because in order to think about and describe the picture, you first had to see it. Thus, your body used its physical sense of sight, and then your mind used the information from that sense to think about what you saw and how to describe it. To Descartes, then, the physical part of you and the spiritual part of you interact, but they are utterly different. That's what dualism is all about.

To Descartes, both aspects of a person are important, but the spiritual aspect (the mind) is what really makes us human. In addition, he was aware that the senses can be fooled. People sometimes **hallucinate** (huh loo' suh nayt') , which means they see things that aren't there. They sometimes hear things that aren't there as well. Your senses of touch, taste, smell, and balance can also be fooled. Thus, you should always be a bit skeptical about what your senses tell you. However, because you can think, you know that you are a real person. In fact, Descartes's most famous words are, "I think, therefore I am." He was convinced that even if the entire physical world was some elaborate illusion, he knew he existed, because he could use his *mind.*

Because Descartes thought the mind was more important to people than their physical nature, he thought that science should be guided by the mind. Do you remember how Francis Bacon thought science should be done? He thought that there were so many counterintuitive things in nature that the human mind alone couldn't be trusted to figure most things out. Instead, everything had to be tested by experiment. While Descartes agreed that experiments are important, he thought that studying the natural world required the understanding of certain truths that could not be understood through experiment. Those truths had to be discovered with the mind, and then experiments could help us fill in the details about how the physical world worked from day to day.

Descartes's separation of the physical world from the supernatural world of the mind affected the study of science greatly. As time went on, natural philosophers began to study the world assuming that it functioned entirely on its own. There was no need for God to "step in" and "fix" the world from time to time, because He was such an incredible Creator that He made the world to run completely on its own. This forced natural philosophers to reexamine the things they were studying, always limiting their efforts to finding a physical explanation for how they worked.

Interestingly enough, even though Descartes's idea of dualism influenced science greatly, most of his actual scientific studies were incorrect. For example, he tried to explain how the planets orbited the sun by suggesting that there was a great, swirling tide in space that pushed them along. Natural philosophers quickly realized he was wrong about that. Many of his concepts of how the human body (and animal bodies) worked were shown to be incorrect as well. However, he did get some things right. He developed some mathematical ideas that helped natural philosophers better analyze their experiments. His writings on optics also helped astronomers build better telescopes, and he also developed a hypothesis about how rainbows form. Even though it wasn't very correct, it helped another natural philosopher (you will learn about him soon) figure out where the colors of the rainbow come from.

As you learned previously, a scientist doesn't have to always be right for him to advance our understanding of God's creation. René Descartes is a perfect example of this truth.

LESSON REVIEW

Youngest students: Answer these questions:

1. Fill in the blanks: Dualism says that people have two natures – a physical one that governs the _____, and a spiritual one that governs the _____.

2. What was Descartes's most famous saying?

Older students: Below the drawing in your notebook, describe how it was made and how it compares to the original picture. Explain how this illustrates Descartes's idea of dualism.

Oldest students: Do what the older students are doing. In addition, explain why Descartes said, "I think, therefore I am."

Lesson 43: Blaise Pascal (1623 – 1662)

Torricelli's experiments with mercury were very interesting to a French natural philosopher who lived at roughly the same time, **Blaise** (bleyz) **Pascal** (pas kal'). Of course, Pascal was fascinated by a lot of different things. He studied mathematics, for example, and at the ripe old age of 16 he wrote his first work of natural philosophy, which ended up improving on the mathematical subject known as geometry. A few years later, he invented a mechanical adding machine, which is often called Pascal's calculator.

This is a portrait of Blaise Pascal.

He was fascinated by Torricelli's experiments for two reasons. First, he was convinced that Torricelli had, indeed, produced a vacuum, and he did several experiments to confirm that fact. Second, he thought that Torricelli's experiment with mercury pointed to a more general rule about the behavior of fluids. He did several experiments with water, and he ended up showing a very important rule about all fluids and the pressure they exert. Perform the following experiment to see what Pascal discovered.

Height and Pressure

What you will need:
- Two straws that can be bent on one end
- Two small glasses, like juice glasses
- A sink with a plug
- Water
- Cellophane tape

What you should do:
1. Put the plug in the sink and turn on the water. You can continue to do the next steps while the sink is filling. In the end, you want the sink to have at least 15 centimeters (6 inches) of water in it.
2. Bend both straws so that the ends that bend point towards each other.
3. Squeeze one of the ends so that you can push it into the end of the other straw, forming a "U" shape out of the straws (see the picture on the next page). Push it in pretty far, because you want the "U" to be airtight.
4. Wrap tape around the place where you have joined the straws. It is best to wrap the tape around that area several times to help make the seal airtight.
5. Fill one of the glasses with water so it is mostly full.
6. Add water to the other glass so it has only about 2½ centimeters (1 inch) of water in it.
7. Set the glasses side by side.
8. Once the sink has a lot of water in it, put the "U" under water, tilting it so the open ends are pointed up (but still under water) and the flat part of the "U" is on the bottom of the sink. You should see air bubbles rising from it as it fills with water.
9. Play with the tilt and squeeze different parts of the "U" while keeping it under water the entire time. Your goal is to get all of the air out of the "U" so that it is completely full of water.

10. Put your index fingers over the open ends of the "U" to trap the water inside.
11. While you keep your index fingers over the open ends, pull the "U" out of the water and turn it over so the open ends are pointed down.
12. Put the "U" into the glasses so that the open ends are both under water, one in each glass. Do not stop covering the ends with your index finger until they are both under water. In the end, your setup should look something like the picture on the left.
13. Watch what happens to the water level in each glass. If you don't see anything happening within a minute, there is probably air in your "U." Try to make sure the seal between the two straws is airtight, and repeat steps 8-12, trying as hard as you can to make sure the "U" stays completely filled with water.
14. Once you notice a change occurring in the water levels, watch the system for a while. Compare the water levels once it appears that the changes have stopped.
15. Raise one of the glasses so its bottom is about halfway up the other glass.
16. Watch how the water levels change in the two glasses, and once again, notice where they end up.
17. Clean up your mess.

What did you see in your experiment? If all went well, you should have seen the water level lower in the glass that was mostly full, while the water level rose in the glass that was mostly empty. Eventually, they ended up coming to the same level. When you raised a glass, the water level should have lowered in the raised glass, while the water level rose in the unraised glass. Eventually, you should have seen that the raised glass emptied and the unraised glass filled until the water level in each glass reached the same height above the counter.

Did the results surprise you? In the end, the water levels had to even out, but not so that there was the same amount of water in each glass. Instead, they had to even out so that the water level was at the same height as measured from the counter. Why is that? Pascal decided that the pressure a liquid exerts depends on the height of the liquid. When you put the "U" in the two glasses with unequal levels, the water in the glass that was mostly full exerted a lot of pressure. That pushed water out of the mostly full glass, through the "U," and into the mostly empty glass. Eventually, however, the height of the water in each glass (as measured from the counter) was the same. At that point, the pressure exerted by the water in each glass was the same, so the water stopped moving between the glasses.

When you raised one of the glasses, the water in that glass was higher above the counter than the water in the other glass. Each glass had the same amount of water in it, but that's not the important thing. The pressure water exerts depends on its *height*. So the water in the raised glass started exerting more pressure than the water in the unraised glass. This pushed water out of the raised glass and into the unraised glass. When the water level in the unraised glass reached the same height above the counter as the water in the raised glass, the pressures were equal again. At that point, the water stopped moving.

Pascal showed that the height of water (or any liquid) affects the pressure with which it pushes. The higher the liquid, the more pressure with which it pushes. We aren't certain this actually happened, but some writers say that Pascal illustrated this dramatically with what is often called his "barrel experiment." He filled a barrel with water, and then put a tall, thin tube on the barrel. He made the seal between the tube and the barrel airtight. As long as the water level in the tube was low, the barrel held the water without leaking. However, when the tube was filled with water so that the level was high, the barrel started to leak.

Now remember, the barrel was full, and the amount of extra water introduced by the tall, thin tube was very small compared to the water that was already in the barrel. As a result, Pascal decided it wasn't the extra water that started making the barrel leak. Instead,

The tube would have been a *lot* taller than what the illustration suggests, so this symbol indicates that a lot of the tube has been cut out to make the illustration fit on the page better.

This illustrates Pascal's "barrel experiment." On the left, the barrel is full of water, but the tube is almost empty. On the right, the tube is filled with water. The height of the water in the tube produces so much pressure that it causes the barrel to leak.

it was the *height* of the water in the tube. That height caused a lot of pressure, and that pressure ended up pushing everywhere the water touched, including the sides of the barrel. That extra pressure pushed so hard on the barrel that the barrel started leaking.

There are really two very important things demonstrated by Pascal's barrel experiment. The first was that the height of a liquid determines the pressure with which it pushes. The second was that when pressure is exerted at one place in an enclosed liquid, the liquid transmits that pressure in all directions, pushing with that pressure against anything it touches. This is called **Pascal's Law**, and if you are doing the challenge lessons, you will learn more about it in the next lesson.

LESSON REVIEW

Youngest students: Answer these questions:

1. Fill in the blank: Pascal agreed with Torricelli (and disagreed with Aristotle) that it is possible for a _____ to exist in nature.

2. Fill in the blank: If one sample of water is higher than the second, the first exerts _____ pressure.

Older students: Make a drawing of your experimental setup and explain what happened in the experiment. Explain what the experiment demonstrates.

Oldest students: Do what the older students are doing. In addition, explain what Pascal's Law says.

Lesson 44: Pascal's Law

In the previous lesson, you learned about Pascal's Law. It says that when pressure is exerted at one place in an enclosed liquid, the liquid transmits that pressure in all directions, pushing with that pressure against anything it touches. Let's do an experiment that demonstrates this, and then I will discuss a very important (and very useful) consequence of the law.

Pascal's Law and Match Heads

What you will need:
- Wooden Matches
- Scissors
- A plastic, ½-liter bottle with a lid, like the kind water comes in
- Water
- An adult to help you

What you should do:
1. Have an adult help you cut the heads off of four wooden matches. You want only the head. There should be no wood sticking out from the head.
2. Fill the bottle to the very brim with water.
3. Put the four match heads in the water so that they float right at the top of the bottle.
4. Put the lid on the bottle as tightly as possible so it forms an airtight seal.
5. Squeeze the bottle as hard as you can. What happens? If nothing happens, have the adult squeeze the bottle as hard as he or she can. Something should happen.
6. Once you have seen what happens, relax your grip so you are still holding the bottle but no longer squeezing it. What happens?
7. Repeat steps 5 and 6 a couple of times.
8. Clean up your mess.

What did you see in the experiment? If things went well, you should have seen that when you squeezed the bottle, the match heads sank. When you relaxed your grip, they floated back to the surface. It's possible that not all of the match heads behaved that way. If too much wood was left on the match head, it would not sink. That's why I had you cut the heads off four matches. While you might have left too much wood on one of them, you probably wouldn't have done that on all four, especially when you were told that there should be no wood sticking out from the match heads.

Why did this happen? A match head weighs less than an equal volume of water, so it floats. However, it is also very **porous** (por' us). That means it has lots of pores (tiny spaces) between the material that makes up the match head. When the match head was floating, there wasn't anything pushing the water into those pores. As a result, the match heads absorbed very little water.

However, when you (or the adult) squeezed on the bottle, you were exerting pressure on the bottle and the liquid inside. Well, the water is a liquid, and since the lid was on the bottle, it was an enclosed liquid. Therefore, Pascal's Law applies. The pressure you exerted on the bottle got transmitted throughout the water, and it pressed on everything the water was touching, including the match heads.

Since the water was pressing on the match heads with the pressure you were exerting on the bottle, it was forced into the pores of the match heads. This made the match heads heavier, and eventually, they became heavier than an equal volume of water. As a result, they started to sink. However, when you stopped squeezing the bottle, the pressure was removed, and as a result, there was no longer any extra pressure pushing water into the pores of the match heads. This caused water to leave the match heads, making them lighter than an equal volume of water, and therefore they began to float again.

Now the key is that the match heads were constantly changing their position in the bottle, sinking or floating based on the pressure with which you squeezed. No matter their position, however, they were sensitive to how you were squeezing the bottle. No matter where the match heads were, they felt the pressure. That means the pressure you were exerting on the bottle was transmitted in all directions.

Of course, that's what Pascal's Law tells us – when pressure is exerted on an enclosed liquid, the liquid transmits it in all directions. It not only makes match heads rise and fall in a water bottle, it also allows us to lift heavy things with only a small amount of force! Have you ever watched an automobile mechanic repair something on the bottom of a car? What does he do? He puts the car on a lift, and the car rises so the mechanic can get underneath, as shown in the picture on the right.

Now cars are pretty heavy. They usually weigh well over 1,000 pounds. How does the lift raise the car up like that? You might think there is some machine that pushes the car up with thousands of pounds of force, but that's not really correct. The machine does not push with a large force, and it doesn't push up. It pushes down! How does pushing down with a small force allow the lift to raise a heavy car up? Pascal's Law.

The lift, which is technically called a **hydraulic** (hi draw' lik) **lift**, uses an enclosed liquid (hydraulic fluid). The machine pushes down on a small surface, and that exerts a pressure on the liquid. As required by Pascal's Law, the liquid then transmits that pressure *in all directions*, pressing against anything it touches. Well, the part that the car is sitting on is *on top* of the

This automobile mechanic is able to stand underneath the car because of a hydraulic lift, which uses Pascal's Law to lift heavy things.

container that holds the liquid. So the liquid presses *up* against it. Because that part is able to move, it rises up in response to that pressure.

That's why the "in all directions" part of Pascal's Law is important. Because the pressure goes in all directions, the hydraulic lift can press down in order to make the car go up. Of course, that's not the end of the story, because the lift uses a small force to lift a very heavy car. How does it do that? Once again, the answer is Pascal's Law.

Pascal's Law tells us that *pressure* is transmitted throughout the liquid, not *force*. Well, the larger the area, the more force you need to use in order to exert the same pressure. So if you want to exert a certain amount of pressure on a small object, it requires only a small force. However, if you want to exert that same amount of pressure on a larger object, it requires a larger force. A hydraulic lift uses this fact to produce an advantage.

A hydraulic lift pushes down with a small force on a small, movable section of the lift, producing a certain amount of pressure.

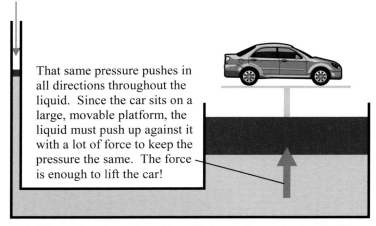

That same pressure pushes in all directions throughout the liquid. Since the car sits on a large, movable platform, the liquid must push up against it with a lot of force to keep the pressure the same. The force is enough to lift the car!

This illustration shows how Pascal's Law allows a hydraulic lift to use a small, downward force to lift a very heavy car.

As shown in the illustration on the left, a hydraulic lift exerts a small force on a small part of the container that encloses the liquid. This produces a certain amount of pressure. That pressure is then transmitted through the liquid in all directions, including upwards. The part of the lift upon which the car is sitting is very large, but the liquid presses up on it with the exact same amount of *pressure*. Since that part of the lift is very large, however, *that same pressure results in a lot more force*, so the liquid presses up with a very large force. The force with which the lift pushes, then, is magnified by the difference in size of the two parts of the lift. This magnification is so strong that a car can be lifted by the hydraulic lift using just a few pounds of force!

Pascal was clearly a brilliant man who helped us understand a lot about mathematics and science. However, he was never fully content with his life until he had an accident that could have killed him. He decided that he survived only through the grace of God, and he decided that he needed to devote himself more fully to the Almighty. As a result, he put aside his scientific and mathematical investigations and concentrated on writing about Christianity. He produced a book called *Pensées* (which means "Thoughts"), which was published after his death. It contains amazing insights into Christianity and the human condition.

When Pascal died, a note was found sewn into the lining of his coat. It read, in part, "Total submission to Jesus Christ and my director. Everlasting joy in return for one day's effort on earth. I will not forget thy word. Amen." [Ben Patterson, *He Has Made Me Glad*, InterVarsity Press 2005, p. 102]

LESSON REVIEW

Youngest students: Answer these questions:

1. What does the word "porous" mean?

2. What is Pascal's Law?

Older students: Write an explanation of what you did in the experiment and why it worked. Be sure to use the word "porous" and Pascal's Law in your explanation.

Oldest students: Do what the older students are doing. In addition, make a drawing like the one above and use it to explain how a hydraulic lift works.

Lesson 45: Pascal and Probability

As I mentioned previously, Pascal didn't limit himself to just one subject. He studied how nature works, he invented things, and he also discovered a lot of new mathematics. Of course, many of the natural philosophers you have studied so far also made contributions to mathematics, but I haven't discussed many of them in depth, because I want to focus on science. However, there is one mathematical discovery that Pascal made that I do want to focus on: **Pascal's Triangle**.

As the drawing on the right shows, it is very easy to construct Pascal's triangle. Put a "1" at the top of a piece of paper, and right underneath that, put two more "1"s side by side. Start the next row with a "1," and then add the numbers

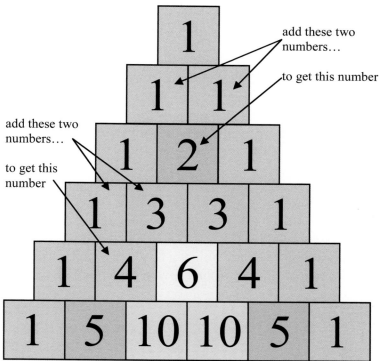

This is Pascal's Triangle. You can make one as tall as you want by following the rules discussed in the text.

above to get the next number for the row. Then finish the row with another "1." For each new row, start with a "1" and then add the two numbers directly above to get the next number. Continue doing that until you get to the end, and finish with another "1." You can do that as much as you want, continuing to make a taller and taller triangle.

Other than making a pretty triangle, what good is this? Perform the following experiment to find out.

Flipping a Coin

What you will need:
- A coin that has an easy-to-recognize "heads" side and an easy-to-recognize "tails" side
- Your notebook or, for younger students, a piece of paper
- A pencil

What you should do:
1. Flip the coin and record whether it ends up being heads or tails.
2. Repeat step 1 a total of 31 more times, so you have recorded the results of flipping a coin 32 times.
3. Count how many heads you ended up getting out of 32 flips.
4. Subtract that number from 32 to get the number of tails.
5. How do the heads and tails compare? Look at the second row in Pascal's Triangle. Notice there are two boxes, each of which has a 1 in it.
6. Now go back and group the flips in sets of two. Your first two results will be one set, your next two results will be the next set, etc. This gives you a total of 16 sets.

7. For each set of two flips, record how many times they both came up heads, record how many times they both came up tails, and record how many times you had one of each (one heads and one tails).
8. Compare how many times you got two heads to how many times you got two tails. Compare that to how many times you got one of each.
9. Look at the second row of Pascal's triangle. Notice it has three boxes. The first and last boxes each have a "1," while the middle box has a "2."

Did you notice that you had about as many heads as you had tails in your 32 flips? There might have been a few more heads than tails (or vice-versa), but they were roughly equal, right? What about when you grouped the results in 16 sets of two? What result did you get the most? It was probably one heads and one tails.

What does this have to do with Pascal's triangle? Well, look at the second row of the triangle. Notice that it has two ones in it. This tells you the probability of something happening when there are two possible results. When you flip a coin once, it can come up as either heads or tails. That means there are two possible results. When that is the case, each result has the same probability. In other words, you are just as likely to get a heads as you are to get a tails. Pascal's triangle tells you this because both boxes in the second row of the column have the same number in them (a "1").

When you flip a coin once, there are two possible results. When you flip it more than once, there are more possibilities. Pascal's triangle tells you how many possibilities there are and how likely each one is.

Now what happened when you grouped your flips in sets of two? If you think about it, when you flip a coin twice, there are three possible results: (1) They might both be heads; (2), there might be one heads and one tails, or (3) they might both be tails. Notice that the next row in Pascal's triangle has three boxes. Also, notice that the first and last boxes have a "1," but the middle box has a "2." This tells you that when you flip a coin twice, there are three possibilities, but they are not all equally likely. The middle option is twice as likely as the other two, because "2" is twice as large as "1."

So Pascal's triangle tells you about the possible outcomes of flipping a coin, or any other activity that has only two answers. If you flip the coin once, there are two possible results, and they are equally likely, because Pascal's triangle shows a "1" and "1" on the row with two boxes. If you flip a coin twice, there are three possible results, and the middle result (one heads and one tails) is twice as likely as the other two, because there is a "2" in the middle on the row that has three boxes.

You can continue this reasoning for all rows of Pascal's triangle. If you flip a coin three times, there are four possible results: (1) all heads, (2) two heads and one tails, (3) two tails and one head, and (4) all tails. If you look at the row of Pascal's triangle that has four boxes, you will see that the chances of (2) and (3) happening are equal, because each of the two boxes in the middle contain a "3." However, those two results are each three times more likely than (1) or (4) happening, since "3" is three times as big as "1."

So why am I telling you about this in a science course? Because this kind of mathematical reasoning is sometimes important in science. Suppose you do an experiment and there are several possible results from the experiment. If you do the experiment 10 times, have you seen all the possible results? You don't know unless you can somehow mathematically determine how many possible results there are and how likely each result is. Pascal and a mathematician named Pierre de Fermat were the first to detail how you could examine such a situation mathematically. As a result, they started the mathematical field known as **probability** – the analysis of random processes to conclude how likely certain results might be.

Do you remember that later in his life, Pascal gave up his scientific and mathematical studies so he could concentrate on writing about Christianity? Well, even though he gave up those studies, he didn't forget them. In fact, he applied his study of probability and how it relates to gambling to Christianity. How in the world did Pascal relate gambling to Christianity? He made an argument for Christianity known as **Pascal's Wager**.

The argument goes like this: If Christianity is true and you believe it, you will give up some earthly pleasures, but you will gain a *huge* reward in the end – an eternity in heaven with the Lord. If Christianity is not true but you believe it anyway, you have given up those earthly pleasures and you get no reward. So in the end, if you follow Christianity you "risk" something – you miss out on some earthly pleasures. However, in exchange for that "risk," you have the possibility of getting a *huge* reward. So in the end, being a Christian is a bit like a bet – you risk losing some earthly pleasures, but if Christianity is true, you get a huge reward.

Pascal argued that since an eternal reward is immensely more valuable than earthly pleasures, Christianity is a good bet. You risk missing out on a few pleasures here on earth, but the eternal joy of heaven outweighs that risk. In addition, the risk you take by not being a Christian is incredibly high – eternal separation from God. That risk is simply not worth a few earthly pleasures. So according to Pascal, Christianity is the best "bet" an intelligent man can make!

LESSON REVIEW

Youngest students: Answer these questions:

1. When it comes to flipping coins, what does Pascal's Triangle tell you?

2. Fill in the blank: Pascal's Wager argues that Christianity is the _____ bet an intelligent man can make.

Older students: Underneath the results you have for flipping the coin, write out Pascal's triangle for at least five rows. Don't look at the picture on the previous page; just follow the rules for making it. Underneath, explain how you made it.

Oldest Students: Do what the older students are doing. In addition, explain how the triangle can be used to predict the results when flipping a coin. As an example, use the fifth row to explain how many possible results there are when you flip a coin four times. In addition, predict what the most likely result will be.

Section 4: The Revolution in the Middle of the 17th Century

This statue honoring Robert Boyle is at Leinster House (where parliament meets) in Dublin, Ireland.

Lessons 46-60: The Revolution in the Middle of the 17th Century

Lesson 46: Thomas Bartholin (1616 – 1680)

Thomas Bartholin (bar' toh lin) was born in Denmark, and his father was a physician. In fact, his father had written a book on human anatomy that was very popular among those who were learning to be physicians. It's not surprising, then, that Thomas was trained to be a physician as well. Once he became a physician, he was obviously good at his job, because the king of Denmark (Christian V) hired Thomas as his personal physician. As his reputation grew, he was convinced to take his father's book and edit it to include some of the more recent discoveries on human anatomy. He did so, adding William Harvey's discovery about blood as well as some of his own discoveries.

One of Thomas Bartholin's contributions to the field of medicine was the first scientific explanation of **refrigeration anesthesia** (an' is thee' shuh). If you don't know what that means, this experiment should clear it up for you.

This is a portrait of Thomas Bartholin.

Cold as an Anesthetic

What you will need:
- Ice
- Water
- A small glass
- A metal paper clip
- An adult to help you

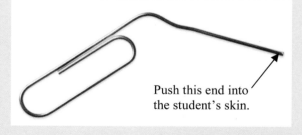

Push this end into the student's skin.

What you should do:
1. Fill the glass about halfway with ice.
2. Add cold water to the glass.
3. Swirl the water and ice so that they mix well.
4. Unfold the paper clip so it looks like the photo above.
5. Put the index finger of your right hand in the ice water mixture.
6. While your finger is soaking, hold out your left hand, palm up.
7. Close your eyes.
8. Keeping your eyes closed, have the adult press the end of the unfolded paper clip onto the tip of your index finger on your left hand. Tell him or her when you first feel the paper clip pressing in, and then have the adult continue pressing harder and harder. Stop him or her when it gets painful.

9. Repeat steps 7 and 8, but this time, pull the finger that you were soaking out of the ice water and use it. Ask the adult if there was a difference in how hard he or she had to press before you noticed it and before it got too painful.
10. Repeat the experiment. This time, you handle the paper clip, and have the adult take your place.
11. Notice the difference between when you were pressing the paper clip into the adult's warm finger and cold finger.
12. Clean up your mess.

What did you see in your experiment? You should have seen that when the paper clip was pressed into a cold finger, it had to be pushed harder in order for you to feel it and for the experience to become painful. That's because we sense pain through **nerve receptors**, and those receptors are much less sensitive when they are cold. Even though Bartholin didn't know about nerve receptors, he understood that cold skin didn't feel as much pain as warm skin. As a result, he suggested that when a surgeon had to cut into a person's skin, the surgeon should first put snow or ice on the area that would be cut. This would reduce the pain that the person would feel.

When something makes a person less sensitive to things like pain, we call it an **anesthetic**. Since the reduced pain you felt in your experiment came from cooling your finger, we could say that your pain was reduced because of a refrigeration anesthetic. Bartholin pointed this out in one of his books. He said that if you covered the skin you were about to cut with snow or ice, the patient would feel a lot less pain when you did what you had to do. However, he made it clear that he didn't invent the process. In fact, he learned it from an Italian natural philosopher named Marco Severino (seh vuh ree' no).

Now I want to make it clear that anesthesia had been used long before Bartholin's time. However, it was typically in the form of a **general anesthetic**, which tries to make the patient less sensitive to pain all over the body. It had been well known for a long time that certain natural chemicals, like opium, would make a person feel so strange that he or she would not be as sensitive to pain. However, the effect was produced over the entire body, and sometimes, it had unpredictable consequences. The refrigeration technique that Bartholin described is a **local anesthetic**: It causes a person to be less sensitive to pain, but only in a particular spot on the body.

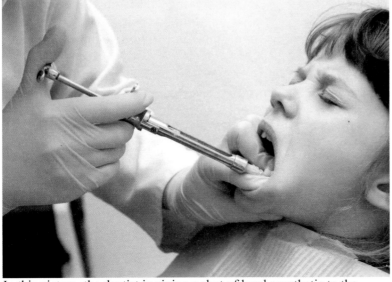

If you go to the dentist to have a tooth filled or removed, the dentist could give you a general anesthetic to deaden the pain, but general anesthetics have risks and longer-lasting consequences. As a result, the dentist will probably give you a shot of something that will reduce the pain you feel, but only in the area near where the dentist gives you the shot. That's a local anesthetic, and in most situations, it is a lot safer than a general anesthetic. Bartholin's discussion of refrigeration anesthesia ended up encouraging the development of other kinds of local anesthetics, which are used in lots of areas of medicine today.

In this picture, the dentist is giving a shot of local anesthetic to the child. The shot hurts, but because it contains a local anesthetic, it quickly makes that part of the mouth less sensitive to pain.

Bartholin's contributions to science don't stop there, however. Remember that he updated his father's human anatomy book. One thing he added was his description of the human **lymphatic** (lim fat' ik) **system**. It turns out that in addition to your blood vessels, there is another system of vessels running throughout your body. These vessels (and the structures that go with them) make up your lymphatic system. While Bartholin didn't understand what the lymphatic system did, he recognized that it was its own system. Others had described parts of the lymphatic system before, but they had all thought it was part of another body system. Bartholin was the first to publish the idea that it was a completely separate system.

So what is the lymphatic system? It is a series of vessels that run throughout the body. Bartholin noted that like veins, the vessels of the lymphatic system have valves that kept the fluid in them flowing in one direction. He showed that the fluid flows to the **thoracic** (thuh ras' ik) **duct**, where the clear fluid inside them (which he called **lymph**) is dumped into a vein. We now know that there is another duct (the right lymphatic duct) where the lymphatic system also dumps its fluid back into the veins. He also showed that there were "bulbs" on the glands, which we now call **lymph nodes**.

Bartholin didn't really know what the lymphatic system did. He just recognized that it was a complete system in the body. We now understand that the lymphatic system takes fluid that collects in the tissues and brings it back to the veins so it can be mixed with the blood. This keeps the tissues from swelling with too much water. The lymph nodes remove from the fluid any particles or microorganisms that could cause health problems before it is dumped back into the veins. The lymphatic system, then, is part of your body's defense against illness.

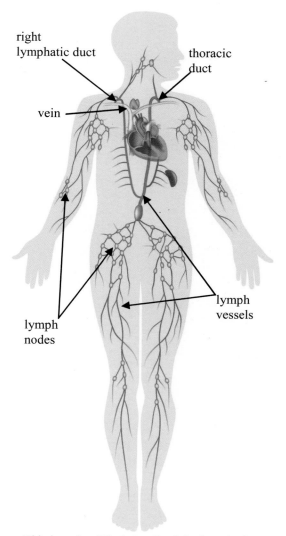

This is a simplified sketch of the lymphatic system.

LESSON REVIEW

Youngest students: Answer these questions:

1. What is an anesthetic?

2. What system in the human body did Thomas Bartholin discover?

Older students: Explain what an anesthetic is and explain the difference between a local anesthetic and a general anesthetic. Also, explain the local anesthetic that Bartholin described. Finally, note what human body system Bartholin discovered.

Oldest students: Do what the older students are doing. In addition, describe the liquid that the lymph vessels carry and what eventually happens to it.

Lesson 47: Otto von Guericke (1602 – 1686)

This is a portrait of Otto von Guericke, painted by Flemish artist Anselm van Hulle.

For a large part of his life, **Otto von Guericke** (gerh' ih kuh) was best known as a politician. His parents were very important political figures in the city of Magdeburg, Germany. He studied law, mathematics, and physics at university, but he came back to Magdeburg and became an engineer in the army of Gustavus II Adolphus, king of Sweden. That ended up bad for him, because he was taken prisoner when the city of Magdeburg fell in 1631. However, Louis I of Anhalt-Köthen (a German prince) paid for his release, and once things had settled down, von Guericke devoted himself to rebuilding the city of Magdeburg. He even became the city's mayor (technically called the bürgermeister) for many years.

Why am I telling you about a politician? Because even though he was very active in the public arena, he was fascinated by natural philosophy. As a result, he spent a lot of his spare time investigating the world around him. He discovered some amazing things, including the power of a vacuum. Do you remember learning about Evangelista Torricelli and his work on vacuums? Well, von Guericke had read Torricelli's work, and it influenced him greatly. As a result, he experimented with making a vacuum. He was eventually able to make a pump that pumped air *out of a container* instead of into a container. As a result, he was able to teach us a lot about what a vacuum can do. Perform the following experiment to see what I mean.

The Power of a Vacuum

What you will need:

- A plastic garbage bag that is tall enough so that you can stand inside it and the top will reach up to your waist (the thicker the plastic, the better)
- A vacuum cleaner with a hose and a small attachment that has bristles around the edge, like the one pictured on the left
- An adult to help you

What you should do:
1. Plug in the vacuum cleaner but don't turn it on.
2. Put the attachment on the hose of the vacuum cleaner.
3. Open the garbage bag and stand inside it.
4. Pull up on the garbage bag so the opening of the bag is around your waist, stomach, or chest. If the bag is so tall that it reaches up to your neck, use a smaller garbage bag. **NEVER, EVER PUT A PLASTIC BAG OVER YOUR HEAD OR MOUTH!!** That can be very dangerous!

5. Put the hose of the vacuum cleaner into the bag with you, and hold the attachment between your legs so that the attachment is securely held in place and the bristles are pushing against one of your legs. See the picture on the right.

6. Turn the vacuum cleaner on.

7. Have the adult help you gather the top of the bag around your waist. You want to try to make a nice seal between the garbage bag, your waist, and the part of the vacuum hose that is at the top of the garbage bag. Eventually, you should get to the point where you have developed enough of a seal that the bag starts pulling in, clinging to your legs and waist.

8. Play around with the bag, trying to get it to cling strongly to your legs.

9. Try to move your legs apart. If you try moving just the bottom part of your legs, you shouldn't be able to do it. You should only be able to pull your legs apart if you move your upper legs, where the attachment is being held. If the bag gets uncomfortably tight, just turn the vacuum off.

10. When you are done, turn the vacuum off and notice what happens.

11. Clean up your mess.

Were you impressed with how strongly the trash bag clung to your legs? Believe it or not, your experiment only gives you a taste of what a vacuum can do. Von Guericke was able to do a much better job than what you did in your experiment. He did a famous public demonstration in Magdeburg that is now called "the Magdeburg hemispheres experiment." In the experiment, he made a metal sphere that was split into two halves. The prefix "hemi" means "half," so a hemisphere is half of a sphere. He put the two hemispheres together and then used his pump to pull air from the inside of the sphere. As a result, the inside of the sphere had a vacuum. Once he was done, two teams of horses were used to try to pull the hemispheres apart, but they couldn't! The vacuum caused the spheres to cling to each other, just as the vacuum in your experiment caused the bag to cling to your legs! When air was let back into the hemispheres, they fell apart on their own, just as the bag in your experiment stopped clinging to you when you turned off the vacuum and air seeped back into the bag.

This statue in Magdeburg depicts Otto von Guericke's famous experiment.

It's important that you understand *why* the garbage bag clung to your legs in your experiment and *why* the horses couldn't pull the two halves of the sphere apart in the Magdeburg sphere experiment. It's not that the vacuum was pulling on the bag or the sphere. It's that *the vacuum caused an imbalance in air pressure.* Think about your experiment for a moment. Before you turned on the vacuum cleaner, there was air inside the bag and air outside the bag. The air inside the bag was pushing out with a certain pressure, and air outside the bag was pushing in with a certain pressure. Those pressures were the same, so the bag didn't do anything unusual.

When you turned on the vacuum cleaner, it started to remove air from the bag. Suddenly, then, there was less air inside the bag. However, there was still the same amount of air outside the bag. So while the air outside was pushing in with the same pressure as always, the air inside couldn't push out with the same amount of pressure. As a result, there was more pressure pushing inwards than there was pushing outwards. This caused the bag to collapse against your legs. As the bag collapsed, a better seal was formed between your body and the bag, so the vacuum cleaner could remove even more air, creating an even greater pressure imbalance. This caused the bag to collapse even more, so that it clung to your legs really strongly.

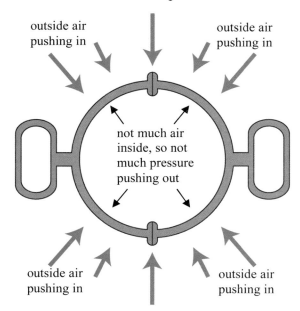

In von Guericke's Magdeburg hemispheres experiment, the vacuum reduced the pressure pushing from the inside out. The pressure from outside pushing in was therefore greater, pressing the hemispheres together.

The reason the bag clung to you so strongly was because the vacuum cleaner had pulled air from the inside. As a result, there wasn't as much pressure fighting against the air pressure that was coming from outside of the bag. The same was true for the two halves of the sphere in von Guericke's experiment. When he pumped air out of the sphere, there was less air inside pressing out. As a result, there was less pressure fighting the pressure of the air that was outside the hemispheres pressing in. This produced a net pressure pushing inwards, which held the hemispheres together so strongly that horses couldn't pull them apart! That should give you some idea about how strong air pressure is!

LESSON REVIEW

Youngest students: Answer these questions:

1. What is a hemisphere?

2. Fill in the blank: In Otto von Guericke's Magdeburg hemispheres experiment, the air pressure pushing from the outside was much _____ than the air pressure pushing from the inside.

Older students: Describe Otto von Guericke's Magdeburg hemispheres experiment, and use a drawing like the one above to explain how it worked.

Oldest students: Do what the older students are doing. In addition, if you don't know the expression, find out what "vacuum packed" means. Explain how it is similar to the experiment you did.

Lesson 48: Otto von Guericke and Electrical Charge

Like most natural philosophers of his day, von Guericke was fascinated by many different aspects of God's creation. As a result, he studied more than just vacuums. For example, he studied electrical charge and what it can do. At that time, very little was known about electricity, but magnetism had been studied for quite a while. You might have already learned, for example, that the Basic Law of Magnetism (that opposite poles attract one another and like poles repel one another) was discovered back in the late 1200s by Petrus Peregrinus. Electrical charges behave similarly to magnets, but there are differences as well.

Von Guericke built a device that would allow him to electrically charge a big ball. Then he showed what that charge could do. Perform the following experiment, which is similar to one that he did.

Electrical Charge

What you will need:
- A balloon (Any shape will do, but it should be larger than your hand when it is inflated.)
- Clean, dry hair (yours or someone else's)
- Thread
- Scissors

NOTE: This experiment works best on a dry day with very clean, dry hair.

What you should do:
1. Inflate the balloon so it is stretched pretty tight.
2. Tie off the balloon so it stays inflated.
3. Use the scissors to cut a 60-centimeter (24-inch) length of thread.
4. Holding the balloon in your right hand, rub it vigorously in your hair.
5. Hold the balloon in front of you (still in your right hand) with the part you rubbed in your hair pointing to the left.
6. Hold the thread in front of you with your left hand so it hangs down in front of you.
7. Move the thread slowly towards the part of the balloon that you rubbed in your hair. When you get close enough, the thread should start to move on its own toward the balloon. At that point, stop moving the thread and see what happens.
8. Eventually, the thread should stick to the balloon. At that point, let go of the thread and see what happens. If it doesn't all fall onto the balloon, move the balloon around until most of the thread is on the balloon.
9. Move the balloon around slowly, watching the behavior of the thread.
10. Hold your left hand (which has let go of the thread) out so that your palm faces the balloon.
11. Slowly move your hand towards the balloon so it is above some of the thread that is attached to the balloon. Don't touch the thread. Just get your hand close to it.
12. Play with the system for a while. You should be able to get the thread to move around a bit by moving your left hand, even though you are not touching the thread.
13. Clean up your mess.

What happened in the experiment? You should have seen that the thread was attracted to the balloon. However, once it was allowed to fall onto the balloon, something odd happened. Some of the thread stayed stuck to the balloon, but some of it rose above the balloon. In addition, when your hand got close to the thread, it started to move in reaction to your hand, even though your hand wasn't touching the thread in any way. As you moved your hand, the thread reacted to the movement.

Von Guericke did a very similar experiment. He didn't use a balloon, of course. Instead, he used a big ball made out of sulfur, a yellow solid that he could mold into the shape that he wanted. He then attached the ball to a pole and a crank, and he used the crank to spin the ball. When he allowed a pad to rub the ball as it spun, it developed an electrical charge. He could feel the charge, because the hairs on his body reacted to it. You probably felt something similar when you rubbed the balloon in your hair. Your hair moved around when you pulled the ball away, because it was reacting to the electrical charge.

This child's hair is attracted to the electrically charged balloon, just as the thread was in your experiment.

Once he had the ball charged like that, he showed that it would pull thread towards it. The more he charged the ball, the farther the thread could be from the ball when it started being pulled towards the ball. He used this ball to attract other things as well. He also noticed that when some things hit the ball, they would then suddenly speed away from the ball. As a result, he showed that, like magnets, electrical charge could be used to both attract and repel (push away) things. However, the attractive nature seemed to be greater than the repulsive nature, because things would first be attracted to the ball. They would only be pushed away once they first touched the ball.

Now von Guericke had no idea why electrical charge could do these things. In fact, it took about 80 more years for someone to develop a basic law of electrical charges like the basic law that already existed for magnets. It took even longer for scientists to understand what was really going on in an experiment like von Guericke's. However, von Guericke at least demonstrated that electrical charge could attract and repel things, just like magnets, and that the more charge there was, the stronger the attraction and repulsion.

Interestingly enough, even though von Guericke's experiments helped other natural philosophers and scientists to eventually understand electrical charge much better, he used his experiment to conclude something that was completely wrong! This happens a lot in science. Good scientists can make many mistakes. Usually, those mistakes are figured out, and often, the process of figuring out the mistakes leads to a better understanding of what is being studied. As I have told you before, then, even the mistakes that scientists make can lead to a better understanding of creation.

What did von Guericke conclude from his experiments? Well, natural philosophers back then understood that there was something called gravity that attracted things to the earth. In fact, since most natural philosophers by this time were convinced that Copernicus was right, they understood that the earth can spin without throwing us all into space because gravity attracts us to the earth, keeping us on solid ground despite the fact that the ground is moving with the earth's rotation. However, they had no idea what caused gravity.

Von Guericke thought that as the earth rotated, the air rubbed up against the earth, giving the earth electrical charge. In other words, von Guericke thought the earth was like his sulfur ball, and the air was like the pad he rubbed up against it. As the air rubbed up against the earth while the earth spun, it charged the earth, just like the pad rubbing up against the sulfur ball as it spun. He thought that this electrical charge is what caused gravity. Just as thread and all sorts of other objects would "stick" to the sulfur ball because the electrical charge attracted them, things "stick" to the earth because the electrical charge of the earth attracts them. We now know this isn't correct, of course, but even that incorrect idea helped other natural philosophers to learn more about both electrical charges and gravity.

These people have jumped out of the plane in the picture. They are falling to the ground because gravity is attracting them to earth. When they release their parachutes, they will fall a lot more slowly so they can land without hurting themselves, but even with the parachute, they will still fall because of gravity.

In addition to his studies on vacuum and electrical charges, Otto von Guericke also tried to understand the weather. He studied a barometer that he made based on Torricelli's work, and he noticed that it would change with the changing weather. He tried to use the barometer to predict the weather. He even suggested that if several barometers were read in several different places, the predictions could become even more accurate. Of course, today we use barometers to help us predict the weather, but we also use several other instruments. Nevertheless, von Guericke's work did help start the science of **meteorology** (mee' tee uh rol' uh jee), the study of weather.

LESSON REVIEW

Youngest students: Answer these questions:

1. Fill in the blanks: When you rubbed the balloon in your hair, you gave the balloon an _____ _____.

2. What did the experiment show that electrical charge can accomplish?

Older students: Describe Otto von Guericke's machine that developed electrical charge and what he used it to do. Explain how your experiment was similar to what he did.

Oldest students: Do what the older students are doing. In addition, discuss how von Guericke tried to use electrical charge to explain gravity. Be sure to note that it is not correct.

Lesson 49: Christiaan Huygens (1629 – 1695)

This portrait of Christiaan Huygens was painted by Caspar Netscher in 1671.

Do you remember learning about Descartes? He had the chance to get to know **Christiaan** (kris' tee ahn) **Huygens** (hoy' gens), because he was a friend of Huygens's father. Descartes was very impressed with young Huygens's mathematical abilities, so he encouraged the boy to learn as much as he could about mathematics. When Huygens went to university, then, it was only natural that he studied mathematics. He also studied law. Historians say that they can see Descartes's influence on Huygens, because Huygens approached his study of nature with the belief that God had designed the world to work on its own. As a result, the universe could be looked at like a big machine that ran without the help of its Designer.

Because of his studies and abilities, Huygens had a great interest in mathematics. In fact, he corresponded with Pascal about mathematical problems related to gambling. He ended up writing a small book about how to calculate your chance of winning when you gamble. He was also interested in the natural world, especially the planets, their moons, and the stars. He worked on improving telescopes so they could see the heavenly bodies more clearly, and because of this, he ended up solving a problem that had perplexed natural philosophers for quite some time. To get an idea of what he did, perform the following activity:

Saturn's Rings

What you will need:
- A tennis ball or baseball
- Two straight pins
- A pen or marker
- A paper plate
- A Ziploc bag
- Scissors
- Tape
- Someone to help you

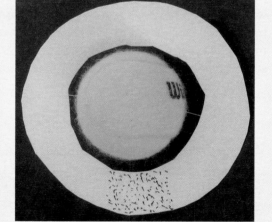

What you should do:
1. Stick a pin into the ball so that the pin stays stuck there.
2. Stick the other pin on the opposite side of the ball.
3. Cut a circle out of the paper plate that is a lot bigger than the ball.
4. Cut a circle inside that circle, making a ring. The inside circle should be large enough to fit the ball inside the ring with a bit of room to spare (see the picture above).
5. Use the pen or marker to make little dots on one section of the ring. The dots should completely fill a small section of the ring, as shown in the picture above.

6. Put the ball inside the ring and use the tape to fasten the ring to the pins. You should now have a ball with a ring around it, as shown in the photo on the previous page.
7. Cut a square that is about 10 centimeters (4 inches) wide out of the side of the Ziploc bag that has no writing on it. Before you remove the square from the bag, however, use the marker or pen to draw an arrow on one side of the square pointing to the top of the bag.
8. Have your helper hold the ball in his hand and move at least 4 meters (13 feet) away from you.
9. Have your helper hold the ball so that the ring is parallel to the floor and the ball is at your eye level.
10. Look at the ball. The ring is hard to see, but you nevertheless see it is there.
11. Hold the plastic square from the Ziploc bag so the arrow is pointed up.
12. Look at the ball through the square of plastic. It's blurry, isn't it? Can you see the ring?
13. Move 2 meters (6 feet) closer to your helper and look at the ball through the plastic. What do you see now?
14. Go back to where you were before (4 meters away from your helper).
15. Have your helper tilt the ball a bit so that the ring slants towards you, with the dots pointing towards you.
16. Repeat steps 10-14. When you look at the ball in step 10, you should see the ring better. You should even see the dots you made.
17. Have your helper tilt the ball even more.
18. Repeat steps 10-14 again. When you look at the ball in step 10, you should see the ring and the dots even better.
19. Clean up your mess and put everything away.

What did you see in your activity? I suspect that you never saw the ring clearly through the Ziploc bag. You probably saw that there was *something* around the ball, but you couldn't tell it was a ring. You probably never saw the dots on the ring when you were looking through the Ziploc bag. Also, while you never saw the ring really clearly through the plastic, it should have been easier to see that there was something around the ball when the ring was tilted towards you.

Why is this important? Remember that Galileo was the first to use a telescope for viewing the stars and planets. It allowed him to discover some wonderful things, like four of Jupiter's moons. However, his telescope was not all that great. The things he saw through it were a bit blurry, like what you saw when you looked through the piece of plastic. As a result, he saw that there was *something* around Saturn, but he couldn't tell what it was. In fact, he described what he saw as "ears" on both sides of Saturn. Christiaan Huygens was able to make a much better telescope than Galileo, and when he looked at Saturn, he found that what Galileo described as "ears" was actually a ring!

Can you see how Galileo would mistake the ring for something else? Think about your activity. When you looked through the Ziploc bag, the ring was really hard to see. However, as the ball was tilted, you saw that there was something around the ball, but you probably didn't see it as a ring. However, when you looked at the ball without looking through the plastic, the ring was clearly visible. Galileo's blurry telescope only showed him there was *something* around Saturn. Huygens's improved telescope showed him it was a ring.

This is a picture of Saturn taken by a modern telescope. You can clearly see it is surrounded by rings.

This photograph was taken by the same telescope at different times over the period of several years. Notice how the rings are easier to see the more tilted the planet appears.

As we have made better and better telescopes, we have found that Saturn doesn't just have one ring. It has several! If you look at the picture on the left, you can see that. With the aid of modern telescopes, we have even determined what makes Saturn's rings. Believe it or not, each ring is made up of dust, rocks, and ice, all orbiting around Saturn just like the moon orbits around earth. That's what the dots on the ring were supposed to represent in your experiment. You couldn't see them when you looked at the ring through the plastic, could you? Even Huygens's improved telescope couldn't. It took astronomers many more years to determine what the rings were made of.

In your activity, I had your helper tilt the ball so that the ring slanted towards you. That was to illustrate one other thing about Saturn. Saturn is tilted in space, and so is the earth. Both planets are also orbiting the sun. As a result, when we observe Saturn at different times, the tilt that we see changes. This made the rings even harder for natural philosophers of Huygens's time to understand, since the rings seemed to change their appearance in telescopes depending on when they were observed.

Christiaan Huygens also used his telescope to discover Saturn's largest moon, which is called Titan. It turns out that Saturn has many moons orbiting around it, but Titan is the largest, so it is the easiest to see with a telescope. When a team of scientists sent a robotic probe to land on Titan, guess what they called the probe? They called it "Huygens," in honor of the man who discovered Titan!

LESSON REVIEW

Youngest students: Answer these questions:

1. Why couldn't Galileo understand that Saturn had rings?

2. What are Saturn's rings actually made of?

Older students: Draw a picture of Saturn and explain why Galileo described its rings as "ears." Explain how Huygens could see that Saturn had a ring, and describe what the rings are made of.

Oldest students: Do what the older students are doing. In addition, draw another picture of Saturn with a different tilt, and explain how the tilt of Saturn made the rings more difficult for the natural philosophers of Huygens's time to understand.

NOTE: The experiment for the next lesson needs to be done outside. Watch the weather to decide when to do science next!

Lesson 50: Christiaan Huygens and Collisions

When one object hits another, what do you call it? Scientists call it a **collision**, and Christiaan Huygens was interested in understanding how collisions work. He ended up discovering a rule that collisions often follow, and it is involved in the following experiment:

Two Collisions

What you will need:
- A large ball that bounces well. The ideal ball is a basketball, but it can be a soccer ball or any other ball that is pretty large and has a nice bounce to it.
- A ball that is much smaller than the first one – the smaller the better. A golf ball, for example, would be great.
- A smooth, hard surface on the ground outside, such as a sidewalk or driveway (Don't do this experiment indoors, as you could break something!)
- Someone to help you (optional)

What you should do:
1. Hold the small ball in your hand as high as you can.
2. Drop the ball onto the hard surface and watch how high it bounces.
3. Get the ball and repeat steps 1-2 twice more, just to get a feel for how high the small ball bounces.
4. Repeat steps 1-2 three more times, but use the large ball instead so you get an idea of how high it bounces.
5. Hold the large ball in your hand, and hold the small ball on top of it, as shown in the picture on the right. Hold them as high as you can. If you are having a hard time doing this, have a helper hold the small ball on top of the big ball just the way it is being held in the picture.
6. Drop the large ball and small ball at the same time, so they both fall towards the hard surface. If you are using a helper, this might require a little work so you both release the balls at the same time.
7. Watch how high the small ball bounces now. In addition, watch how high the large ball bounces.
8. Repeat steps 5-7 twice more to make sure you have a good idea of how both balls bounce when they are dropped together like that.
9. Put the balls away and go back inside to complete the lesson.

What did you see in your experiment? Individually, both the small ball and the large ball bounced, but they didn't bounce as high as the height from which you released them, did they? What happened, however, when the small ball was placed on top of the large ball and they were both dropped together? The large ball should have barely bounced at all, and the small ball should have bounced much higher than the height from which you released it. What explains this unusual result?

In order to understand what happened in the experiment, you first have to realize that there are two collisions involved. First, the large ball collided with the flat surface. When that happened, the surface forced the ball to stop and change directions. As a result, the large ball bounced back up.

When that happened, the large ball then collided with the small ball, which was still falling down. That collision shot the small ball high into the air.

The next thing you have to understand is that when something is moving, it develops **momentum** (moh men' tum). The larger its momentum, the harder it is to stop. Well, if you think about it, the faster something moves, the harder it is to stop. After all, if someone tosses a ball to you gently, you will be able to catch it and stop it easily. However, if someone throws that same ball with a lot of speed, it is harder to catch and stop. So the faster an object is moving, the larger its momentum.

That can't be the entire story, however. Think about stopping a baseball, and then think about stopping a wad of paper that is the same size as the baseball and is moving at the same speed. Which would be easier to stop? The wad of paper, right? Why is that? Because the wad of paper weighs less than the baseball. The heavier something is, the harder it is to stop.

Even though they are moving at the same speed, the truck has a lot more momentum than the car, because it is much heavier.

So there are two things you have to consider when something is moving. You have to think about its speed and its weight. The faster something is going, the harder it is to stop. In addition, the heavier something is, the harder it is to stop. Christiaan Huygens realized that in order to get an idea of how hard a moving object is to stop, you need to consider both its weight and its speed. If you do that, you would be thinking about what scientists call the object's momentum, which tells us how hard it is to stop it or make it change the way it is moving.

Now you can finally understand why the small ball bounced so high in your experiment. When the large ball was forced by the surface to bounce up, it collided with the small ball that was still coming down. Both balls were moving pretty quickly, but the large ball had a lot more momentum, because it weighed a lot more than the small ball. When the two balls collided, the small ball gave its momentum to the large ball, and the large ball gave its momentum to the small ball.

Think about what that means. The small ball was moving down. What happened when the large ball got the small ball's momentum? It started moving down as well. So as soon as the large ball hit the small ball, it stopped moving up. Instead, it started moving down, because it got the small ball's momentum. What happened to the small ball? It got the large ball's momentum. Since the large ball was moving up, that means the small ball started moving up. In other words, the small ball got hit by the large ball. This pushed the small ball, like it had been hit by a bat.

So now you know why the large ball didn't bounce very high when it was dropped with the small ball on top of it. It bounced off the surface, but as soon as it hit the small ball, it started moving down instead of up, because it got the small ball's momentum. But why did the small ball bounce so high? Well, it got the large ball's momentum, which was really big. It was big because the large ball weighs a lot. So the small ball got a large amount of momentum.

Now remember what momentum is based on: the speed of the object *and* its weight. The small ball got a lot of momentum, but it has only a small amount of weight. How can something with a small amount of weight carry a lot of momentum? It has to have a lot of speed! The small ball can't change its weight, so if it suddenly gets a lot of momentum, what has to happen? It has to speed up!

This tells you why the small ball bounced so high once it hit the large ball. The small ball got a lot of momentum from the large ball. However, the small ball didn't weigh very much. In order to have all the momentum of the large ball, then, it had to start moving really quickly. This, of course, made it shoot really high in the air.

Christiaan Huygens understood that momentum is important in collisions like the one the large and small ball experienced in your experiment. He decided that the total momentum in a collision must stay the same. That's why the small ball gave its momentum to the large ball, and the large ball gave its momentum to the small ball. That way, the total momentum of the two balls remained the same. This is often called the **Law of Momentum Conservation**, and Huygens was the first to recognize it.

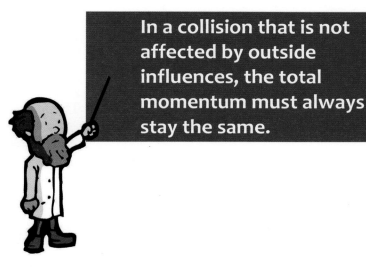

In a collision that is not affected by outside influences, the total momentum must always stay the same.

LESSON REVIEW

Youngest students: Answer these questions:

1. Fill in the blanks: An object's momentum depends on its _____ and _____.

2. Fill in the blank: During the collision in your experiment, lots of things changed. However, the total _____ of the two balls remained the same.

Older students: Explain momentum in your own words, including what two things about an object determine its momentum. Also, state the Law of Momentum Conservation.

Oldest students: Do what the older students are doing. In addition, use the Law of Momentum Conservation to explain the results of your experiment.

Lesson 51: Christiaan Huygens and Clocks

If you have been doing the challenge experiments, you already learned in Lesson 28 that Galileo could not use the clocks of his day to measure time in his experiments. They were just not very good at keeping time. Even in Huygens's day, clocks were very unreliable when it came to telling time. This was unfortunate not only for natural philosophers who were doing experiments, but also for sailors.

In those days, sailors told time by using a sundial, looking at the height of the sun in the sky, or observing the stars at night. They were surprisingly good at knowing what time it was. However, that only told them what the *local* time was. You might already know that the time of day depends on where you are. Think about two friends who grew up together in South Africa. As adults, one moves to Sydney, Australia, and the other moves to New York City in the United States. Suppose the friend in Australia wants to phone his friend in the United States. He has to think about the time very carefully, because it is 16 hours *earlier* in New York City than it is in Sydney. If he calls his friend at 5 PM Sydney time, it will be 1 AM in New York City, and his phone call would probably wake his friend up!

The time of day changes depending on where you are because the earth rotates. As some parts rotate into the sun's light, other parts rotate out of the sun's light. This makes a big difference. The farther west you are, the earlier in the day it is. Even in a single country, the time can be different depending on where you are.

Because the earth rotates, the time of day depends on where you are. Notice that in the countries farther west (like the UK and the US), it is earlier than in the countries that are farther east (like Japan).

In the United States, for example, it is three hours earlier in Los Angeles, California than it is in New York City. Ancient sailors could make a pretty good estimate of where they were on the ocean if they only had some way to measure what time it was at the port where they started their voyage. That way, they could compare the local time they measured on the ship to the time back at the port where they started. That would give them a good estimate for how far east or west they had traveled.

During Christiaan Huygens's day, however, clocks couldn't keep time well enough, especially on the rocking and rolling deck of a ship. As a result, sailors had a difficult time knowing how far east or west they had traveled once they left port. Huygens wanted to change that, so he worked on building a clock that would tell time in a reliable way. Of course, in order to do that, he needed something that happened at a steady rate. If you did challenge lesson 28, you know that Galileo used water leaking from a hole in a bowl to keep time in his experiments. Huygens, however, knew he had to use something that lasted longer than a leaky bowl, so he took a different idea from Galileo and applied it to clocks. Perform the following experiment to see what he did.

Pendulums

What you will need:
- String
- Two washers or nuts
- Scissors
- A stopwatch
- Someone to help you

What you should do:
1. Cut a 60-centimeter (2 feet) length of string.
2. Tie one washer to one end of the string.
3. Have your helper hold the string in the middle so the washer hangs down about 30 centimeters (12 inches) from his or her hand.
4. Tell your helper to keep his or her hand still, and pull the washer to the right of where it is hanging. In a moment, you will release the washer and watch it swing back and forth. In other words, you are making a pendulum like the ones you made in lesson 24.
5. Hold the stopwatch in your other hand.
6. When you release the washer, start the stopwatch.
7. Watch the washer swing to the left and then back to the right. When it reaches the point where you originally released it, count that as 1 swing.
8. Continue to watch and count the swings until you have counted a total of 10. At that point, stop the stopwatch.
9. Record how long it took for the pendulum to make 10 swings back and forth.
10. Repeat steps 4-9 again, but this time, have your helper hold on to the very end of the string. That way, the washer hangs down about 60 centimeters (2 feet) from his or her hand.
11. Tie the other washer to the end of the string so that there are now two washers tied there.
12. Repeat steps 4-9 again with your helper holding the string in the middle so the washers hang down about 30 centimeters (12 inches) from his or her hand.
13. Repeat steps 4-9 one more time with your helper holding on to the end of the string so the washers hang down about 60 centimeters (2 feet) from his or her hand.
14. Clean up your mess.

What did you see in the experiment? You should have noticed that it took the pendulum longer to swing 10 times back and forth when your helper held the end of the string as compared to when he or she held the middle of the string. However, when you added the second weight, it shouldn't have made much of a difference. The pendulum should have taken about the same amount of time to swing back and forth 10 times when the string was held in the center, regardless of the number of washers. In the same way, the pendulum should have taken about the same amount of time to swing back and forth 10 times when the string was held at the end, regardless of the number of washers.

Huygens determined that this is a property of pendulums. The time they take to swing back and forth depends only on the length of the pendulum. In science, we say that the time it takes a pendulum to swing back and forth is the **period** of the pendulum. In your experiment, then, you measured the time it took for 10 periods to pass. If you wanted to determine the period of your pendulum, you would divide your measurement by 10. In the end, then, Huygens showed that a pendulum's period depends only on its length. Galileo had already shown that its period didn't depend on how far it was pulled before it was released, so putting those two facts together, Huygens was able to design a clock that used a pendulum to keep time. Not surprisingly, it was called a **pendulum clock**.

It worked because each time the pendulum swung one way, it would move a wheel. When it swung the other way, it would move the wheel some more. By determining the period of the pendulum, Huygens could decide how much each swing should turn the wheel so that the wheel could move the second hand on the clock one click each second. Huygens's first design produced a clock that lost only 15 seconds each day. In other words, his clock would record that 23 hours, 59 minutes, and 45 seconds had passed when 24 hours had actually passed. That sounds bad, but prior to Huygens's clock, the best ones tended to lose 15 *minutes* each day!

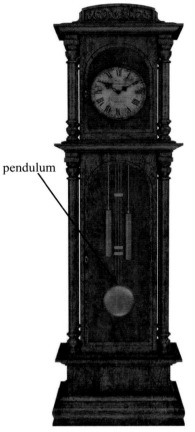

pendulum

This grandfather clock uses its pendulum to keep track of time.

Even though the pendulum clock was a great improvement over any other clock that was around, it still wasn't good enough to be used by sailors. The rocking and rolling of the ship produced problems for the pendulum, and even when the seas were calm, losing 15 seconds each day was a real problem on a voyage that lasted several weeks! Huygens continued to work on different designs for clocks, but none of them were reliable enough for sailors. In the end, it would take almost another 100 years for someone to produce a clock that would be of help to sailors when it came to determining how far they had traveled east or west of their port on long voyages.

While pendulum clocks were not good enough for sailors, they were wonderful for people who wanted to keep time in their homes or laboratories. As a result, they quickly became a standard way to tell time. Nowadays, we have significantly better ways to keep time, so pendulum clocks are rarely used anymore. However, you might find one from time to time in a person's home, especially if the person likes old collectable items, which are usually called **antiques** (an teeks'). Tall pendulum clocks are sometimes called "grandfather clocks."

LESSON REVIEW

Youngest students: Answer these questions:

1. Why is the time of day different in Sydney, Australia than it is in New York City in the U.S.?

2. (Is this statement True or False?) The period of a pendulum depends only on how much weight is hanging on the end.

Older students: Explain why the time of day is different depending on where you are on the earth. Also, describe what the period of a pendulum is and what determines it.

Oldest students: Do what the older students are doing. In addition, explain how Christiaan Huygens used a pendulum to make a significantly more accurate clock than what was available up until then.

Lesson 52: Christiaan Huygens and Light

Even though Huygens helped us understand Saturn's rings, determined the Law of Momentum Conservation, and helped us to keep better track of time, he is best remembered for his studies of light. In particular, he solved a mystery that had stumped the natural philosophers of his day. Do the following quick experiment to see what that mystery was.

A Surprising Property of Light

What you will need:
- A flashlight
- Scissors
- An adult to help you
- A dark room
- A straight piece of cardboard that is as wide as your bathtub and at least 10 centimeters (4 inches) tall

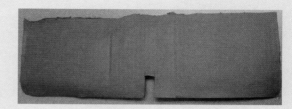

What you should do:
1. Have the adult help you cut a rectangular slot out of the middle of the cardboard. It should start at the bottom and be about 2 centimeters (¾ of an inch) wide and 4 centimeters (1½ inch) tall. See the picture above.
2. Take the flashlight into a dark room and turn it on.
3. Stand at one end of the room and shine the flashlight on the wall at the other end. You should see a nice, round spot of light where it hits the wall.
4. In a moment, you are going to cover the flashlight with your piece of cardboard so the light shines only through the slot. Then, you are going to shine it at the wall just like you did in the previous step. Before you do that, however, predict what you will see. Say the prediction out loud.
5. Cover the flashlight with the cardboard so that the only way light can get to the other side of the room is to go through the slot you made.
6. Point the covered flashlight at the wall. Notice the shape that the light makes on the wall.
7. Pull the cardboard away from the flashlight. How did the light on the wall change?
8. Keep the cardboard, but put away the flashlight.

What did you expect to see when you shined the covered flashlight on the wall? Most people expect to see a spot of light that is shaped like the slot. Is that what you saw? No. Instead, you saw a spot of light that looked a lot like it did before you covered it. About the only real difference was the brightness. The spot of light on the wall was dimmer when you covered it with the cardboard, but other than that, it looked pretty much the same as it did without the cardboard.

Did the result of the experiment surprise you? Similar experiments surprised natural philosophers at this point in history. Why did light behave this way when it encountered something in its way? Why didn't the shape of the object it encountered change the shape of the light? Christiaan Huygens figured out why, but to understand his explanation, you need to continue your experiment.

Light is a Wave

What you will need:
- The slotted piece of cardboard you made previously
- A bathtub

🖐 A turkey baster
🖐 Someone to help you

What you should do:
1. Put the plug in the bathtub and add enough water so the water level is about ¾ as tall as the slot in the cardboard. The water level should not exceed that height.
2. Have your helper fill the turkey baster and go to one end of the bathtub.
3. Have your helper hold the turkey baster high above the tub and drip water from the baster into the tub.
4. Watch the ripples that appear as a result of the water being dripped into the tub. You might have to move your head around a bit to get a good look at the ripples.

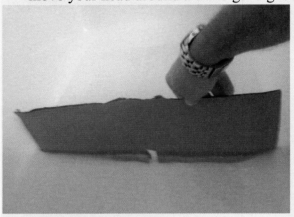

5. Put the cardboard in the water near the end where your helper is. The slot should be on the bottom, and the cardboard should cross the tub like a water barrier so the only way water can get past the cardboard is to go through the slot. See the picture on the left. Don't worry that it is getting wet.
6. Have your helper fill the turkey baster again.
7. Have your helper hold the turkey baster high above the tub and drip water from the baster into the tub near where the cardboard is. The water should not drip on the cardboard, but it should drip near one side of the cardboard, centered on the slot.
8. Watch the ripples that occur on both sides of the cardboard. Once again, feel free to move your head around a bit to get the best look possible at the ripples.
9. Notice how the ripples behave once they have passed through the slot.
10. Drain the tub and put everything away.

What did you see in the experiment? When your helper first dripped water into the bathtub, you should have seen ripples going out in circles from where the drops were hitting the water. When you put the slotted cardboard in, the ripples hit the cardboard, and most of them stopped. However, the ripples that hit the cardboard at the slot went through. How did they behave on the other side of the slot? Did you notice that they started going out in circles again? The ripples were smaller on the other side of the slot, but they had exactly the same shape as the ripples that were made by the dripping water.

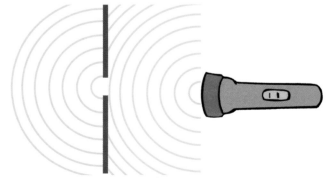

Because light can be thought of as a wave, when it hits a barrier with an opening, it ends up spreading out from the opening in the same way it spreads out from the light source.

Christiaan Huygens realized that this was the key to understanding the first part of your experiment. The light didn't take the shape of the slot when you blocked the flashlight with the cardboard because *light acts as a wave.* When a wave hits a slot like the one in the cardboard, it doesn't take the shape of the slot. Instead, it spreads out from the slot, just as if it started out there.

Just as the water waves looked pretty much the same coming out of the slot as they did coming from the original drops of water, light waves look pretty much the same coming out of the slot as they did coming out of the flashlight. That's why the flashlight's light looked pretty much the same with or without the slotted cardboard once it hit the wall. Of course, it was dimmer, because a lot of the light was blocked, just as the waves in the tub were smaller on the other side of the cardboard.

If you don't completely understand this, don't worry about it very much. Natural philosophers of this time period didn't completely understand waves, and even to this day, scientists don't completely understand light. All you really need to understand is that to describe certain behaviors of light, Christiaan Huygens understood that you had to think of light like a wave on the water. As a result, the scientific description of light as a wave was born. You might have already learned about the Law of Reflection and the process of refraction. If so, you might be interested to know that Huygens could explain those processes using his idea of light behaving like a wave.

Now although Christiaan Huygens didn't completely understand light or waves, he did understand one thing: The marvels that he was investigating through natural philosophy were made by

God. In one of his books, he wrote, "I suppose nobody will deny but that there's somewhat more of Contrivance, somewhat more of Miracle in the production and growth of Plants and Animals, than in lifeless heaps of inanimate Bodies, be they never so much larger; as Mountains, Rocks, or Seas are. For the finger of God, and the Wisdom of Divine Providence, is in them much more clearly manifested than in the other." (Christiaan Huygens, *The Celestial Worlds Discover'd*, http://www.staff.science.uu.nl/~gent 0113/huygens/huygens_ct_en_b1.ht m, retrieved 08/02/2013)

Christiaan Huygens thought that the behavior of light was best explained by thinking of it as waves moving out from the light source, much like these waves in the water are moving out from the center of the photo.

LESSON REVIEW

Youngest students: Answer these questions:

1. (Is this statement True or False?) When the flashlight was covered with the slotted cardboard, it was dimmer, but it had the same shape as when it was not covered.

2. Fill in the blank: Huygens believed that light behaves like a _____.

Older students: Describe what you did in the first part of your experiment and what you predicted you would see when you covered the flashlight. Describe what you actually saw, and then explain how Christiaan Huygens thought light must behave in order to understand the result.

Oldest students: Do what the older students are doing. In addition, make a drawing like the one on the previous page, and explain how it relates to both light and your experiment.

Lesson 53: Robert Boyle (1627 – 1691)

This portrait of Robert Boyle was painted by Johann Kerseboom.

While Christiaan Huygens was studying astronomy, light, motion, and time, **Robert Boyle** spent a lot of time trying to turn inexpensive metals (like lead) into precious metals (like gold). This pursuit was known as **alchemy** (al' kuh me). Unlike most of the people who had practiced alchemy before, however, Boyle was also committed to studying creation and learning what he could about it through experimentation. So as he did experiments related to alchemy, he used those experiments to help him learn more about how substances change when exposed to other substances. As a result, most science historians consider him to be the father of modern **chemistry**, the scientific discipline that studies substances and how they can be changed.

At this time in history, chemistry was considered a dirty, smelly process that was useful in the creation of medicine, but not much else. As a result, it was not thought to be something a serious natural philosopher would do. Instead, people who made medicine for doctors were the ones who usually did what we call chemistry today. In fact, if you go to England, you will find that your doctor will tell you to go to the "chemist" to get the medicine you are being prescribed. In the U.S., we call such people **pharmacists**, but in England, they are usually called "chemists," because that's all chemistry was considered good for back in Boyle's day!

Boyle set out to change that view of chemistry, because he thought it was an excellent way to understand more of God's creation. His best-known book is called *The Sceptical Chymist* (yes, that's how he spelled it), and in it, he tried to convince chemists that they should strive for more than just making new substances. Instead, they should try to figure out why their experiments work. In addition, they should try to develop some general principles that would help natural philosophers better understand the world around them.

The book is set up as an argument between three different views. One is the view of Aristotle, which says that all substances are made up of four elements: air, water, fire, and earth. This view was still popular in Boyle's day, even though a lot of Aristotle's teachings had been shown to be incorrect. The second view was that all substances are made up of three elements: mercury, salt, and sulfur. This was the view that was popular among many alchemists. The third was Boyle's view: that all things are made up of tiny particles, which he called **corpuscles** (kor' pus sulz). The properties of any substance were determined by these corpuscles and how they interacted with one another.

In Boyle's view, these corpuscles came in many shapes and sizes and were in constant motion. When two substances are mixed together and something new is produced, it is because the mixing of the substances had caused a change in the way these corpuscles interacted.

Now like most natural philosophers, he was wrong about a lot of things. Nevertheless, today we recognize that all substances are made of tiny particles that we call atoms. In most substances, those atoms link up to form other particles called molecules. Molecules come in many shapes and sizes, and they are in constant motion, just as Boyle suggested. Perform the following experiment to see what I mean.

Art in Motion

What you will need:
- Milk (Whole milk is best, but any cow milk other than skim milk will work.)
- A pan and a stove or a microwave
- Four colors of food coloring (They need to be liquid, not gels.)
- A Q-tip
- Dishwashing soap
- A small bowl
- A large plate that can hold a thin layer of milk
- An adult to help you

What you should do: 
1. Have an adult help you use the pan and stove or the microwave to warm the milk. Don't get it boiling; just warm it like you might do for making hot chocolate.
2. Put the plate in a location where it won't be jostled.
3. Pour the warm milk so it forms a thin layer on the plate (see the picture on the right).
4. Add a small amount of dishwashing liquid to the small bowl. It doesn't need to be much.
5. Roll one end of the Q-tip around in the dishwashing liquid so it gets soaked with it. Leave it in there as you do the next steps.
6. Put two drops of one color of food coloring near the center of the plate. It should float on the milk.
7. Repeat step 6 for each color, getting them close together (see the picture on the right). If they touch, that's not a problem.

8. Pull the Q-tip out of the dishwashing liquid and put the end that is soaked with it into the milk right in between all four colors of food coloring.
9. Hold the Q-tip so that the liquid-soaked end is pushing against the bottom of the plate for a couple of seconds and then lift the Q-tip out of the milk completely.
10. Watch what happens to the colors.
11. Clean up your mess and put everything away.

What did you see in the experiment? Once you put the Q-tip in the milk, the colors should have started moving around and mixing, making pretty patterns in the milk. The colors should have continued moving for a little while, even after you took the Q-tip out of the milk. Why is that? Well, milk is a mixture of many different things, including water, fats, vitamins, and proteins. The fats don't mix well with the water, so they float around as little globs. As Boyle suspected, the water and the globs of fat (as well as the vitamins and proteins) are in constant motion. Well, it turns out that soap molecules are fairly long, and one side is attracted to water, while the other side is attracted to fats.

When you added the soap to your experiment, its molecules were attracted to the water and the fat globs. Because the water and fat globs were moving around, however, the soap molecules were pulled along as they were attracted. Well, the food coloring was in the way of this merry chase, so as the soap started moving around to attach itself to the water and fats, it started mixing the food coloring around, making the pretty swirls of color you saw in your experiment! Eventually, the soap got evenly mixed in the milk so that all the soap molecules were attached to some fat and water, and the chase ended. As a result, the colors stopped moving.

Now even though the colors stopped moving, that doesn't mean the fat, water, and soap molecules stopped moving. They continued to move, but since the soap molecules had found the water and fat that they were attracted to, they weren't pushing the colors around as much. However, if you waited long enough, you would still see the colors mixing. They would just mix very slowly.

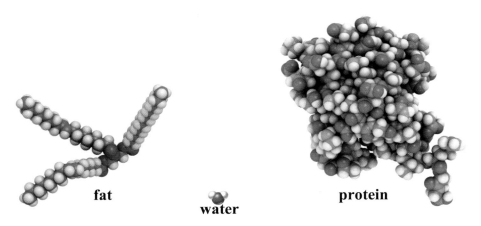

fat   **water**   **protein**

So even though a plate of milk doesn't look like it's moving, the water molecules, fat molecules, protein molecules, and vitamin molecules that make it up are in constant motion, just as Boyle thought.

Milk has many molecules in it, including water, proteins, and fats. These models give you an idea of what such molecules look like. While Boyle didn't understand molecules, he did realize that matter is made up of tiny particles that come in many shapes and sizes, and those particles are in constant motion.

LESSON REVIEW

Youngest students: Answer these questions:

1. What is alchemy?

2. Fill in the blanks: Boyle correctly understood that all matter is made up of particles that come in different _____ and sizes and are in constant _____.

Older students: Explain the difference between chemistry and alchemy. In addition, explain what Boyle got right in terms of what makes up all substances.

Oldest students: Do what the older students are doing. In addition, try to guess why you warmed the milk in your experiment. Don't worry if you are wrong. Think of a reason and write it down, and then check the answers. Correct your guess if it was wrong.

Lesson 54: Robert Boyle and the Vacuum

As you've already learned, most natural philosophers prior to the Scientific Revolution didn't think a vacuum could exist. However, Evangelista Torricelli showed that it could exist, and Otto von Guericke made a pump that produced a vacuum and used it to show how powerful a vacuum can be. Boyle was fascinated by what von Guericke had done, and he set out with his assistant (a man you will read about in a later lesson) to make improvements on the design of von Guericke's pump. He ended up producing something much better, which he called a **pneumatic** (noo mat' ik) **engine**. Today, we call it a vacuum pump.

Boyle began doing experiments with his vacuum pump, and he discovered something that was rather startling to him. The following experiment is nothing like the one he did, but it does illustrate what he discovered.

An Annoying Sound

What you will need:
- Two round balloons of the same size (Somewhere between 13-20 cm [5-8 inches] when inflated work best.)
- A hex-head nut (This is the kind of nut that fits on a bolt and is tightened with a wrench. The nut has six flat sides on the outside.)
- A penny

What you should do:
1. Insert the hex-head nut through the opening of one balloon so it is inside the balloon.
2. Insert the penny through the opening of the other balloon so it is also inside the balloon.
3. Blow up each balloon and tie it off. The balloon doesn't have to be blown up all the way. Just blow it up so that it is stretched tight but still small enough to hold easily in one hand, as shown in the picture on the right. Try to make the balloons the same size.
4. Hold the balloon that has the hex head nut in it as shown in the picture on the right.
5. Start twirling the balloon in your hand so the nut starts moving inside. Keep twirling until the nut starts rolling around along the sides of the balloon. You'll know when you get it right, because you'll hear an annoying noise!
6. Repeat step 5 with the balloon that has the penny in it. Do you hear the same noise?
7. Pop the balloons and recover the penny and nut. Throw the remains of the balloons away and put the penny and nut back where they belong.

What happened in the experiment? When you got the hex head nut rolling inside the balloon, it made a really annoying noise, didn't it? However, when you did the same thing with the penny, you didn't get that noise, did you? Why?

Think about the differences between the penny and the hex head nut. The penny is solid, but the nut has a hole in the center. The penny is thin, while the nut is thick. Also, the penny's sides are smooth, but the nut has six flat sides, which means there are six corners where those sides touch one another. Both the penny and the nut were rolling along their sides in the balloon, so the difference in the sides is responsible for the difference in the two systems.

As the nut rolled along the sides of the balloon, those six points kept punching into the side of the balloon. This caused the sides of the balloon to start vibrating, and as they did that, they started pushing the molecules in the air around. This caused the air molecules to "clump together" when the sides of the balloon vibrated outwards, and it caused them to "spread out" as the sides of the balloon vibrated inwards. As a result, clumps of air molecules followed by spread-out air molecules started traveling away from the balloon.

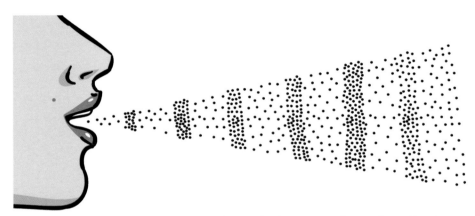

When you talk or sing, the molecules in the air clump up and spread out, forming a sound wave that travels through the air.

If you've learned much about sound, you might recognize that description. It's what we call a **sound wave**, and it's the way sound is produced. When you hear something, it's because a series of clumps and spread-out areas of molecules (sound waves) have entered your ears. When you speak, you produce sound waves that then travel through the air so that it can be heard by someone else.

People didn't know this back in Boyle's time, but both Leonardo da Vinci and Galileo wrote about experiments that indicated sound was a vibration in the air. Boyle did an experiment that helped to demonstrate that this is true. He put a ringing bell in a glass container and then used his vacuum pump to pull air out of the chamber. Guess what happened? At first, he could hear the bell ringing inside the container. However, as he pumped air out of the container, the bell's ringing got softer and softer. Eventually, it disappeared altogether. When he disconnected the pump and allowed air to flow back into the container, he could hear the bell ringing again.

So Boyle showed that without air, sound could not travel from the bell to his ears. In addition, however, he showed that the *amount* of air affected the volume of the bell. When only a small amount of air was in the container, the bell could be heard, but its sound was soft. The more air that was let into the container, the louder the bell became. This was important, because it really showed that air was a very important part of what makes us hear sound. This lent a lot of support to the idea that sound travels through the air in waves, such as what is illustrated above.

Boyle didn't limit his experiments with air to sound. He realized that air was important to a great many things we take for granted. For example, he put a candle into a glass container and pumped the air out of the container. The candle, of course, went out. If you studied Roger Bacon (c. 1214 – 1294), you might remember that he was the first to show that a candle in a sealed container eventually stopped burning. In addition, you might have learned that Leonardo da Vinci showed that a burning candle actually uses up something from the air. Boyle's experiment added to the evidence that there is something in air that a fire needs in order to burn.

This painting was made by Joseph Wright of Derby in 1768. It shows a natural philosopher doing Boyle's experiment in which a bird is placed in a glass container and the air is pumped out of the container, causing the bird to die.

He also did some very careful (but somewhat gruesome) experiments on animals to show that the reason we breathe is in order to get something from the air. In an experiment, he put a bird in the glass container and pumped the air out of the container. The poor bird, of course, died as a result. This experiment apparently became famous, because as the vacuum pump became more popular, traveling natural philosophers (who were often more showmen than scientists) would do the experiment to the amazement and horror of the people who came to see the show.

This experiment, of course, showed that air was necessary for an animal to live. You might think this is obvious, since animals breathe.

However, many natural philosophers thought that perhaps the motion of the lungs was the important aspect of breathing, and that the air simply helped that motion. However, Boyle showed that was incorrect. He had his assistant (you will learn about him soon) cut open a dog and push air into its lungs. He showed that even when the lungs did not move, the animal stayed alive as long as old air was allowed to leak out of the motionless lungs and fresh air was allowed to enter them. While the experiment was bad for the dog, it allowed natural philosophers to understand that it's the air that is being breathed, not the motion of the lungs, that keeps animals (and people) alive. Now please understand that while scientists still use animals in their experiments, they are much more humane to the animals than the people in Robert Boyle's time were!

LESSON REVIEW

Youngest students: Answer these questions:

1. Fill in the blanks: The noise in your experiment was made because the nut caused the sides of the balloon to vibrate, which produced a _____ _____.

2. What did Boyle show was necessary for fire, life, and sound?

Older students: Explain why the nut, and not the penny, caused the strange sound in your experiment. In addition, explain Boyle's experiment with the bell and why it lent support to the idea that sound is a vibration in the air.

Oldest students: Do what the older students are doing. In addition, explain the other experiments that show how air is necessary for fire and for animals to live.

Lesson 55: Robert Boyle and His Law

Because Boyle spent a lot of time doing experiments with his vacuum pump, he ended up learning a lot about pressure and how it affects gases. Remember, the air around you presses against everything it touches. However, if you pump air out of a container, there is less air, and the air that remains cannot press against things as strongly. As you get rid of the air in a container, then, the pressure inside that container goes down. This can lead to an interesting effect, as shown in the experiment below:

Boyle's Law

What you will need:
- 🖐 A small jar, like a baby food jar (Be sure any labels on the jar are removed so it is very easy to see inside the jar.)
- 🖐 A funnel whose large opening is bigger than the jar
- 🖐 Some Play-Doh
- 🖐 A small balloon (It needs to fit inside the jar when it is just barely inflated.)
- 🖐 A wall mirror

What you should do:

1. Blow into the balloon so that it is just barely inflated and then tie it off. The sides of the balloon should not even be fully stretched out. It should look something like the balloon in the picture on the far left.
2. Put the balloon into the jar.
3. Roll the Play-Doh into a tube that is long enough to go all the way around the top of the jar.
4. Put the tube of Play-Doh around the top of the jar so it sits on the lip of the jar securely (see the picture on the near left.)
5. Turn the funnel upside down and press the large opening down over the jar. It should squeeze the Play-Doh, forming a seal between the jar and the funnel. In the end, your setup should look like the picture on the bottom left.
6. Take your jar/funnel system into the room with the wall mirror.
7. Stand in front of the wall mirror.
8. Put the small end of the funnel in your mouth as if it is a straw.
9. Hold the jar so that you can easily see the balloon in the mirror, even though the end of the funnel is in your mouth.
10. While you are watching the balloon, suck on the end of the funnel like you would a straw. You are trying to suck air out of the jar.
11. Stick your tongue on the opening of the funnel so air doesn't rush back into it, and then exhale.
12. Repeat steps 10 and 11 several times to get as much air out of the jar as possible. The most effective strategy is to suck, seal, and exhale very quickly over and over again. If it is easy to suck on the funnel, you need to redo steps 3-7 again because you don't have a good seal between the jar and the funnel.

13. You should have seen a change in the balloon while you were doing all that sucking. To see how much change occurred, watch the balloon and pull your tongue off the opening of the funnel so that air rushes back in. What happens to the balloon?
14. Clean up your mess.

What happened in your experiment? If all went well, you should have seen the balloon inflate a bit as you sucked air out of the jar. When you let the air back into the jar, the balloon should have gone back to being barely inflated. Why did this happen? The balloon was tied off, so the same amount of air was in the balloon the entire time. However, as you sucked air out of the jar, there was less air pressing on the balloon. As a result, the air pressure *outside the balloon* decreased. The air pressure *inside the balloon* stayed the same, however, and as a result, the air in the balloon was able to expand a little, inflating the balloon a bit more.

So, in fact, there are two ways to inflate a balloon. The easy way, of course, is to just blow into the balloon. The hard way is to get rid of a lot of the air around the balloon. That would cause the pressure outside the balloon to decrease, and what air was inside the balloon would expand, inflating the balloon. It turns out that you were only able to suck a small amount of air out of the jar, so the effect you saw was pretty small. However, if you have a good vacuum pump and a good airtight seal in the container, the effect can be really dramatic. The two pictures below show the results of a similar experiment. In this case, however, a container with a really good seal and a vacuum pump were used. As you can see, the balloon inflated dramatically as the vacuum pump pulled air out of the container.

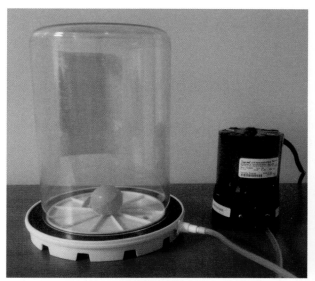 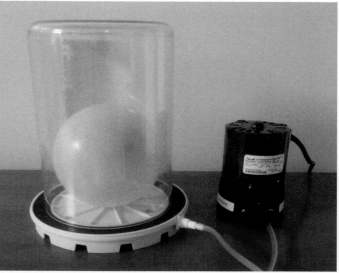

On the left, a barely-inflated balloon was put into a container with an airtight seal that was connected to a vacuum pump. The vacuum pump was then turned on, and as it pumped air out of the container, the balloon grew, as shown on the right.

This is one of the things that Boyle discovered while doing experiments with gases and a vacuum pump. He found that as pressure decreases, the volume that a gas occupies increases. Similarly, when the pressure increases, the volume of a gas decreases. In science we would say that the pressure and volume of a gas are **inversely related**. Do you know what the word "inverse" means? It means opposite. So when two things are inversely related, they behave opposite to each other. When one goes up, the other goes down. That's how pressure and volume are related. When pressure goes up, volume goes down. When pressure goes down, volume goes up. Since one does the opposite of what the other is doing, we say they are inversely related to one another.

Now it's important to realize that this inverse relationship holds, no matter which thing you change. In your experiment, you decreased the pressure by sucking some air out of the jar. As a result, the volume increased. However, what if instead of changing the pressure, you changed the volume? Well…the pressure would do the opposite. So if you increased the volume, the pressure would decrease. If you decreased the volume, the pressure would increase.

What happens if you squeeze an inflated balloon too hard? It pops, right? Well, when you squeeze a balloon, you are decreasing the volume that the air inside the balloon can occupy. As a result, its pressure increases. The more you decrease the volume, the more the pressure increases. Eventually, the pressure inside the balloon gets so large that it breaks the walls of the balloon, and the balloon pops!

The balloon this woman is squeezing might pop because she is reducing the volume of the air inside, which increases its pressure.

Now it's important to note that Boyle went a step further than just showing that pressure and volume are inversely related. He actually did some math to show exactly how the two were related. As a result, he came up with a mathematical equation that told him exactly how much one would change if you changed the other. That equation is now called **Boyle's Law**, and you will learn about it in high school chemistry.

Robert Boyle taught us a lot about the natural world, and he was always sure to give God the credit for its amazing design. His last words to the Royal Society, a scientific organization that he helped to create, were "Remember to give glory to the One who authored nature." [Dan Graves, *Scientists of Faith*, Kregel Resources 1996, p.63] When he died, he left a large sum of money that was dedicated to sponsoring lectures that would provide evidence for the Christian faith. These lectures, called the Boyle Lectures, are still going on today!

LESSON REVIEW

Youngest students: Answer these questions:

1. What does it mean when two things are inversely related?

2. If I increase the pressure of a gas, what does its volume do?

Older students: Draw two pictures that show your experiment before you started sucking air out of the jar and after you sucked air out of it. Use those pictures to explain what Boyle discovered about gases, being sure to use the term "inversely related."

Oldest students: Do what the older students are doing. In addition, explain why squeezing a balloon can cause it to pop.

NOTE: If you are doing the challenge lessons, the experiment for Lesson 58 must sit for several days. You should try to start it by tomorrow at the latest.

Lesson 56: Marcello Malpighi (1628 – 1694)

Do you remember studying about William Harvey back in Lesson 38? He figured out that blood must circulate in the body, because it just wasn't possible for anyone to make the amount of blood that flowed through the heart every day. He decided that the arteries carried blood away from the heart, and the veins brought it back to the heart. However, he didn't know exactly how that happened, because he couldn't find anything that connected the arteries to the veins. That's where the Italian natural philosopher **Marcello** (mar chel' oh) **Malpighi** (mal pee' gee) comes in.

By the mid-1600s, many natural philosophers were aware of the fact that lenses could be used to make faraway things appear to be near and small things appear to be large. Indeed, as you have already learned, Galileo used someone else's design to make a telescope with which he studied the heavens. He also used the same principle to make a microscope. Other natural philosophers did the same so that they could better study very small things.

This is a portrait of Marcello Malpighi.

Malpighi did too, but he used his microscope to observe animal and plant anatomy. As a result, he discovered things that no one else had ever seen! For example, when he used his microscope to study veins and arteries, he found that there were tiny blood vessels connecting them! In other words, he found the missing piece to William Harvey's puzzle of how blood circulates through the body. He determined that blood flows away from the heart in arteries, and those arteries branch into smaller and smaller arteries. Those tiny arteries are connected to veins by even tinier blood vessels, so that blood can flow from the arteries to the veins. Once in the veins, the blood is then taken back to the heart.

The very tiny blood vessels that connect the arteries to the veins are called **capillaries** (kap' uh lehr' eez), and they are so tiny that they cannot be seen without a microscope. So now you have the complete picture of the human circulatory system. The heart pumps blood into the arteries, which carry the blood away from the heart. It eventually flows into capillaries, and those capillaries take it to the veins, where it can be carried back to the heart.

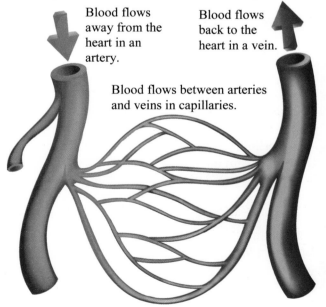

Blood flows away from the heart in an artery.

Blood flows back to the heart in a vein.

Blood flows between arteries and veins in capillaries.

This illustration shows how arteries and veins are connected by capillaries. Please note the colors are false. They are just there to distinguish between arteries and veins.

While the discovery of arteries is one of Malpighi's major achievements, he discovered many other things when he studied anatomy with a microscope. The following experiment illustrates another one of his discoveries.

Fingerprints

What you will need:
- An old compact disc (CD) that can be completely ruined
- A candle that can stand on its own or is in a holder (It should make a large flame.)
- Something to light the candle
- A magnifying glass
- An adult to help you

What you should do:
1. Put the candle in a place where it will be safe to light.
2. Have the adult light the candle and monitor the experiment.
3. Hold the CD so the shiny side is down and put it over the candle. The flame should actually touch the shiny surface of the CD.
4. Slowly move the CD back and forth over the candle. After a few moments, pull it out of the flame and look at the shiny side. It should be black where it touched the candle.
5. Repeat steps 3 and 4 several times so that about half of the shiny side of the CD is black from the candle's soot.
6. Blow out the candle.
7. Turn the CD over so the blackened side is facing up, and set it on the counter. Allow it to sit for a while to cool.
8. Take your index finger (the one you use to point at things) and lay it down into the black soot. You want the entire bottom of the finger from the last knuckle to the end pressing into the black soot.
9. Pull your index finger straight up out of the soot.
10. Look at the print your index finger left behind. Examine it with the magnifying glass.
11. Have the adult do the same thing with his or her index finger right next to the print your finger left behind.
12. Examine the adult's print with the magnifying glass and compare it to yours. Do you see any differences, other than the size?
13. Clean up your mess.

What did you see in the experiment? You should have seen that your index finger left a pattern of swirls and curves behind. Of course, that's one of your **fingerprints**. Every person's fingers have a pattern of curves and swirls, and each person's pattern is unique. No two people have the same fingerprints. You should have noticed that your fingerprint and the adult's fingerprint were quite different from each other.

Malpighi was not really the first to notice that fingers (and palms and feet and toes) have these patterns of swirls and curves. However, he was probably the first to discuss them in the context of human anatomy. As a result, modern scientists have named a particular layer of the skin (the Malpighian layer) after him. He also didn't realize that each person's fingerprints are unique. That wasn't considered until about 100 years later. Nowadays, of course, people can be identified by their fingerprints. It is a common way for crime scene investigators to determine who was involved in a crime. They gently spread dust on a surface, and the dust sticks to the oils that are left behind from people touching the surface. The dust shows the fingerprints, which can then be used to identify people.

Malpighi also studied plants quite a bit. He noticed that if he picked off the leaves from a seedling, the plant would stop growing. This told him that leaves probably were important for making nutrition for the plant. As you probably already know, that's exactly what leaves do. They make food for the plant.

This made Malpighi think a bit. He figured that water must be important to the food-making process, since plants need a lot of water. He concluded that there must be some way for water to go from the roots of a plant to its leaves. Also, he realized that if he was right about what leaves do, there must be some way for the food to travel from the leaves to the rest of the plant. He used his microscope to look at roots, stems, and leaves, and he found what appeared to be tubes running through all those structures. He decided that those tubes must carry water and food in the plant.

He decided to test his idea by **girdling** a tree. That means he cut all the outer wood away in a ring around the entire tree. He then noticed that a sweet liquid (we call it **sap**) dripped down from the top of the girdle, but nothing rose up from the bottom of the girdle. This told him that the tubes in that part of the tree carried food from the leaves down to the roots of the tree so the roots could grow.

This tree was girdled by the Wisconsin Department of Natural Resources in order to see if it contained a parasite known as the emerald ash borer.

Nowadays we understand that while animals have blood vessels that carry blood throughout the body, most plants have tubes that carry things throughout the plant. Some of those tubes carry water up from the roots to the leaves, while other tubes carry food down from the leaves to the rest of the plant.

LESSON REVIEW

Youngest students: Answer these questions:

1. What type of blood vessel did Marcello Malpighi discover? What similar things did he find in plants?

2. What do we call the pattern of swirls and ridges found on the tips of your fingers?

Older students: List the two human-anatomy-related discoveries made by Marcello Malpighi that are discussed in this lesson, and discuss how one of them related to William Harvey's work. Also, discuss what similar structures Malpighi found in plants.

Oldest students: Do what the older students are doing. In addition, explain what girdling a tree is and how Malpighi used that to confirm his suspicions about leaves making food for a plant.

Lesson 57: Robert Hooke (1635 – 1703)

This is how artist Rita Greer imagines Robert Hooke in his lab. Note his microscope on the shelf behind him. It is in front of his book, *Micrographia*.

Do you remember that Robert Boyle had an assistant? His name was **Robert Hooke**, and he helped Boyle with his experiments for seven years. During that time, he developed a reputation for having a keen eye for observation and a strong talent in mathematics. Some historians say that he might have actually done a lot of Boyle's work, since Boyle was not known for his observational or mathematical skills. This is probably true to at least some extent. Do you remember the cruel dog experiment that showed animals breathe to get air? Many books credit Boyle with that experiment, when Hooke was the one who actually did it.

After working for Boyle, Hooke started doing his own scientific investigations, which led to a lot of wonderful discoveries. Like Malpighi, he knew how lenses could be used to make small things appear larger, so he built his own microscope and started looking at all sorts of natural things. He drew very detailed illustrations of what he saw and eventually published them in a book that is called *Micrographia*. The prefix "micro" means "small," and "graphia" refers to writing. So the book contained his writings and drawings of things that are very small. Interestingly enough, there is no portrait that historians can be certain is of Robert Hooke. As a result, we don't really know what he looked like. The drawing shown here is just how one artist imagines him.

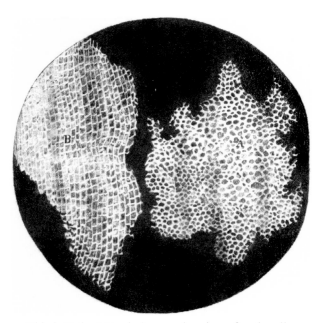

This is Robert Hooke's own drawing of cork cells.

Despite the fact that we don't know what Robert Hooke looked like, we do know what his book *Micrographia* looked like, because copies of it have survived. It contains detailed drawings of living and nonliving things magnified to the point where all sorts of wonderful details are visible. For example, the picture on the left is his own drawing of what he saw when he looked at cork through his microscope. Cork is a kind of wood, so it comes from a living organism – a tree. When Hooke looked at it under the microscope, he saw that it was made of tiny rectangles stacked together. He called those rectangles **cells**, because they reminded him of the cell that a monk lives in at a monastery – a tiny, rectangular room that contained little besides a bed and a wardrobe. We now know that all living things are made up of tiny units, and we still call them "cells," in honor of Robert Hooke.

What Hooke saw under the microscope fascinated him, and it opened up a world that had been long ignored by many people. To give you an idea of just how different things look when viewed under a microscope, do the following activity.

Magnified Things

What you will need:
- Your notebook or, for younger students, a piece of paper
- Colored pencils or crayons

What you should do:

Look at the pictures shown below. They are of things that you have probably seen before, but as they appear under a microscope. Draw each picture in your notebook (or on the paper) and try to guess what it is. Write your guess down underneath each drawing. You'll see if you were right later.

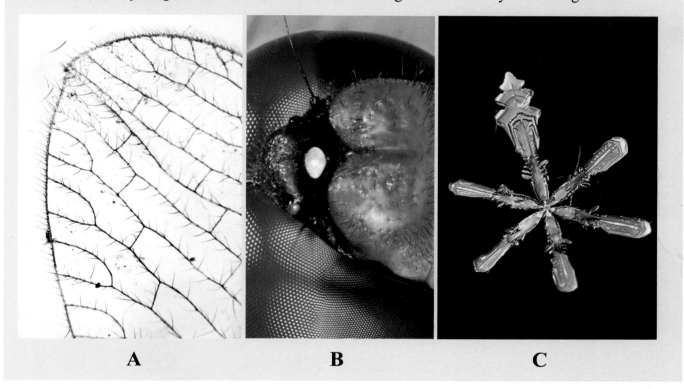

A   B   C

Do you have any idea what you are looking at in these three pictures? They certainly don't look like anything you've seen in nature using just your eyes, do they? Here's how Hooke described what he saw through the microscope:

> …whereas in natural forms there are some so small, and so curious, and their designed business so far removed beyond the reach of our sight, that the more we magnify the object, the more excellencies and mysteries do appear; And the more we discover the imperfections of our senses; and the Omnipotency and Infinite perfections of the great Creatour. [Robert Boyle, *Micrographia*, Observation 5: Of watered Silks, or Stuffs]

Hooke is saying that with our limited sight, we can't see all the intricate designs that God used in His creation. However, the microscope allows us to see some of them, and we can't help but stand in awe of God's mighty power! In case you were stumped by the photos on the previous page, here is what you were drawing:

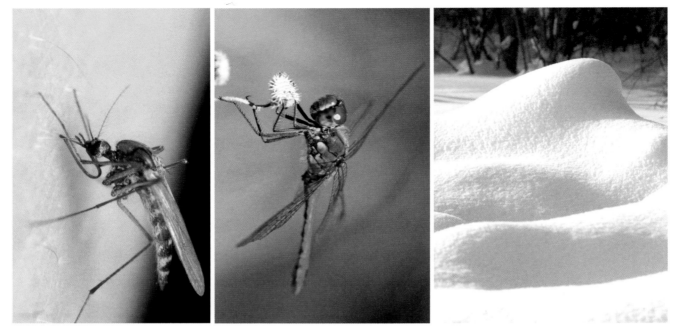

A (mosquito's wing)   B (dragonfly's face)   C (a single snowflake)

Are you surprised by any of these things? I have to confess that I would not have recognized the mosquito's wing, and even though I have seen drawings of individual snowflakes, I wouldn't have thought that's what picture "C" on the previous page was showing!

Hooke's *Micrographia* opened up a whole new world of study to the natural philosophers of his day. As others have followed in his footsteps, we have learned an enormous amount about the unseen world that exists all around us!

LESSON REVIEW

Youngest students: Answer these questions:

1. Fill in the blank: All living organisms are made of tiny units called _____.

2. Did you guess correctly on your drawings? If not, cross out your incorrect guess and write the correct answer for what you have drawn.

Older students: If you didn't guess correctly on your drawings, cross out your incorrect guess and write the correct answer for what you have drawn. Also, explain what Hooke saw when he looked at cork under the microscope and what he called them. Also note that we now know all living organisms are made up of them.

Oldest students: Do what the older students are doing. In addition, although Hooke saw that cork was made up of cells, he didn't see anything inside those cells. However, we now know that there are all sorts of things inside plant cells. Why didn't Hooke see what was inside the cells? Write down your answer and correct it if it is wrong.

Lesson 58: Robert Hooke and Fossils

Do you remember learning about Conrad Gesner in Lesson 17? He was doing work in the mid-1500s, and he wrote a book on fossil objects. However, he didn't use the word "fossil" the same way we use it today. To him, anything that a person could dig up from the ground was a fossil, so that included stones, gems, and other interesting things underground. Not surprisingly, his book made a lot of natural philosophers more interested in studying things that you can dig up from the ground, so over the roughly 100 years between Gesner's work and Robert Hooke's work, a lot of people had examined a lot of things that had been dug up from the ground.

This hunk of rock holds fossils from shelled sea animals called ammonites. In Hooke's day, most natural philosophers did not recognize them as remains of once-living creatures. They thought such things were just interestingly-shaped rocks.

Because so many natural philosophers were examining things they dug up from the ground, it was well known that some of these "fossils" looked a lot like the things you saw when studying animals. For example, some fossils looked like seashells. Some looked like bones found in animals. Some even looked like plants. However, like Gesner, most natural philosophers believed that all these things were just interestingly-shaped rocks. Why did they look like the things you find in the world of animals and plants? Most thought there was a "shaping force" in nature that helped to determine the shapes of everything in the natural world. As a result, it wasn't surprising that some rocks looked like some plants and animals. They had all been molded under the influence of this "shaping force."

Robert Hooke's studies led him to believe that this thinking was wrong. He was the first to look at fossils under the microscope, and he found something amazing. For example, when he looked at stones that were shaped like pieces of wood under the microscope, they had essentially the same structures as found in a piece of rotten oak wood he had examined under the microscope. The same held true for animal-shaped rocks. Rocks shaped like seashells had the same microscopic details as seashells that had been recently collected from the beach. This led Hooke to conclude something that was amazing at the time – these interestingly shaped rocks were the remains of once-living creatures! Now please understand that others (such as Leonardo da Vinci) had reached that conclusion before Hooke. However, Hooke was the first to offer strong evidence to back up the conclusion.

Not only was Hooke's conclusion amazing, it was very controversial. After all, natural philosophers knew what happened after a living thing died. It **decomposed**. In other words, it rotted away. If you pile a bunch of leaves on the ground, they don't turn into leaf-shaped rocks! They turn into dirt. A dead squirrel doesn't turn into a squirrel-shaped rock! It turns into dirt. If these interestingly-shaped rocks really were the remains of once-living organisms, how did they become hard as rocks? Even something like a seashell, which starts out hard, doesn't look anything like a rock. How could a seashell change from its shiny, chalky properties into those of a seashell-shaped rock? Hooke thought he had the answer, which is illustrated in the following experiment.

Petrifaction

What you will need:
- A kitchen sponge that is okay to ruin
- Scissors
- Epsom salt (available at any drugstore)
- Water
- A pan
- A stove
- A spoon for stirring something hot
- Two bowls
- Two small plates
- Two small rocks

What you should do:
1. Fill the pan with enough water so you will be able to fill both bowls about halfway with it.
2. Have an adult help you heat the pan on the stove until the water is boiling.
3. While you are waiting for the water to boil, cut the sponge into two pieces that will each fit comfortably in one of the bowls. If you want, you can cut them into interesting shapes.
4. Put one piece of sponge into one bowl and the other piece into the other bowl.
5. Once the water is boiling, have an adult help you pour enough hot water into one of the bowls so that the sponge would be completely covered if it sank to the bottom.
6. Put the pan back on the stove, but not on the hot burner.
7. Add lots of Epsom salt to the water in the pan.
8. Use the spoon to stir the Epsom salt and the water. If all the Epsom salt dissolves, add more. In the end, you want to be sure you have dissolved as much Epsom salt in the water as you possibly can. There should be extra, undissolved Epsom salt when you are done.
9. Have an adult help you pour the solution of Epsom salt and water into the other bowl so that once again, the sponge would be covered if it sank to the bottom. It's not a problem if some of the undissolved Epsom salt gets into the bowl.
10. Allow the bowls to cool.
11. Once the bowls are cool, place a rock on each sponge so that it sinks. That way, both sponges are covered in the liquid in which they are soaking. Let the bowls sit for a couple of hours or so.
12. After the bowls have been sitting for a couple of hours, remove the sponge that was sitting in the water and put it on one small plate.
13. Remove the sponge that was soaking in the Epsom salt solution and put it on the other plate.
14. Wait a few days until both sponges are dry. Once they are dry, pick them up and compare them. Clean up your mess.

What did you see when you compared the two sponges? Most likely, there wasn't anything unusual about the sponge that had been soaking in plain water. What about the sponge that had been soaking in the Epsom salt solution? It should have become pretty hard. It probably wasn't as hard as a rock, but it was a lot harder than the other sponge, wasn't it?

Why did the sponge get so hard by soaking in the Epsom salt solution? The Epsom salt that was dissolved in water started diffusing into the sponge. Do you know what **diffusion** is? It is the process by which substances move around so as to even out their concentration. When you first poured the solution on the sponge, there was no Epsom salt in the sponge and a lot of it in the solution. As the sponge sat in the solution, then, some Epsom salt moved into the sponge so that the Epsom salt was evenly spread throughout the bowl and the sponge.

Over time, however, the water that had also soaked into the sponge evaporated. As the water evaporated, the Epsom salt couldn't stay dissolved anymore, so it became solid again, like it was in the container you got it from. The Epsom salt became solid right on the sponge, and that ended up making the sponge harder.

Robert Hooke suggested that this is what happened with the living organisms that eventually turned into fossils. He thought that when some living things die, they might end up soaking in water that had a lot of minerals dissolved in it. As the dead organism soaked in this solution, its tissues would absorb the minerals, causing it to become as hard as stone.

It turns out that Hooke was correct…at least for some fossils. There are several ways that a fossil can form, but one way is through a process called **petrifaction** (pet' ruh fak' shun), which is sometimes called "petrification." This process happens essentially like Hooke suggested. A dead

organism ends up soaking in water that has a lot of minerals dissolved in it. Over time, those minerals replace the decomposing tissue in the organism, turning the organism as hard as stone. If you have ever been to the Petrified Forest in Arizona (or a similar place), you have seen the results of petrifaction. There, you can find tree remains that are as hard as rock. They are the remains of real trees that were petrified over time. Hooke's investigations helped natural philosophers understand that fossils really are the remains of once-living organisms, and that has helped us learn a lot about the kinds of plants and animals that have lived on earth throughout its history.

This is a piece of petrified wood. It is as hard as rock, but you can tell it was a tree at one time. The colors come from the different minerals that were dissolved in the water in which this tree soaked when it died.

LESSON REVIEW

Youngest students: Answer these questions:

1. Fill in the blanks: Robert Hooke showed that fossils are the remains of _____-_____ _____.

2. What do we call the process where minerals replace the decomposing tissues of an organism?

Older students: Explain why Hooke decided that fossils must be the remains of once-living organisms. Also, explain the process of petrifaction.

Oldest students: Do what the older students are doing. In addition, do some research to find another way that fossils are formed. Check the answers to make sure you are correct.

Lesson 59: Robert Hooke and His Law

Although Robert Hooke is probably best known for his work with a microscope, the law that bears his name (**Hooke's Law**) has nothing to do with small things. In fact, it has to do with springs. Like Christiaan Huygens, Hooke wanted to produce better clocks, so he looked for something that could be used for that purpose. While experimenting with springs, he discovered something very important. The following experiment helps you visualize what he found.

Spring Oscillations

What you will need:
- A Slinky (It can be small or large, plastic or metal.)
- A stepladder or platform that is a couple of meters (six feet) high and an easy place from which to drop objects
- An adult to help you

What you should do:
1. Hold the Slinky in one of your hands so that most of the coils are scrunched up together and only a small part of the Slinky is hanging down from your hand.

2. Hold your hand so the Slinky is hanging down right in front of your face (see the picture on the left).
3. Use your other hand to steady the Slinky so that it hangs still in front of you without bouncing up and down.
4. Pull down on the hanging end of the Slinky. Don't pull it too far. Just under 10 centimeters (4 inches) is plenty.
5. Let go of the end you just pulled down. Watch what happens.
6. Have the adult set up the stepladder and climb as high as is safe on it.
7. Have the adult hold the very top of the Slinky in front of the ladder so it is hanging down, fully extended.
8. Stand so the Slinky is between you and the ladder.
9. If you can touch the Slinky, steady it so it stops bouncing. If you can't reach it, just wait a little while so the bouncing settles down.
10. Watching the position of the bottom of the Slinky closely, have the adult release the top of the Slinky. What happens?
11. Repeat steps 6-10 so you can watch it happen again.
12. In case you didn't find anything unusual about what happened, keep the Slinky and stepladder out so you can repeat steps 6-10 again once you have read my discussion of the experiment.

What did you see in the first part of the experiment? When you pulled on the Slinky, it stretched down, and when you released it, the bottom started traveling upwards. After a few moments, however, it eventually stopped and started traveling downwards again. After a few more moments, it eventually stopped moving downwards and started moving upwards again. This happened over and over. If you were really patient, you could watch this process for a long, long time until the motion finally came to a rest. However, you probably got bored long before that happened.

Why did the Slinky behave like that? Well, when you steadied the Slinky so it didn't bounce up and down anymore, it was stable. Scientists call this the spring's **equilibrium** (ee' kwuh lib' ree uhm) **position**. That's the position the spring will stay in if there are no other forces pulling or pushing on it. When you pulled it down, though, you added another force, and that caused the Slinky to stretch. This made the Slinky pull against you in an attempt to return to its equilibrium position. However, your pull was just as strong as the spring's pull, so the end of the spring couldn't move back.

This is where Robert Hooke's discovery becomes important. He found that when a spring is pulled away from its equilibrium position, it pulls back with a force that becomes stronger the farther the spring is pulled. If you pull the spring just a little bit away from its equilibrium position, the spring fights you with just a little bit of force. If you pull the spring farther from its equilibrium position, however, the force with which the spring pulls back becomes stronger. This is called Hooke's Law, because Robert Hooke is the one who figured it out.

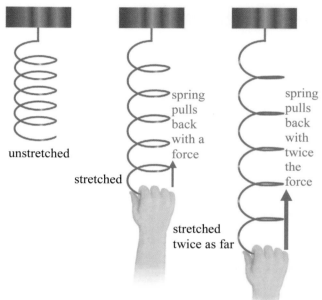

So when you were holding the Slinky stretched out, it was pulling back against you with a certain amount of force. When you let go, there was nothing fighting the force, so the end of the spring started moving back to its equilibrium position. But think about what this means. The closer the end of the Slinky got to its equilibrium position, the smaller the force pulling on it became! When the end of the Slinky reached the equilibrium position, *there was no force pulling on it at all.*

Even though there was no force pulling on the end of the Slinky once it reached its equilibrium position, the end of the Slinky didn't stop moving. After all, it had built up a lot of speed moving back to its equilibrium position, and that speed had nothing fighting it. As a result, the end of the Slinky kept moving. However, as it moved above its equilibrium position, the Slinky began fighting again.

Hooke's Law says that the farther you stretch a spring, the harder it pulls back. If you stretch a spring twice as far, it pulls back with twice the force.

This is another aspect of Hooke's Law. It didn't matter whether the spring was being stretched (like you did when you pulled down on the Slinky) or scrunched up (like what happened as the end of the Slinky moved up past its equilibrium position). Either way, the spring fights to get back to its equilibrium position. As a result, when the end of the Slinky moved above its equilibrium position, the Slinky started pushing down, trying to get back to its equilibrium position.

Well, as the Slinky got more scrunched up, it started pushing with more force. Eventually, the force was able to stop the end of the Slinky from moving up any farther. At that point, however, the Slinky was really scrunched up, so it was pushing with a lot of force. This caused the end of the Slinky to start moving down again, back to its equilibrium position.

So do you see what's going on here? Because the Slinky pushes or pulls with a force that gets stronger the farther it is from its equilibrium position, the end of the Slinky kept getting pushed or pulled in the direction of that position. However, because it had built up speed by the time it got there, it couldn't stop. It passed the equilibrium position, causing the Slinky to start pushing or pulling in the opposite direction. In the end, it "wanted" to stay at its equilibrium position, but every time it got there, it had so much speed that it overshot the equilibrium position and had to "try" again.

Scientists call what you saw **oscillation** (os' uh lay' shun) – the regular, back-and-forth movement across a specific point. In this case, the end of the Slinky was moving back and forth

When you swing, you are oscillating, because you are moving back and forth across the point where the swing hangs when no one is using it.

across the equilibrium position – always trying to get to the equilibrium position, and always overshooting it because of its speed. Anything that moves back and forth across a fixed position is oscillating. For example, when you swing back and forth on a swing set, you are oscillating. The point across which you are oscillating is the position the swing had when it was just hanging from the swing set. That's its equilibrium position.

But what about the second part of the experiment? If you were watching closely enough, you should have seen that the bottom of the Slinky hovered in midair until the Slinky was completely scrunched up. In other words, the top of the slinky fell towards the bottom, but the bottom did not rise or fall. It just "hovered" there until the top fell down to meet it. This effect is much more difficult to explain, but it is based on the same idea. As the Slinky falls, it pulls up on its bottom part. The force with which it pulls up is exactly equal to the force with which gravity is pulling down. As a result, the bottom of the Slinky can't rise or fall. It just hovers there until the Slinky is all scrunched up. At that point, there is nothing pulling up on the bottom of the Slinky anymore, so it can fall with the rest of the Slinky.

Even though Robert Hooke didn't have a Slinky, he did have a lot of springs, and experimenting with those springs allowed him to come up with Hooke's Law. You'll learn the mathematics behind his law when you study physics in high school.

LESSON REVIEW

Youngest students: Answer these questions:

1. Fill in the blank: Hooke's Law says that the farther you stretch a spring, the _____ it pulls back.

2. What does it mean for something to oscillate?

Older students: Draw two pictures to illustrate your experiment. The first should have you stretching the Slinky, and the second should have the bottom of the Slinky moving up once you released it. Explain what the Slinky was doing, being sure to use Hooke's Law and the word "oscillation."

Oldest students: Do what the older students are doing. In addition, explain why a guitar string vibrating is an example of oscillation, and describe its equilibrium position.

Lesson 60: Robert Hooke and the Planets

Hooke not only built and used microscopes, he also built and used telescopes. He made several improvements to the existing design of telescopes and, as a result, was able to study some astronomical things in stunning detail. For example, even though most of his book *Micrographia* was about what he saw through his microscope, he also reported on some of the things he saw with his telescope. He published detailed drawings of parts of the moon's surface, showing the craters, hills, and valleys that cover it.

As he studied the moon, planets, and stars, he was driven to explain why the planets behave in the way they do. By this time in history, most natural philosophers agreed with Copernicus. They understood that the planets orbit around the sun. They also understood that Kepler's Laws really worked. As a result, the motion of the planets was regular and predictable. However, there were a few good ideas about *why* this was true. Robert Hooke suggested something that turned out to be exactly right. The best way to explain Hooke's suggestion is to start with an experiment.

Forces and Orbits

What you will need:
- A 1½-meter (5-foot) length of strong string (not thread)
- Scissors
- A plastic bottle (1-liter bottles are best, but a ½-liter bottle will do. It should be one you can ruin.)
- A baseball or tennis ball
- Some paperback books
- Two plastic bags
- An adult to help you

What you should do:
1. Cut the top off the plastic bottle so that you have the opening and a small portion of the bottle right below the opening (see the picture on the right).
2. Put the baseball or tennis ball into one of the plastic bags and twist up the opening so that it forms a tight roll.
3. Tie the bag closed with one end of the string.
4. Thread the other end of the string through the bottle opening, so the threaded top of the bottle is closest to the bag that holds the ball.
5. Tie the other end of the string to the other bag, but tie it so you can still put things in the bag.
6. Put one book in the bag to which you just tied the string.
7. Hold the top of the bottle with one hand and pull on the ball so that the bag with the book is lifted up.
8. Let go of the ball and see if the book falls back down. If so, the book and its bag are heavier than the ball and its bag. If not, add another book and try again. Before you continue, you need to have enough weight in the book bag so it can pull the ball up as it falls down.
9. Go outside to a nice open space. If it's cold, that's not a problem. Just bundle up.

top of the plastic bottle

bag with the ball inside

bag with the books inside

10. Hold the top of the bottle with your strongest hand and start twirling it above your head so that the ball starts orbiting your hand (see the picture on the left).
11. Once you get the ball twirling, start twirling it faster and see what happens to the bag with the books.
12. Once you see what happens when the ball twirls faster, start slowing down how fast you twirl the ball and notice what happens to the bag with the books.
13. Play around with this for a while, making the ball twirl faster and slower and noticing what happens to the bag of books.
14. Choose a good speed for the ball to twirl so that the bag of books doesn't rise or fall, and have the adult come and kneel next to you. Make sure the adult is low enough that the ball and string don't hit his or her head!
15. When the ball is moving away from anything that might break (like a window!), have the adult cut the string right above the bag of books. Watch what happens to the ball.
16. Pick up the ball and string and put everything away.

What did you see in the experiment? First, you should have seen that although the ball was lighter than the bag of books, it could lift the books up if it was twirling fast enough. When you slowed the ball down, the bag of books fell. It should have been fairly easy to find a speed where you could twirl the ball around, and the books would not rise or fall. They would just hang in one spot. When the adult cut the string, however, the bag of books fell, and the ball went flying off in whatever direction it was traveling when the string was cut. The ball didn't fly in a curve, however. It flew straight.

Without the string being pulled on by the bag of books, the ball wouldn't travel in a circle. Instead, it traveled in a straight line. That's the way the ball "wanted" to travel. However, it couldn't, because the string kept pulling on it. The weight of the books in the bag pulled down on the string, which caused the string to pull the ball towards the top of the plastic bottle. This changed the ball's direction. As a result, rather than traveling straight, it traveled in a circle. The important thing to understand here is that it's the force of the string that kept the ball moving in a circle. Without that force, the ball would have just kept traveling in a straight line, like it did when the adult cut the string.

Believe it or not, this is the same reason the planets orbit the sun! The sun and planets are all attracted to one another by the **gravitational force**. This force exists between any two objects that have matter in them. When you drop something, it falls to the ground because the object you drop has matter in it, and the earth has matter in it. As a result, there is a gravitational force between them. The object falls to the ground because it is attracted to the earth by this gravitational force. Well, the sun also has a lot of matter in it (a lot more than the earth), so there is a very strong gravitational force attracting the earth (and all the other planets) to the sun.

Why don't the planets just fall into the sun like a dropped object falls to the earth? Because the planets are already moving! They are all "trying" to travel in straight lines, like the ball on the string in your experiment. However, just like the ball on the string, they aren't allowed to move in a straight line, because there is a force pulling them towards the sun. Because the planets are traveling so quickly, the best that force can do is change their direction, making them travel around the sun rather than into the sun.

Robert Hooke was the first to propose this. He recognized that if you have an object moving in a straight line and then apply a force that pulls on it, the force will end up making the object orbit the point to which the force is pulling it. The object "tries" to go straight, but the force pulls on it, changing its direction towards the source of the pulling force. If the force is really big or the object is moving really slowly, in the end, the object will be pulled to the center by the force. If the force is very weak or the object is moving very quickly, the object will eventually move away. However, if the force and speed are just right, the object will end up orbiting around the source of the force!

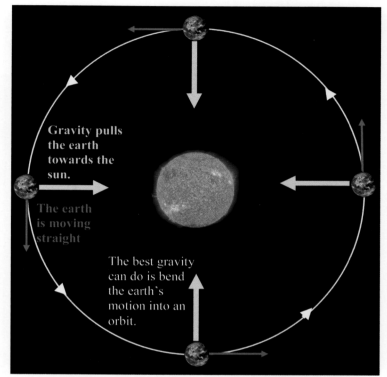

Gravity pulls the earth towards the sun.

The earth is moving straight

The best gravity can do is bend the earth's motion into an orbit.

Planets orbit the sun because the gravitational force can bend their motion into an orbit, but it is not strong enough to pull them in.

Now Robert Hooke wasn't the first one to mention gravity; he was the first to accurately describe how it controls the motion of the planets around the sun. Later on, you will learn about another natural philosopher who worked out even more of the details, allowing us to have an even better understanding of the process.

Before we leave Robert Hooke, it is important to note that natural philosophy was not the only thing he did. In fact, he was a very well-respected **architect** (ar' kih tekt'). That's what we call people who design buildings. In 1666, London experienced a terrible fire that destroyed thousands of homes and many churches. Hooke was a leader in the effort to rebuild the city after the fire.

LESSON REVIEW

Youngest students: Answer these questions:

1. What did Robert Hooke make to help him better observe the moon, planet, and stars?

2. What bends the motion of the planets into an orbit around the sun?

Older students: Make a drawing like the one above and use it to explain why the planets orbit the sun.

Oldest students: Do what the older students are doing. In addition, explain your experiment in your own words and discuss how it is similar to the way in which planets orbit the sun.

NOTE: The experiment in Lesson 63 needs to sit for several days. You should start it soon.

Section 5: The Revolution Near the End of the 17th Century

This statue of Sir Isaac Newton is at the Oxford Museum of Natural History.

Lessons 61-75: The Revolution Near the End of the 17ᵗʰ Century

Lesson 61: Giovanni Cassini (1625 – 1712)

When Italian-born astronomer **Giovanni** (jee oh vah' nee) **Cassini** (kuh see' nee) was young, he loved studying the night sky. This led him to study **astrology** (uh strah' luh jee). As you might have already learned, astrology is the odd belief that the movement of the stars and planets in the sky affects a person's future. While some people today still believe in it, most understand that astrology is just a superstition. However, it was incredibly popular in the ancient world, and even during the Scientific Revolution. Natural philosophers you have already studied, such as Galileo, used astrology regularly. In fact, anyone studying to be a doctor had to learn astrology, since it was thought that the movement of the stars and planets could affect a person's health!

Although Cassini started out as a strong believer in astrology, the more he studied the heavens and the predictions of astrologers, the more he realized that astrology just couldn't be correct. Over time, then, he spent less and less time on astrology, and more and more time on astronomy – the scientific study of the heavens. As a result, he made many discoveries that have aided the progress of science. One of the more interesting things he studied is demonstrated in the following experiment.

This is a painting of Cassini done by Léopold Durangel in 1879. He did the painting based on an engraving that was done of Cassini when he was alive.

Scattering Light

What you will need:
- A mug used for hot beverages or a very well-insulated cup and a glove
- Water
- A pan and stove to boil water
- A flashlight
- A dark room
- An adult to help you

What you should do:
1. Have an adult help you get the water boiling on the stove and then pour it into the mug until the mug is nearly full.
2. Turn on the flashlight.
3. Hold the mug by its handle (or the cup with a glove) in your right hand and take it into the dark room with the flashlight in your left hand.
4. Make sure the only light in the room is coming from the flashlight.

5. Hold the flashlight in your left hand in front of you at eye level and shine it to the right so that the beam of light passes in front of you across your field of vision. Look straight ahead, and observe what you see.
6. Without moving the flashlight, hold the mug in front of you so the light coming from the flashlight travels across the top of the mug (see the picture on the left). Once again, look straight ahead and observe what you see.
7. Bring the mug and flashlight together so the flashlight touches the mug and shines right over the top of it. Once again, look straight ahead and observe what you see.
8. Slowly move the flashlight around the mug so it is always pointed to the center of the mug as it moves. How does what you see change as you move the flashlight?
9. Put everything away.

What did you see in the experiment? You should have noticed that as you looked straight ahead in step 5, you could see what was in front of you, because the light hit the wall of the room and bounced around, allowing you to get a dim view of the room. What happened when you put the mug under the light, however? You should have seen the steam rising from the mug. It should have looked like little sparkles of light rising from the mug. As you brought the flashlight near the mug, the steam should have made interesting shapes in the flashlight's beam, and the "sparkles" should have been easier to see when the flashlight was at some positions and harder to see when the flashlight was at other positions.

The glow you see in the photo is called zodiacal light, and it was first studied scientifically by Cassini.

Why did this happen? Well, when the flashlight was shining from left to right, the light traveled in front of your eyes, but you didn't see that light. The light you were seeing was the light that reflected off the wall of the room. However, when you put the mug in front of the light, some of that light bounced off the steam and ended up hitting your eyes. As a result, you saw flashes of light as it bounced off the steam. Scientists call this **scattered light** – light that is bounced in different directions by particles that it hits as it travels. So the steam was scattering light, and some of that light scattered into your eyes.

What does this have to do with astronomy? Well, Cassini noticed that on clear nights just after sunset or right before sunrise, a glow would often shoot up from where he assumed the sun was just below the horizon, as shown on the left. This glow was most noticeable in the spring and autumn. It puzzled Cassini, because he knew he shouldn't be able to see the sun's light, since the sun was below the horizon. Nevertheless, it was there. Cassini wrote his ideas about what caused it, and a Swiss mathematician named Nicolas Fatio de Duillier became interested in it. Together, they determined that it is caused by dust and other particles between the sun and the earth. Those particles scatter the sun's light, making it visible, much like the steam scattered the flashlight's light. We now call this **zodiacal** (zoh dye' uh kuhl) **light**.

Cassini discovered many other things as well. For example, he studied the planet Saturn quite a bit. Remember the telescope Christiaan Huygens made, which was good enough to see that Saturn was surrounded by a ring? Well, Cassini used an even better one, which showed that there is a gap in the ring. We now know that there are several gaps, and that Saturn has multiple rings rather than just one

ring. Cassini found the largest gap, and as a result, it is now called the **Cassini division**. He discovered four moons orbiting Saturn in addition to the one Huygens discovered. Because he discovered so much about Saturn, an unmanned spaceship that is currently orbiting and studying Saturn is called the "Cassini spacecraft," in honor of him.

Cassini discovered the largest gap in Saturn's rings, which is called the Cassini division. Interestingly enough, this picture was taken by the Cassini spacecraft!

Cassini not only studied Saturn; he also studied the other planets. He made detailed drawings of Mars, and he also determined how long it took Mars and Jupiter to make a full rotation. In other words, he measured the length of a day on Mars and Jupiter! He and another natural philosopher, Jean Richer were also the first to make a correct measurement of how far Mars is from the earth. They used parallax, which you learned about in Lesson 3.

Even though he started his career thinking that the earth was the center of the universe, the more he studied astronomy, the more he found that this arrangement didn't fit the facts. As a result, he eventually changed his mind and sided with Copernicus. If you study history, you might hear Cassini called by another first name. This is because he ended up moving from Italy to France. He did so much work in France that he started being called by the French version of his name – Jean-Dominique Cassini. It didn't seem to displease him, so depending on which book you read, you might see him called by that first name instead of the Italian version (Giovanni).

LESSON REVIEW

Youngest students: Answer these questions:

1. What is scattered light?

2. Name two things Cassini initially believed but later changed his mind about based on the facts.

Older students: Describe what you saw in your experiment, using the term "scattered light." Explain how that relates to Zodiacal light.

Oldest students: Do what the older students are doing. In addition, I think Cassini is a great model of a real scientist, because he allowed his own studies to change his mind on certain subjects. Discuss why Cassini changed his mind and why that shows he was a good scientist.

NOTE: The experiment in Lesson 74 requires two cardboard tubes from a roll of toilet paper and three cardboard tubes from a roll of paper towels. You should start saving them now.

Lesson 62: Francesco Redi (1626 – 1697)

This is a picture of the Francesco Redi award, which is given to scientists who have made significant contributions to our understanding of poisons and how they harm the body.

A year after Cassini was born in Italy, another great natural philosopher was born. His name was **Francesco** (frahn ches' koh) **Redi** (ray' dee), and he was the son of a physician. Not surprisingly, he also became a physician and gained a lot of fame in his profession. In fact, he was the personal physician for two different Grand Dukes of Tuscany. Not content with just following the medical practices of the time, however, he did a lot of his own investigations into life and the things that threaten it. As a result, he helped us understand a great deal about the natural world.

For example, Redi performed a lot of experiments on snake bites. It was well known at the time that bites from some snakes were much worse than bites from others. A bite from some kinds of snake could kill a grown man in under an hour, while a bite from many other kinds of snakes is not life-threatening at all, as long as it is cleaned and bandaged. Redi was interested in how best to treat snake bites, so he experimented with vipers, which were the most dangerous snakes he could find.

Natural philosophers knew that vipers producd a poisonous venom, and that's what caused their bites to kill people. However, not much was known about how the snake produced the venom or how the bite could be treated. Redi demonstrated a very effective method for treating a venomous snake bite, the first part of which is demonstrated by the following experiment.

Restricting Blood Flow

What you will need:
- A 30-centimeter (12-inch) length of string
- An adult to supervise (As discussed in the introduction to the book, this should be the case for *all* experiments. For this experiment, I just want to emphasize it.)

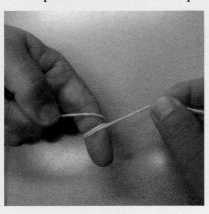

What you should do:
1. Hold one end of the string in your left hand, but make sure the index finger of that hand stays extended.
2. Using your right hand, loosely wrap the other end of the string around the index finger of your left hand near the top knuckle. Wrap it around twice, as shown in the picture on the left.
3. Look at the index finger around which you wrapped the string.
4. While continuing to look at the index finger, pull the string with your right hand so it tightens up. The string that's wrapped around your finger should tighten up, causing just a bit of pain.

5. Hold the string tight for 10 seconds, but no more. This is where the adult supervision is important. If you hold the string tight for too long or hold it too tightly, it could damage your finger!
6. After 10 seconds, unwrap the finger quickly and see how it changes.
7. Repeat the experiment once more, making sure you understand what the tightened string does to your finger.
8. Put the string away.

What did you see in the experiment? You should have seen that when you tightened the string, the tip of your finger got much redder, while the part of the finger below the string got paler. When you unwrapped the string, however, the colors went back to normal. Now this probably didn't surprise you, but it was the first step that Redi said was necessary to treat a venomous snake bite.

By tightening the string around your finger, you were restricting how the blood could flow. As was known from the time of Galen, veins are usually closer to the surface of the skin, while arteries are deeper in the body. As a result, when you tightened the string, you shut down the veins in your finger by pinching them closed. However, the arteries in your finger were not completely closed. That's because the string wasn't tightened strongly enough to push through all that tissue and completely pinch the arteries closed. They were partly closed off, but not completely closed off.

Now remember, the veins carry blood back to the heart, while the arteries carry blood away from the heart. So, since the veins were completely closed in your finger, blood could not flow from the tip of your finger back to your heart. As a result, it just stayed in the tip of your finger. However, your arteries were not completely shut down, so they kept bringing blood to the tip of your finger. As a result, blood kept "piling up" in the tip of your finger. Blood kept being added, but no blood could go away.

That's why the tip of your finger turned dark red. Because the blood was piling up, there was more blood in it than usual. At the same time, there was less blood in your finger below the string, because the blood that was supposed to be flowing through that part of the finger and back to the heart wasn't there. This made your finger paler than normal right below the string. Of course, when you unwrapped the string, the blood could flow normally again, and in a few seconds, everything returned to normal.

Medical doctors call what you made a **ligature** (lig' uh chur), and it can be used to restrict how the blood is flowing when a patient is being treated. According to Redi, this was crucial in helping a person survive a venomous snake bite. Redi's experiments made him realize that a snake injects its venom into the blood. If you could keep the blood in the region of the bite from flowing back to the heart, the venom wouldn't make its way around the body. As a result, he

This western diamondback rattlesnake (a snake with a venomous bite) injects its venom into a person using the fangs shown in this picture.

suggested that the first step in treating a venomous snake bite is to apply a ligature behind the bite so as to keep the venom from spreading.

Of course, that's only the first step of the procedure. The next step is to get the venom out of the area where the bite happened. How do you do that? One option is to suck the venom out of the wound and spit it on the ground. The more you can suck out of the wound, the less likely the person will be to die from the venom.

This suggestion went against the accepted view of Redi's time. You see, most people thought that drinking the venom from a snake would be just as deadly as getting bit by the snake. However, Redi's careful experiments showed that this simply wasn't the case. A snake's venom was only fatal if it was injected into a person's blood by the snake. When it is swallowed, the venom is destroyed by the digestion process. It probably doesn't taste very good, and it might make you sick to your stomach, but it won't kill you. Now, please note that modern medicine has determined that applying a ligature to a snakebite victim and trying to suck out the venom is not a good treatment for snakebites. So while Redi was ultimately wrong about how to treat snakebites, he at least helped us understand them better.

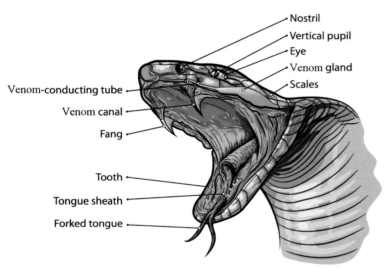

Redi showed that a snake makes its venom in glands that exist behind its fangs.

Redi dispelled a few other myths about venomous snakes with his experiments. For example, it was thought at the time that a snake's venom was made in its liver. However, Redi showed that this wasn't the case. Instead, he showed that all snakes with a venomous bite have glands behind their fangs, and that's where the venom is made. He also showed that a snake's venom is just as deadly even when the snake is dead. This was important, because it was thought that one reason some snakes had a venomous bite was because they were angry, and that emotion somehow made their bite venomous. Redi showed that the snake's "emotions" had nothing to do with its venom.

LESSON REVIEW

Youngest students: Answer these questions:

1. What is a ligature?

2. What two things did Francesco Redi say should be done to treat a venomous snake bite?

Older students: Describe what a ligature is and what it does. Explain how Redi thought that this helps a person who has been bitten by a venomous snake. Also, explain what else Redi said should be done to treat the snake bite and why that won't kill the person doing it.

Oldest students: Do what the older students are doing. In addition, there are two types of snake venom. Do some research to find out what they are and how they work.

Lesson 63: Francesco Redi and Spontaneous Generation

Back in Redi's day, people had some very odd ideas. Belief in astrology is an example, but here's another one: **spontaneous generation**. It's the belief that living things can come from nonliving things. Why did people have this idea? Perform the following experiment to find out.

"Spontaneous" Mold

What you will need:
- A fresh tomato
- A large pot for boiling water
- Water
- A knife
- A small plate
- A plastic container with a lid (like a Tupperware container) that is small enough to fit into the pot but large enough to hold half a tomato
- Kitchen tongs
- An adult to supervise (As discussed in the introduction to the book, this should be the case for *all* experiments. For this experiment, I just want to emphasize it.)

What you should do:
1. Add enough water to the pot that you can completely submerge the plastic container.
2. Have the adult help you get the water in the pot boiling.
3. Have the adult help you cut the tomato in half.
4. Once the water is boiling, drop both halves of the tomato in the water.
5. While the tomato halves are still in the boiling water, have the adult help you grab the plastic container with the kitchen tongs and completely submerge it in the boiling water. **The water is very hot, so don't let it get near your hands.**
6. Hold the plastic container in the boiling water for about 30 seconds and then pull it out, dumping any excess water into the pot. Put the container down on the counter near the stove.
7. Use the tongs to get one half of the tomato that is in the boiling water, and place it in the container.
8. Use the tongs to grab the lid for the container, and submerge it in the boiling water for about 30 seconds.
9. Use the tongs to place the lid on the container so it covers the top of the container.
10. Use the tongs to grab the other half of the tomato that is still in the water and put it on the small plate.
11. Allow everything to cool.
12. Once things are cool, use your fingers to secure the lid on the container.
13. Move the container and plate to a place they won't be disturbed and let them sit for a few days.
14. Clean up your mess.
15. Check the tomato half on the plate twice a day. Eventually, you should see something growing on it. When you see something growing on that tomato half, open the plastic container and see if there is something growing on the tomato half that is in the container.

What was growing on the tomato? It was a living organism called **mold**. This organism grows on lots of rotting things, such as breads and fruits. If you only think about half of the tomato that was out on the plate, what might you conclude from your experiment? No one put any mold on the tomato, and it certainly didn't crawl there! Nevertheless, it appeared on the tomato after a few days. One reasonable conclusion is that the mold came from the tomato. Somehow, the rotting tomato did something to produce a living organism.

This is why people believed in spontaneous generation. They saw examples of living things appearing on nonliving things, even when there was no evidence that the living things were put there or had crawled there. As a result, spontaneous generation was something that pretty much every natural philosopher in Redi's day believed.

Now, of course, you probably know that the mold didn't come from the tomato, which is what the tomato in the container demonstrated. It shouldn't have had any mold on it, because mold doesn't come from rotting tomatoes. Instead, mold grows from something called **spores**, which are very tiny and travel in the air. They can only be seen with a microscope, and they act a bit like seeds. They find a good place to land, and then they develop into a mold. The container kept the spores in the air from landing on the tomato inside it, and as a result, no mold grew on that tomato. The reason you had to put everything in boiling water beforehand is that there are spores everywhere, so the container and the tomato already had spores on them. By boiling everything, you killed the spores that were already there before the experiment started.

In Redi's day, the issue wasn't mold. It was flies. People noticed that if you left rotting meat out, it would eventually have tiny insects called **maggots** crawling all over it. Even if you put it in an open jar high on a shelf where no crawling creature could reach it, maggots would still develop. This made many people conclude that the rotting meat must somehow turn into maggots. Redi didn't believe this, and he developed an experiment to show that it wasn't true.

He put meat in several different jars. Some of the jars he left open. Others he sealed airtight. Others he covered with a cloth that had very tiny holes in it. The holes would let air into the jars, but they kept out any flying insects that might fly into the jars. The only place maggots appeared was on the meat in the open jars. They never appeared in the sealed jars or the jars covered with cloth. This showed that *something* was bringing the maggots to the meat.

To demonstrate this, he put maggots in a jar covered with cloth and waited. After a while, flies appeared! That told him that maggots turn into flies. There was no way flies could get into the jar, since it was covered. Nevertheless, flies appeared, because the maggots became flies! So Redi not only demonstrated that maggots do not come from decaying meat, he also showed that when a fly's egg hatches, a fly is not what comes out. Instead, a white, crawling insect called a maggot comes out. That maggot then eventually develops into a fly!

Redi showed that maggots (top) are really just baby flies (bottom). If you feed maggots and wait, they will turn into flies.

I have mentioned this before, but I want to emphasize it by mentioning it again. In many scientific experiments, we use a **control** – a "standard" sample against which all other samples can be compared. In your experiment, for example, you used two tomato halves. The only difference between the two halves was that one was covered, while the other was not. You compared what happened to the tomato half in the container with what happened to the tomato half that was left out in the open. The one that was left out in the open was the control. It showed you what happens when a tomato is left out. You compared the covered tomato to the control to see what effect covering the tomato in a container would have.

Redi did essentially the same thing. His uncovered jars were the controls of the experiment. They showed what was already known to happen. He then compared them to the covered jars and, as a result, he was able to conclude something very important. As far as historians can tell, this is actually the first example of an experiment that used a control. Nowadays, such experiments (we called them **controlled experiments**) are common. However, as far as we know, Redi was the first to perform one and write about it.

gall

Interestingly enough, you might think that Redi's experiment destroyed the notion of spontaneous generation altogether. Unfortunately, it did not – even for Redi! While Redi's experiment convinced him (and pretty much all other natural philosophers who read about it) that maggots don't come from decaying meat, even Redi thought there were some examples of living things coming from nonliving things.

For example, Redi studied **galls**, which look like tumors that form on many kinds of plants. They end up developing into living organisms that feed off the plant and harm it. We call such organisms **parasites** (pehr' uh sites). Redi wanted to believe that insects somehow laid eggs in the plant, and those eggs eventually formed galls. However, he could never show how that happened. As a result, he thought that perhaps they formed from dead tissue in the plant. Even though he was wrong about that (we now know galls can form as a result of a parasite getting into the plant), he studied parasites so much that he is often called the father of parasitology, which is the study of parasites.

The "ball" on this goldenrod plant is a gall that contains parasites that harm the plant.

Of course, Redi wasn't the only one who continued to believe in spontaneous generation. Most natural philosophers believed in some form of spontaneous generation for another 200 years before another great natural philosopher (Louis Pasteur) finally demonstrated that it just doesn't happen.

LESSON REVIEW

Youngest students: Answer these questions:

1. What is spontaneous generation?

2. What did Francesco Redi demonstrate about maggots, besides the fact that they don't come from rotting meat?

Older students: Describe Redi's experiment and how it showed that maggots do not come from decaying meat. Point out the control Redi used in the experiment and discuss what he did to show that maggots are really just baby flies.

Oldest students: Do what the older students are doing. In addition, explain what a gall is and what a parasite is.

Lesson 64: Antoni van Leeuwenhoek (1632 – 1723)

This portrait of Antoni van Leeuwenhoek was painted by artist Jan Verkolje in about 1680.

As you already know, microscopes had been used by natural philosophers really since the time of Galileo. You might be surprised to read that Dutch tradesman **Antoni van Leeuwenhoek** (ley' vuhn hook) is sometimes credited with inventing the microscope. That's not true, of course. The microscope was invented long before he was born. Why do people say he invented the microscope? Because he took the microscope to a whole new level!

Van Leeuwenhoek was born into a family of tradesmen, and he became one as well. He was a fabric merchant, a wine inspector, a lens maker, and even a bit of a politician. Then he saw a copy of Hooke's masterpiece, *Micrographia*. It fascinated him, and he decided to put his own lens-making skills to work to build a microscope of his own so that he could learn more about this tiny world Hooke had illustrated. This is where van Leeuwenhoek excelled. He made microscopes that were so much better than anyone else's that he could see things no one had ever seen before! What made his microscopes so good? Perform this experiment to see for yourself.

Sometimes Smaller is Better

What you will need:
- A piece of cardboard (no bigger than 18 cm [7 in] by 10 cm [4 in])
- Clear plastic wrap
- Tape
- Scissors
- A medicine dropper
- Water
- An adult to help you

What you should do:
1. Have an adult help you cut a rectangle out of the center of the cardboard. It should be about 5 cm (2 inches) wide and 3 cm (a bit more than 1 inch) tall.
2. Have the adult help you get a piece of plastic wrap that is bigger than the hole, but smaller than the piece of cardboard.
3. Stretch the plastic wrap over the hole and tape it to the cardboard. As you are taping, make sure the plastic wrap is stretched so that when you are done, there are no wrinkles in the part that is over the hole.

4. Turn the piece of cardboard over so the plastic is on the bottom.
5. Use the medicine dropper to put a full drop of water on the plastic. Don't put it in at the center of the hole. It should be off to one side a bit.

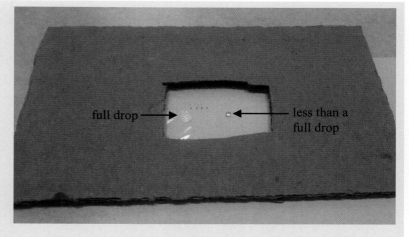

full drop →   ← less than a full drop

6. Now use the medicine dropper to put much less than a full drop of water on the plastic. Do this by touching the plastic with the end of the medicine dropper before you squeeze the bulb. Then just barely squeeze the bulb until a very tiny amount of water comes out. Once that happens, pull the medicine dropper away. You might have to do this a couple of times to get it to work, but eventually, you should have something like what you see in the picture above, where there is a full drop of water on the left and a much smaller drop of water on the right.
7. Carefully lift the cardboard so as not to disturb the drops, and place it on this book, well below the words you are reading right now. The plastic, of course, should be touching the book so the water drops don't get on the pages.
8. After you get done reading this line of instructions, slide the cardboard on the page so you can see the white box below through the plastic. Once it is there, position it so the large drop of water is right over one of the tiny x's that is in the box. Look at the drop from above, and see how much larger it made the x. You can move it around to see how it magnifies other x's in the box. Next, do the same thing with the smaller drop. Once you have looked at the x's through both drops, slide the cardboard away so you can read the rest of the instructions.

```
x x x x x x x x x x x x x x
x x x x x x x x x x x
```

9. Did the drops magnify the x's differently? They should have. One drop should have magnified better than the other. If you didn't see that, try again. Which drop gave the best magnification?
10. Clean up your mess.

What did you see in the experiment? You should have seen that the smaller drop of water magnified much better than the larger drop of water. You probably already know that a curved piece of glass (or drop of water) can magnify what is underneath it because of refraction. What this experiment shows you, however, is that the curve itself makes a difference. The tighter the curve, the stronger the magnification.

Antoni van Leeuwenhoek was a master at making very tiny balls of glass that were nearly perfect. As a result, his microscopes were better than anything that had ever been made at the time! This was quite impressive, because the other microscopes being used at the time had two lenses in them, just like a telescope. Van Leeuwenhoek was able to make a better microscope with a single ball of glass as its only lens!

What did van Leeuwenhoek see with his incredible, tiny balls of glass? He saw a world of activity that had never been seen before. There were all sorts of tiny creatures that moved about doing incredible things. He called them "animalcules" (an ih' mal kyulz) which takes the word "animal" and adds the Latin suffix that means "little." In other words, he called them "little animals." We now know they aren't really animals. They are microscopic creatures called **protozoa** (proh' tuh zoh' uh) and **bacteria**. They move about, just as animals do, but they are completely different from animals. The pictures below give you an idea of some of the things he saw.

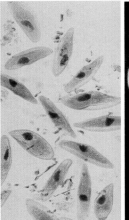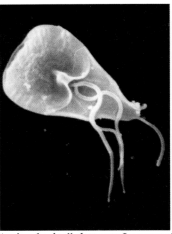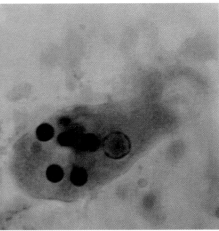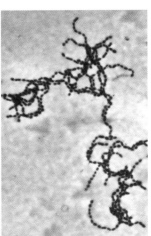

These are some of the "animalcules" that van Leeuwenhoek described seeing with his microscope. The left three pictures are of protozoa, and the last one on the right is of bacteria. They are all creatures made up of a single cell, but the protozoa are a lot larger than the bacteria.

Van Leeuwenhoek found microscopic creatures in nearly everything he examined with his microscope, which led him to the conclusion that they exist nearly everywhere in creation. It turned out that he was right! From a drop of pond water to a piece of wet dirt, you can generally find microscopic creatures. As the serious study of nature tends to do to people, van Leeuwenhoek's discoveries made him marvel at God's handiwork. He wrote,

From all these observations, we discern most plainly the incomprehensible perfection, the exact order, and the inscrutable providential care with which the most wise Creator and Lord of the Universe had formed the bodies of these animalcules, which are so minute as to escape our sight, to the end that different species of them may be preserved in existence. [Abraham Schierbeek, *Measuring the invisible world: The life and works of Antoni van Leeuwenhoek*, Abelard Schuman 1959, p. 171]

When it came to the wonders of nature, van Leeuwenhoek understood Who was responsible for them!

LESSON REVIEW

Youngest students: Answer these questions:

1. What did Antoni van Leeuwenhoek make that allowed his microscope to magnify things so well?

2. What do scientists call the things that van Leeuwenhoek called "animalcules?"

Older students: Explain what van Leeuwenhoek was able to do in order to make his microscopes magnify things so well. Also, discuss what he called the microscopic organisms he saw and what scientists call them today.

Oldest students: Do what the older students are doing. In addition, offer a possible explanation for the fact that when some people use a microscope made exactly as van Leeuwenhoek's was made, they see protozoa, but they don't see bacteria. Check your explanation and correct it if it is wrong.

Lesson 65: Antoni van Leeuwenhoek on Populations and Spontaneous Generation

When van Leeuwenhoek peered through his tiny glass beads and saw the incredible microscopic world, he was amazed by what he saw. He wrote:

> The motion of most of them in the water was so swift, and so various, upwards, downwards, and roundabout, that I admit I could not but wonder at it. I judge that some of these little creatures were above a thousand times smaller than the smallest ones which I have hitherto seen…Some of these are so exceedingly small that millions of millions might be contained in a single drop of water. [Alan Gillen, T*he Genesis of Germs: The Origin of Diseases and the Coming Plagues*, Master Books 2007, p. 51]

Notice that last line. He wrote that millions of millions of them might be contained in a single drop of water. The more he investigated the microscopic world, the more he wanted to know how many actually existed in a drop of water!

When scientists try to count the number of living things, we say that they are estimating the **population**. Suppose you were in van Leeuwenhoek's shoes. How would you try to determine the population of microscopic organisms in a drop of water? You couldn't just count them all. Remember, he said that millions of them could be in a drop of water! That would take too long to count! How would you do it? Perform the following experiment to see how van Leeuwenhoek did it.

If you were to count all the penguins that exist on this island, you would know its penguin population.

Estimating a Population

What you will need:
- A bag of small candies like Reese's Pieces, M&Ms, or Skittles
- A ½-cup measuring cup
- A measuring tablespoon
- A knife (It doesn't need to be sharp.)

What you should do:
1. Open the bag of candies and pour the candies into the ½-cup measuring cup. Continue to pour until the candies spill out over the edge of the measuring cup.
2. Lay the back side of the knife on the handle of the measuring cup and then pull it all the way across the top of the cup so the knife pushes away all candies that are not level with the top of the cup. This is called "leveling off" the measuring cup. That way, you know you have exactly ½ cup of candies.
3. Clear away all the candies that have spilled out as a result of your pouring and leveling off.

4. Scoop out a tablespoon of candies from the measuring cup. Scoop deeply so it is overflowing with candies. Don't worry if some of the candies spill out. Just keep track of them so you can put them back in the measuring cup in a moment.

5. Once you have your tablespoon overflowing with candies, use the back side of the knife to level off your tablespoon.

6. Collect all the candies that spilled out of the measuring cup and tablespoon in steps 4 and 5 and put them back in the cup. Now you should have a tablespoon of candies as well as a ½-cup measuring cup that is no longer full of candies, because you have removed a tablespoon of them.

7. Carefully pour the candies from the tablespoon out on the table and count them. Write that number down.

8. Now count the candies that are still in the measuring cup and add it to the number of candies that were in the tablespoon. That will tell you the total number of candies in ½ of a cup. Write that number down.

9. There are 8 tablespoons in ½ of a cup. If you multiply the first number you got (the number of candies in the tablespoon) by 8, how does it compare to the second number you got (the total number of candies in the ½ measuring cup)?

10. Clean up your mess, and ask your parent if you can have some of the candy. Don't whine or beg!

When you multiplied the number of candies in the tablespoon by 8, what did you get? Was it close to the total number of candies in the ½-cup measuring cup? It should have been. It might have been off by 2 or 3, but it should have been close. After all, there are 8 tablespoons in ½ of a cup. If you take the number of candies in a tablespoon and multiply in by 8, it should tell you roughly how many candies fit in ½ of a cup.

This is what Antoni van Leeuwenhoek did to estimate the population of microscopic organisms in a drop of water. He used his glassmaking skills to make a glass tube that was divided into about 30 sections. His measurements of the glass tube indicated that each section held a very tiny

It would be hard to count all the jelly beans in this picture. However, if you count the number of jelly beans in the blue square and multiply by 16 (the number of blue squares that would fit in the picture), you would get a good idea of how many there are.

amount of water. In fact, it would take water from 2,730 sections to make a single drop! He looked at the water in several sections to see that they all held about the same number of organisms. He then counted 1,000 organisms in a single section. He multiplied that number by 2,730, which gave him an estimate for the number of organisms in a drop of water. His answer was two million, seven hundred and thirty thousand (2,730,000)!

So van Leeuwenhoek took a small sample, counted the organisms in the sample, and then multiplied that by the number of samples that should fit into a drop of water. This allowed him to estimate the number of organisms in a drop of water. You did the same thing. You took a sample of candies (one tablespoon), counted the candies in that sample, then multiplied by the number of tablespoons in ½ of a cup to get the number of candies in ½ of a cup.

Do you see the genius behind van Leeuwenhoek's idea? He didn't have to count every organism to get an idea of the population. He just counted a tiny sample and then multiplied by how many samples should fit into a drop of water. Of course, his result wasn't exact. The only way to get an exact result would be to truly count every organism. However, his result gave a number that was probably close to the exact number, and as a result, we call it a **population estimate**.

He went on to apply this method to estimate other populations as well. For example, he took the population of Holland at the time and then calculated how many countries the size of Holland would fit on earth. He then multiplied the population of Holland by that number to estimate how many people could live on the earth, at least with personal space that each person in Holland had. His estimate was 13 billion people. Currently there are between 7 and 8 billion people living on earth. Scientists continue to use this method to estimate the populations of all sorts of organisms on earth.

Now van Leeuwenhoek did his work in the same time period as Redi, but Leeuwenhoek was convinced that spontaneous generation was not possible. For example, at the time, natural philosophers thought that insects called wheat weevils were produced by decaying wheat. However, van Leeuwenhoek's careful observations showed that they came from eggs that had been laid on the wheat. In his microscopic studies, he saw that even the tiniest organism could only come about through other living organisms reproducing themselves. He said these organisms, "…must surely convince all of the absurdity of those old opinions, that living creatures can be produced from corruption of putrefaction." [Abraham Schierbeek, *Measuring the Invisible World: The Life and Works of Antoni van Leeuwenhoek*, Abelard Schuman 1959, p. 171] In other words, living things don't come from dead things. They only come from other living things.

This insect is a wheat weevil.

LESSON REVIEW

Youngest students: Answer these questions:

1. Fill in the blank: The number of deer in a given state would be called that state's deer _____.

2. What did van Leeuwenhoek think of spontaneous generation?

Older students: Make an illustration to help explain how van Leeuwenhoek was able to estimate the population of microscopic organisms in a drop of water. While the method doesn't give an exact answer, explain why it is very useful. Also, write down what van Leeuwenhoek thought about spontaneous generation.

Oldest students: Do what the older students are doing. In addition, try to come up with a situation in which van Leeuwenhoek's method could come up with an incredibly wrong answer. Check your answer and correct it if it is wrong.

NOTE: The next two lessons each require a different fresh flower, and the experiment for the very next lesson needs to sit overnight. You should start it the day before your next day of science.

Lesson 66: John Ray (1627 – 1705)

This portrait of John Ray is by an unknown artist.

As you have already learned, most of the natural philosophers throughout history were devout Christians. Many of them were priests or preachers, and natural philosophy was just one more means by which they learned about God. Many of these priests and preachers were important in their churches, but some were little-known country preachers who became famous because of what they learned about nature. Science historians call these people **parson-naturalists**. The term **parson** used to refer to a particular kind of priest, but nowadays, it usually refers to any preacher who lives in a country setting. A naturalist is someone who observes and studies nature to learn more about it. So a parson-naturalist was a country preacher who observed and studied nature to learn more about it.

One of the most famous parson-naturalists was **John Ray**. He was curious about all of God's creation, but he especially loved to study plants. He made it his mission (with the help of a friend) to describe and document every plant in England. While he probably did not completely succeed, he did end up publishing a book that described and discussed 18,600 different plants! I am not sure how many different plants existed in England in Ray's day, but you have to admit that it was a valiant attempt at completing his mission.

Because he wanted to document every plant in England, he was concerned about plant **classification**. As you know, scientists like to classify things so they can better understand what they are studying. One very important part of classification is determining the **species** to which an organism belongs. Do you recognize that word? It refers to a group of organisms that are very, very similar to one another. They might not be identical to one another, but they are more similar to each other than they are to any other group of organisms.

For example, people are all part of a specific species, called *Homo* (ho' mo) *sapiens* (say' pee uhns). There are a lot of differences among people, but overall, people are more similar to other people than they are to cats or dogs, right? In the same way, there is a lot of difference between a Siamese cat and a tabby cat, but once again, those cats are much more similar to one another than they are to dogs and humans. As a result, cats belong to their own species, *Felis* (fee' lis) *catus* (kay' tus). Dogs also belong to their own species, *Canis* (kan' us) *familiaris* (fuh mih lee air' us).

When it comes to classifying organisms, determining the species is important. It is important to know the groups of organisms that are most similar to each other. You might remember from Lesson 18 that Conrad Gesner thought natural historians could classify plants by their flowers. However, John Ray disagreed. Perform the following experiment to learn one reason why.

What Color is that Flower?

What you will need:
- ✋ A flower with petals that are light in color (White would be ideal, but any light color will do. A flower bought from a store will work, or you can pick one from outside.)
- ✋ A small glass (like a juice glass)
- ✋ Food coloring
- ✋ Scissors
- ✋ A spoon
- ✋ Water

What you should do:
1. Add warm water so the glass is ¾ full.
2. Add 10-20 drops of dark food coloring, like blue.
3. Stir to mix the food coloring with the water.
4. Have an adult help you cut the flower's stem under running water. The stem should be cut so that it is not much taller than the glass, and it should be cut diagonally so the stem will not sit flat at the bottom of the glass.
5. Put the flower in the glass. The blossom of the flower should be above the lip of the glass.
6. In your notebook (or on a sheet of paper if you are doing the "youngest student" review exercises), write down a description of the flower. Be sure to note what color the petals are.
7. Put the glass and flower in a place where it will not be disturbed until tomorrow.
8. Once the glass and flower have been sitting for at least 12 hours, look at the flower. Compare it to the description you wrote yesterday. Has anything changed?
9. You can keep the experiment going for a while to see how much change will occur. Once you are done, however, be sure to clean up your mess!

What did you see in the experiment? You should have seen the flower change color. Depending on the flower, the dark color from the food coloring might have spread throughout the flower, or it might have shown up in spots or stripes on the petals of the flower. Either way, what does that tell you? It tells you that the color of a flower is affected by what's in the water that the plant takes in. As a result, two plants that are really the same can produce different-looking flowers, depending on where they are planted.

Sometimes, this effect can be rather remarkable. Consider the pictures on the right. Both of the flowers shown there come from the same species of plant: the lacecap hydrangea (hi drain' juh). Their colors are different only because of the soil in which they were grown. So even though these two plants really are more similar to one another than to any other type of plant, they can produce flowers that look rather different. Because of this, John Ray realized that flowers probably weren't the best means by which natural philosophers should classify plants. In fact, Ray spent a lot of time trying to find out what features of a plant changed depending on where it was located and what features stayed the same. He decided

Even though they look very different, these flowers come from the same species.

that the only features you could use to classify plants were the aspects that were the same regardless of where the plant was.

So what features did Ray use to classify plants? One of the most important was whether or not it produced flowers. You might have already figured out that there are some plants that never produce flowers, while other plants do. To Ray, that seemed like a very important feature, and it was one of the first things he used to classify them. Scientists today still make the distinction between plants that produce flowers and those that don't.

When studying the flowering plants, Ray noticed another thing that helped him classify them. He saw that when they first sprouted from the ground, some flowering plants produced a single first leaf, while other flowering plants produced two leaves right away. He decided that was an important way to classify flowering plants, and scientists today still agree. As you might have already learned, we call those first leaves **seed leaves**. The flowering plants that produce only one seed leaf are called **monocots**, while the flowering plants that produce two seed leaves are called **dicots**. Those classifications are very broad, and many species fit into each. How did John Ray suggest that scientists should classify species? He said that if two living organisms could reproduce (make a new living organism) and that new organism could mature and also reproduce, then those two organisms are part of the same species. That's still how scientists classify species.

The seedling on the left is a monocot, as it has only one seed leaf. The seedling on the right is a dicot, since it has two seed leaves.

In all of his studies, Ray was keenly aware that he was looking at the result of God's handiwork. In fact, one of his last books was called *The Wisdom of God Manifested in the Works of Creation*. In it, he tried to use God's creation as a means of better understanding His wisdom and power.

LESSON REVIEW

Youngest students: Answer these questions:

1. (Is this statement True or False?) Two plants of the same species will always produce identical flowers.

2. What is the difference between a monocot and a dicot?

Older students: Use the results of your experiment to give one reason why the features of their flowers aren't the best means by which we can classify plants. Discuss the two ways Ray classified plants that are still used by scientists today.

Oldest students: Do what the older students are doing. In addition, write out this question and your answer: A horse and a donkey can reproduce. Their offspring are called "mules." Mules, however, cannot reproduce. Are horses and donkeys part of the same species? Check your answer and correct it if it is wrong.

Lesson 67: Nehemiah Grew (1641 – 1712)

John Ray helped us understand how to better classify plants, and he also tried to better understand the function of flowers in the plants that make them. After all, flowers are very pretty, but there's probably more to them than just that. The plants that make them spend a lot of energy on them, so they must do something for the plant. However, flowers aren't always there. Thus, whatever they do, it must be something that is only needed at certain times.

Nehemiah Grew studied the same issue. He was very interested in plants and actually made a lot of the same observations as Marcello Malpighi, who you learned about in Lesson 56. While Grew was a bit younger than Malpighi, their work did overlap, and it is thought that they borrowed from one another's work. Grew's actual profession was that of a physician, but like most natural philosophers in this time period, he spent a lot of time studying things other than his profession. Because of his detailed studies, he was able to determine the basics of what a flower does for a plant. To best understand what he taught us, let's start by examining a flower in some detail.

This woodcut of Nehemiah Grew was done by an unknown artist.

The Parts of a Flower

What you will need:
- 🖐 A flower that looks something like the picture on the right – It should have obvious stalks in the center, and one stalk should be noticeably different from the rest. A lily is ideal. It's best if most of the stalks look a bit "fuzzy," because you want some pollen to be on them.
- 🖐 A plain white sheet of paper
- 🖐 A magnifying glass

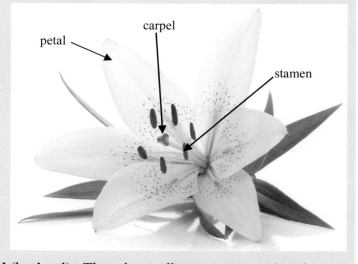

What you should do:
1. Look at the flower and identify the parts labeled in the picture on the right. The stalk near the center of the flower that looks different from all the other stalks is the **carpel** (kar' pul). The other stalks are **stamens** (stay' menz).
2. Lay the sheet of paper flat on a table or desk.

3. Turn the flower upside down and shake it vigorously above the paper. You should see something that looks like dust falling on the paper. That "dust" is called **pollen**. If you don't get any pollen falling on the paper, use your fingers to gently rub the top of one of the stamen. If there is any pollen at all, it should rub off.
4. Use the magnifying glass to look at the pollen.
5. One by one, pull the petals off the flower. Be sure to pull them off right where they attach to the stem.
6. Now you should see the stamens and the carpel more clearly. Look at each of them near the bottom where they attach to the stem. Do you notice a difference between the bottom of the carpel and the bottom of the stamens?
7. Pull the stamens off the flower, once again, making sure to pull them off where they attach to the stem. Look at one of the stamens carefully. You should be able to see that the pollen you shook off onto the paper comes from the top of the stamen.
8. Pull the carpel off the flower.
9. Holding the carpel in your hand, look at the top of it with the magnifying glass.
10. Turn the carpel upside down and touch the top of the carpel to some of the pollen that is on the paper. What happens?
11. Look at the top of the carpel with the magnifying glass again. Notice how the pollen sticks to the top of the carpel.
12. Clean up your mess.

The parts of the flower that you examined were well known in Nehemiah Grew's time. In fact, as far as we know, John Ray was the first to use the terms "petal" and "pollen," so these things were being studied by all those who wanted to learn more about flowers. However, Grew spent a lot of time studying the pollen he collected from different species of flowering plants. He showed that while pollen came in many different shapes, a given species of plant always produced the same pollen.

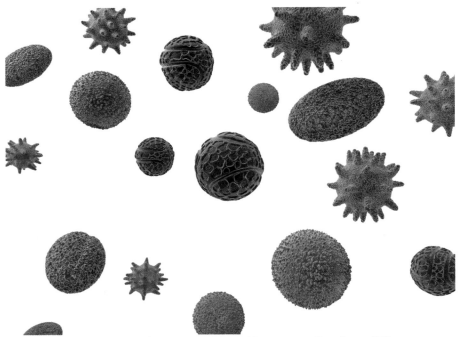

This drawing shows you what you would see if you put pollen from different species of flowering plants under a microscope.

Grew had also noticed, like other natural philosophers, that pollen could be blown out of a flower and carried on the wind. He thought that perhaps the pollen on one flower could be carried by the wind to a flower on a different plant. Since each species of flower seemed to have its own kind of pollen, if the flower it landed on was from a different species of plant, nothing would happen. However, if the flower it landed on was from the same species of plant, the pollen would be recognized by the flower and something could happen.

What could happen? Well, think back to your experiment. When you touched the top of the carpel to some pollen that was on the paper, what happened? The pollen stuck to the carpel, didn't it? Grew suggested that when the pollen from one flower landed on the carpel of another flower from the same species, the two could interact to form a seed. Of course, the seed could then grow into another plant. According to Nehemiah Grew, then, the purpose behind a flower is reproduction. The pollen from one flower lands on the carpel of another flower, and they interact to form a seed. That seed then becomes another plant of the same species.

petal of the flower

strawberry forming from the carpel

Well…guess where the seed of a flowering plant forms? It forms at the base of the carpel. If you watch a flower over time, you will find that it is beautiful for a while. Eventually, however, the petals curl up and fall off the flower. The base of the carpel begins to swell, and eventually, a structure is formed that has at least one seed it in. So in the end, Nehemiah Grew was the first to really figure out why flowering plants make flowers: The flowers allow them to reproduce by sending pollen from one plant to another. The stamens produce the pollen, and the carpel "catches" the pollen and uses it to make a seed.

This picture shows an unripened strawberry (which holds the plants' seeds) developing from the flower of a strawberry plant. Seeds come from flowers whose carpels have caught pollen from a plant of the same species.

Grew not only taught us about the function of flowers in flowering plants; he also urged us to remember what we are actually studying when we study the natural world. He said, "For all Nature is as one Great Engine, made by, and held in His Hand." [Robert Bingham Downs, *Landmarks in Science: Hippocrates to Carson*, Libraries Unlimited 1982, p. 140] It is important to remember that as you continue to learn science. In science, we are studying a wonderful creation that has been designed, built, and sustained by God!

LESSON REVIEW

Youngest students: Answer these questions:

1. There are two kinds of stalks in most flowers. What do we call them?

2. What is the function of flowers in flowering plants?

Older students: Draw a picture of a flower that includes the parts you studied in your experiment. Explain what the flower does for a plant as well as what the stamens and carpel do.

Oldest students: Do what the older students are doing. In addition, when pollen is carried on the wind, it can enter your nose. For some people, this causes allergies. Most people's allergies are not caused by all species of plant, however. Usually there are specific species, like those of the ragweed variety, that cause the most allergies. Explain why you think some species of plants are more likely to cause allergies with their pollen than others. Check your explanation and correct it if it is wrong.

Lesson 68: Sir Isaac Newton (1643 – 1727)

This portrait of Sir Isaac Newton was painted by Sir Godfrey Kneller in 1689.

It is now time to learn about the greatest natural philosopher of the entire time period covered by this course. Some (including me) would say that he might very well be the greatest natural philosopher who has ever lived. I am talking about **Sir Isaac Newton**. Born on Christmas day in 1643, he was the son of a farmer. As he grew into adulthood, his mother tried to get him to be a farmer as well. He hated it, however, so he went to Cambridge University and studied mathematics. He was forced to leave when the university was closed due to the plague. While this was bad for most people, it ended up being great for Newton, because he started studying on his own and ended up making incredible discoveries in both mathematics and natural philosophy.

These discoveries ended up making him quite famous. Queen Anne knighted him in 1705, and when he died, the English poet Alexander Pope wrote the following:

Nature and nature's laws lay hid in night;
God said "Let Newton be" and all was light.

Even though he discovered all sorts of wonderful truths about God's creation, he realized that he had barely scratched the surface of all that should be learned. Towards the end of his life, he wrote:

I do not know what I may appear to the world, but to myself I seem to have been only like a boy playing on the sea-shore, and diverting myself in now and then finding a smoother pebble or a prettier shell than ordinary, whilst the great ocean of truth lay all undiscovered before me. [Martin Garrett, *Cambridge: A Cultural and Literary History*, Interlink Books 2004, p. 192]

Believe it or not, there is so much to discuss about Newton's discoveries that we will spend most of the rest of the course on them!

We'll start by discussing what Newton taught us about light. You probably already know that the white light we see coming from the sun or from a light bulb is actually composed of all the colors of the rainbow. During Newton's time, that wasn't really understood. Natural philosophers knew that certain pieces of glass (called **prisms**) would make a rainbow if white light was shined through them at certain angles. However, they didn't really understand why. During Newton's time, most natural philosophers thought that the prism did something to add color to the white light. Newton disagreed. He thought that the rainbow came from the light itself. The only thing the prism was doing was separating the colors of the light. He ended up showing that he was right, but before you learn how, I want you to do an experiment.

Adding Colors of Light

What you will need:
- A plain white sheet of paper
- A magnifying glass
- A string of colored Christmas tree lights
- A room that can be made dark

What you should do:
1. Go into the room and plug in the string of Christmas tree lights. Keep the room light on for now.
2. Set the paper down on a flat surface.
3. Set the magnifying glass on top of the paper.
4. Find a section of lights where the colors red, green, and blue appear right next to one another or at least near one another.
5. Hold the string of lights so those three colored bulbs are easy to reach.
6. Turn off the room lights so the only light that exists in the room is coming from the Christmas tree lights.
7. Hold the red bulb over the magnifying glass as shown in the picture above. Try to shade the light coming from the other bulbs so it doesn't reach the magnifying glass. In the end, the entire magnifying glass should light up red, as shown in the picture above.
8. Repeat step 7, but use the blue bulb instead of the red one.
9. Repeat step 7 once again, but this time use the green bulb.
10. Hold the red bulb and blue bulb so they are side by side and touching each other. Now hold them both over the magnifying glass. What color do you see now?
11. Hold the red bulb and green bulb so they are side by side and touching each other. Now hold them both over the magnifying glass. What color do you see now?
12. Hold the red bulb, blue bulb, and green bulb so they are side by side and touching each other. Now hold them over the magnifying glass. What color do you see now?
13. Put everything away.

What did you see in the experiment? If all went well, when you put a single bulb over the magnifying glass, you should have seen the magnifying glass light up with its color. However, when you put two bulbs over the magnifying glass, you should have seen a new color. The red and blue bulbs should have made a pinkish color called "magenta," and the red and green bulbs should have made a light yellow color. What did you get when you put all three bulbs together, however? You should have gotten white.

Did that surprise you? You probably already knew that white light could be broken down into the colors of the rainbow: red, orange, yellow, green, blue, indigo, and violet. But did you know that you could add those colors back together to make white light again? You didn't actually add *all* those colors together, but you did add three colors that span the rainbow. That was enough to get white light back. In fact, we call red, green, and blue the **additive primary colors**. This means they can be added together to make *any* color, including white.

Newton didn't add primary colors together, but he did something very similar. He let white light shine through a prism, just like other natural philosophers did. After that, however, he went a step further. He allowed the rainbow of colors that were produced by that prism to go into *another* prism that was turned the opposite way. Guess what happened? The second prism put those colors back together, and as a result, white light came out of the prism. Now think about what that tells us.

In Newton's day, most natural philosophers thought that a prism *added* colors to light. However, if that's what a prism did, you would expect Newton's second prism to add even more colors. Instead, it combined the colors again, making white light. That tells you white light is made of all colors of the rainbow, and all a prism does is separate those colors out. If you do it right, however, you can use a prism to add those colors back together to form white light again.

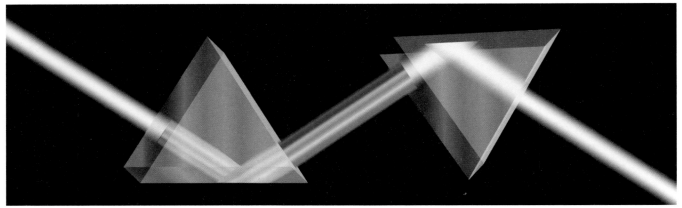

Newton showed that a prism will separate white light into the colors of the rainbow, and if a second prism is placed correctly, it will add those colors back together to make white light again.

So Newton showed that all colors are merged in white light. He started experimenting with individual colors of light, examining how they reflected off things. This led him to conclude that all the colors we see in nature are the result of colors being separated from white light. When you see a red object, for example, it appears red because the only color that reflects off of it is red. All the other colors of the rainbow are absorbed by the object, and the only light that hits your eyes after reflecting off the object is red. That makes it appear red to you.

Now before I end this lesson, I want to make a very important point. You used red, green, and blue light to make white light. As I said, those are the *additive* primary colors. However, what happens if you mix red paint, blue paint, and green paint? Do you get white paint? No! You get a dark brown, almost black paint. That's because adding paints (or inks) is different from adding light. If you continue to study science, you will eventually learn about the *subtractive* primary colors, which are what you have to use if you are mixing paints or inks.

LESSON REVIEW

Youngest students: Answer these questions:

1. What are the three additive primary colors?

2. If an object appears green to you, what kind of light does it reflect? What does it absorb?

Older students: Draw a picture of Newton's two-prism experiment as shown above. Explain how this shows that prisms don't add color to light, but instead, they separate white light into its colors.

Oldest students: Do what the older students are doing. Also, think about a computer monitor or a television set. It makes only three colors of light, but it can display millions of different colors. Explain how that's possible, and indicate what those three colors are. Check your answer and correct it if it is wrong.

Lesson 69: Isaac Newton and Diffraction

Isaac Newton explained a lot about color and how we see it. However, there were other aspects of light that he had a hard time explaining. Do you remember learning about Christiaan Huygens? He did experiments that seemed to indicate that light is a wave. Newton didn't believe that. He thought of light as a stream of particles. Just as Huygens could explain reflection and refraction using his wave theory of light, Newton could explain reflection and refraction with his particle theory of light. However, there was one thing Newton could not explain with his particle theory. Do the following experiment to see what it was.

Diffraction

What you will need:
- An index card
- A pushpin
- A lamp that can be moved
- A room that can be darkened

What you should do:
1. Use the pushpin to make several holes near the short edge of the index card. You want the holes to vary in size, from the smallest you can possibly make with the pushpin to one that is as wide as the widest part of the pin.
2. Fold the index card in half along its short side.
3. If the lamp has a shade, remove it so the bulb is bare.
4. Put the lamp at one end of the room and turn it on.
5. Turn off all other lights in the room so that the only light in the room comes from the lamp.
6. Stand about 1 meter (3 feet) from the lamp.
7. Hold the index card so the short end without the holes touches your nose and the end with the holes in it is in front of your eyes. See the picture above.
8. Close one eye, and with your open eye, look at the light bulb on the lamp through the smallest holes. Do you see anything unusual? Look at the center of the hole as well as the edges of the hole.
9. Use your open eye to look through another hole. Once again, look for anything unusual.
10. Repeat step 9 until you have looked through every hole you made. You should have seen something unusual that was more noticeable the smaller the hole.
11. Don't put anything away yet. You might want to do the experiment again once you have read the lesson.

What did you see in the experiment? If things went well, you should have seen dark lines in the holes. Despite the fact that you were looking through the holes at a light bulb, there should have been dark lines in the holes. Also, along the edges of the holes, you should have seen tiny rays of light shooting out from the hole.

What explains the things you saw? Let's start with the rays of light shooting out from the holes. The only light in the room was coming from the lamp, so those rays of light must have traveled through the hole. In general, we think of light as traveling in a straight line. The light leaves the lamp and travels in straight lines that go off in every direction. Since you were looking at the light through the tiny holes, the only light you should have seen is light that traveled straight from the lamp, through the hole, and into your eyes. But that's not all you saw, was it? You saw a lot of light like that, but you also saw lines of light traveling outward from the hole. Where did they come from?

Those lines of light came from the lamp, but when they hit the edges of the hole, they actually *bent around those edges* and began traveling in a new direction.   This bending of light around the edge of an obstacle is called **diffraction** (dih frak' shun), and it was something Newton couldn't explain with his particle theory of light. In his theory, the particles should have traveled straight from the lamp. If they went in the hole, they would go through the hole and hit your eyes. If they hit the index card, they would stop and never reach your eyes. There would be no reason for particles of light to bend around the edges of the hole, as the light in your experiment clearly did.

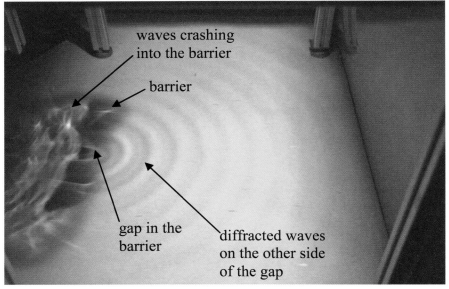

waves crashing into the barrier

barrier

gap in the barrier

diffracted waves on the other side of the gap

This is a picture of an experiment where waves are made in water. The waves hit a barrier with a gap in it, and they diffract.

When you studied Christiaan Huygens, however, you learned how waves naturally bend around the edges of obstacles that they hit. Look, for example, at the picture on the left. It is showing an experiment where waves are made in a tank. The waves are flat, but they hit a barrier. They can't travel through the barrier except at a gap in the barrier. Do you see what the waves do when they hit that gap? They bend around it, forming a half circle of waves that go out from the gap. You saw that in the experiment you did when you learned about Huygens. While Newton's particle theory of light couldn't explain diffraction, Huygens's wave theory could.

Now what did you notice about how the size of the hole affected what you saw? The light rays shooting out from the hole should have been easier to see in the smaller holes. That's something Newton saw in his experiments as well. If the hole was really big, light didn't seem to bend around the edge much at all. However, the smaller the hole, the more light seemed to bend around the edge. So diffraction depends on the size of the hole. The smaller the hole, the more the diffraction.

But that's not the only thing you saw in your experiment, is it? In fact, it probably wasn't even the most noticeable thing. What you probably saw most clearly in your experiment was a pattern of dark lines inside the hole. Despite the fact that you were looking at the bright bulb of a lamp, there were dark lines in the hole. It should have looked like there was fuzz that was blocking up parts of the hole. However, there wasn't fuzz in the hole. Instead, those dark lines came from the light itself!

But wait a minute. How can light create dark lines? Once again, it is because light can behave like a wave. Think about two waves on the ocean moving towards each other. What happens when the highest part of one wave (called the **crest** of the wave) hits the highest part of the other wave? They will add together to make a wave that is twice as large, right? But what happens when the highest part of one wave hits the lowest part of the other wave (called the **trough** of the wave)? The trough of the one wave will cancel out the crest of the other wave, and there won't be a wave there at all!

So waves can interfere with one another. When their crests meet, they add together to make a really big wave. When one wave's trough meets another wave's crest, the waves cancel one another out. Well, if you think of light as a wave, what happens when a light wave gets cancelled out? There isn't any light anymore, so there is darkness. That's what those dark lines you saw in the small holes were. They were places where the waves of light interfered with each other in a way that cancelled them out. As a result, there was darkness.

This illustration shows two sets of waves formed by dropping two stones in water. Look what happens in the area where the waves overlap. You get some places where the waves are bigger, and some places where they are smaller. That's the way waves interfere with one another, and it explains the dark lines you saw in your experiment.

Now if you don't completely understand all this, don't worry. The key thing to realize is that the only way to explain the results of your experiment is to think of light as a wave. Newton's particle theory, therefore, simply couldn't explain diffraction. You might think that means Newton's particle theory is wrong, but that's not quite true! It turns out that light sometimes behaves like a particle, and it sometimes behaves as a wave. This is one of the properties of light that is not fully understood, even today. When you take science in high school, you will learn more about this interesting fact!

LESSON REVIEW

Youngest students: Answer these questions:

1. Fill in the blank: When light bends around an obstacle, we call it _____.

2. Which theory of light can explain the answer to #1: the particle theory or the wave theory?

Older students: Use words to explain what you did in your experiment as well as what you saw. Explain what diffraction is and which theory of light (particle or wave) can explain it.

Oldest students: Do what the older students are doing. Also, explain how the dark lines in your experiment were formed.

Lesson 70: Isaac Newton's Universal Law of Gravitation

When Newton began studying the world around him, it had been more than 100 years since Copernicus had published his heliocentric view of the universe. It had been more than 30 years since Galileo had published his book that showed strong evidence in support of Copernicus's view. More importantly, it had been more than 40 years since Kepler published the last of his three laws governing the motion of the planets. Nevertheless, there were still some who doubted the heliocentric view of the universe. Newton, however, was convinced that the sun does sit at the center of the solar system and that all the planets orbit around it.

But Newton wanted to know more. He wasn't satisfied just to know how the solar system was *arranged*. He wanted to know how it worked. What kept the planets in motion around the earth? Why did the planets travel around the sun in ellipses rather than in perfect circles? He used telescopes to study the heavens, but in the end, it was mathematics that gave him the answers to his questions. In studying Kepler's Laws, he was able to determine that all the planets were attracted to the sun by a force called **gravity**, and the strength of that force depends on two things. Perform the following experiment to learn about one of the two things upon which the force of gravity depends.

A Rocking Candle

lighter end tilted up

heavier end tilted down and melting faster

What you will need:
- 👋 A tapered candle that is 15 centimeters (6 inches) long or can be cut down to that length.
- 👋 A lighter
- 👋 Two tall glasses that are the same height
- 👋 Aluminum foil
- 👋 Two straight pins
- 👋 A serrated knife (like a steak knife)
- 👋 An adult to help you

What you should do:
1. Cover the area where you are working with aluminum foil.
2. If the candle is longer than 15 centimeters (6 inches), have the adult help you use the serrated knife to cut it down to 15 centimeters (6 inches).
3. Have the adult help you use the lighter to melt down the back end of the candle until you can light the wick there. Allow the flame to burn for a minute so that it makes a nice, strong flame, and then blow it out.
4. Have the adult help you light the other end of the candle (the end you normally light) so that it produces a nice, strong flame as well. Blow it out.
5. Push one straight pin into the candle about halfway down its length. Push it until it is about halfway through the candle. **Be careful! Don't let the pin slip and stick into you!**
6. Push the other straight pin in the other side of the candle, directly opposite the first straight pin. Once again, push it until it is about halfway through the candle. **Again, be careful!**
7. Set the two glasses in the middle of the aluminum foil covering so that they are close together.
8. Set the candle between the glasses so that each pin rests on one of the glasses.

9. The candle will not balance, because one side is heavier than the other. That's fine. Use the knife to push down gently on the lighter end of the candle so the candle tilts with the heavier end pointing down. (See the picture on the previous page.)
10. Have the adult light both ends of the candle. **Be careful! Don't get too close to the flames!** As it is burning, continue to push gently on the lighter end of the candle so that the candle stays tilted. You should notice that the end that is tilted down (the heavier end) melts faster than the end that is tilted up (the lighter end). At this point, your experiment should look like the picture on the previous page.
11. Allow the candle to burn like this for a while. Eventually, the end that is tilting up will start to fall down. At that point, pull the knife away and watch what happens. Watch for a while.
12. Once you are done watching the behavior of the system for a while, blow out the flames and clean up your mess.

What did you see in your experiment? If all went well, you should have seen the candle rock back and forth. Why did this happen? Well, think about the situation. When you started, one side of the candle had more wax than the other side. As a result, the candle would tilt so that side was pointed down. You held the candle so it remained tilted, with the heavier side pointing down. Well, because the flame tended to rise, the end that was pointed down had the flame right on the wax, and the wax melted quickly. The wax was melting on the other side, but not as quickly, because the flame wasn't really touching the wax.

As you held the candle, then, it lost wax from the heavier end faster than it did from the lighter end. As a result, the heavier end started getting lighter faster! Eventually, so much wax melted off the heavier end that it became the lighter end. At that point, the candle started to tilt the other way. When that happened, however, the flame changed. The end that just started pointing down lost wax more quickly than the end that started pointing up. As a result, it eventually became the lighter end again, and the candle tilted the other way.

The candle continued to rock back and forth because the amount of wax on each end kept changing. One end would get heavier, and that would cause the candle to tilt so that the heavier end was pointed down. As soon as that happened, however, the heavier end started losing wax more quickly and then became the lighter end, which caused the other end to tilt down. That happened over and over again.

But *why* did the candle tilt so that the heavier end always went down? Well, gravity was pulling on both sides of the candle, but the more weight there was, the stronger gravity could pull. As a result, the side of the candle with the most weight was pulled more strongly to the earth, so the candle always tilted to the side that had the greater weight.

Because there is more weight on this end, gravity pulls it down with more force.

Gravity pulls harder on the side of the teeter-totter that has more weight. As a result, it tilts to that side.

Newton determined that all objects are attracted to all other objects, as long as they have **mass**. What is mass? It is a measure of how much matter is in an object. The more matter an object has, the heavier it is and the larger its mass. For example, in your experiment, the side of the candle that had the most wax was the heavier side. It was also the side with more mass.

Newton used Kepler's Laws and mathematics to show that gravity is affected by mass. The more mass two objects have, the more strongly they are attracted to one another. In your experiment, both sides of the candle were attracted to the earth by gravity, but the side with the most mass was attracted to the earth more strongly. As a result, the candle always tilted so the side with the most mass was pointed down.

Newton was also able to show something else about gravity. This wasn't shown in your experiment, but Kepler's laws and some math told him that the *closer* two objects are to each other, the *stronger* gravity attracts them to one another. If you put these two facts together, you come up with **Newton's Law of Universal Gravitation**:

The force of gravity between two objects increases as the mass of either object increases, and it increases as the distance between them decreases.

Newton actually came up with a mathematical formula that describes exactly how the force of gravity increases with increasing mass and decreasing distance. If you end up taking high school physics, you will learn that formula and how to use it.

LESSON REVIEW

Youngest students: Answer these questions:

1. What happens to the gravitational force between two objects if one of them loses some mass?

2. What happens to the gravitational force between two objects if they are pushed closer together?

Older students: Write down Newton's Law of Universal Gravitation. Then make a drawing that illustrates your experiment and use the first part of the law to explain why the candle rocked back and forth.

Oldest students: Do what the older students are doing. Also, try to explain why the gravitational force between the sun and Jupiter is *smaller* than the gravitational force between the sun and the earth, despite the fact that Jupiter has a lot more mass than the earth. Check your explanation and correct it if it is wrong.

Lesson 71: Isaac Newton and His First Law of Motion

We will return to the concept of gravity in a little while. However, to fully understand how gravity affects objects, you need to learn a bit more about motion. Newton developed three laws of motion that still guide our understanding of the way things move. Not surprisingly, we will start with his first law of motion, which is best illustrated by experiment.

Inertia

What you will need:
- A tall glass with a wide opening
- A pie pan or the top from a round storage tin
- A cardboard tube from the center of a roll of toilet paper
- An egg
- A Ping-Pong ball
- Water
- Adult supervision (As I mention in the introduction, this should be the case for *every* experiment. I want to emphasize it here, however, because it's possible for the student to hit the glass and send it flying. The adult should coach the child to avoid that.)

What you should do:
1. Fill the glass at least ⅔ full of water.
2. Set it on a flat surface like a counter or table.
3. Set the pie pan (or storage tin lid) on top of the glass so the lip is pointed up.
4. Stand the cardboard tube on top of the pie pan so it is at the very center of the glass's opening.
5. Put the egg on top of the cardboard tube with the widest end of the egg sitting in the tube. The egg should not sink into the tube. It should sit on top of it, as shown in the picture on the left. If your egg is too small, squeeze the tube so that it flattens up a bit. That should make the opening at the top of the tube less wide, allowing you to set the egg on top without it sinking into the tube much.
6. Hold your hand at the level of the pie pan so your palm is facing the pie pan.
7. Hit the pie pan hard with your palm so that it goes flying straight off the glass. Stop your palm before it hits the glass, and **do not** hit the pie pan at an angle so that it flips up. Hit the side of the pie pan straight on so it slides straight off the top of the glass.
8. What happened to the egg? If you ended up with a smashed egg, you didn't hit the pie pan so it moved straight. You might have hit it so it flipped up as it flew off the pan. Try it again, being sure to hit the pie pan straight. Alternatively, the egg might have sunk too deep into the tube. You want the egg to just be barely sitting at the top of the tube. If it sinks into the tube, squeeze the tube more to flatten out the top so that the egg barely sits on top of it.
9. Repeat the entire experiment using the Ping-Pong ball instead of an egg.
10. Clean up your mess and put everything away.

Hit it like this so it slides straight off the glass.

What did you see in your experiment? If all went well, you should have seen the pie pan or storage tin lid fly straight off the glass. The cardboard tube should have gone flying off as soon as the lip of the pan or lid hit it. However, the egg didn't go flying off, did it? It fell straight into the glass of water, didn't it? Why?

The egg fell into the water because of Newton's First Law of Motion. Here is what it says:

> An object at rest will stay at rest until acted on by an outside force. An object in motion will stay in motion until it is acted on by an outside force.

Everything in your experiment (the glass, the water, the pie pan, the tube, and the egg) started out at rest. They would have stayed like that forever if nothing had hit or jostled them. However, you hit the pie pan. As a result, it started to move in the direction you hit it. It was pretty slick, so there wasn't much friction between it and the tube. This means the pie pan couldn't exert much force on the tube. This allowed it to slide underneath the tube without moving the tube much. As it continued to slide, however, the lip hit the tube. At that point, the tube was acted on by a strong force (the lip hitting it), so it began to move as well.

The egg was at rest this whole time. Since the tube was just touching the egg at its edges, there wasn't much friction between the tube and the egg. As a result, the tube couldn't exert much force on the egg when it started moving, so the egg stayed at rest, just as Newton's First Law says it should. Once the tube flew away, however, there was nothing fighting the force of gravity which was pulling the egg down, so the egg fell. Since it hadn't moved from its position right above the glass, however, it fell straight down into the glass.

In other words, the egg was at rest, and it resisted being moved. The tube moved, but there wasn't enough friction to force the egg to move with it, because the egg resisted any change from being at rest. What about the Ping-Pong ball? It didn't fall into the glass, did it? That's because it couldn't resist the change in motion nearly as well as the egg. The egg resisted a change from being at rest, and there wasn't enough friction to overcome its resistance. The Ping-Pong ball couldn't resist the change as well, so it went flying off in the direction that the tube pushed it. The ability of an object to resist a change in its motion is called **inertia** (ih nur' shuh). In your experiment, the egg had more inertia than the Ping-Pong ball, so it was able to resist being moved better than the Ping-Pong ball.

Have you ever seen the trick where someone quickly pulls the tablecloth off of a table that is set with dishes? It's a hard trick to do, but those who practice it can usually pull the tablecloth out from under the dishes without disturbing them much. They'll end up pretty much where they were before the tablecloth was pulled out from under them. Don't try this yourself! It takes a lot of practice, which usually results in some broken dishes at first! When the trick is done right, it's because of Newton's First Law. The dishes are at rest and will stay at rest until acted on by an outside force. If the tablecloth is slick enough and it is pulled straight and fast enough, friction is not strong enough to overcome the inertia of the dishes. As a result, the dishes aren't pulled off the table.

It's important to realize, however, that the tablecloth trick and your experiment illustrate only one part of Newton's First Law. Go back and read it again. The law also says that when an object is in motion, it will stay in motion until acted on by an outside force. This is utterly different from what Aristotle taught. He thought all objects "wanted" to be at rest, so unless a force was constantly applied, an object would eventually come to rest.

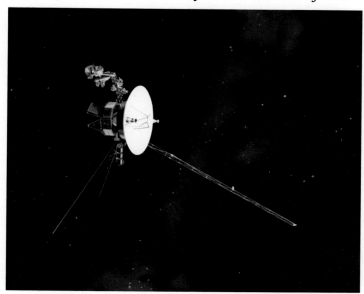

Newton, of course, realized that wasn't true. He realized that objects in motion tend to come to rest because *friction* is an outside force working *against* the motion. Without friction, the object would continue in motion, no matter what. Now, of course, Newton wasn't the first to have this realization. Galileo made the point years before him. However, Newton was the first to set it down in a law that was part of a series of laws which helped us understand motion.

This is an artist's conception of a Voyager spacecraft in space. Voyager 1 has traveled out of our solar system because of Newton's First Law.

We now know, of course, that Galileo and Newton were right. If you get rid of friction, an object in motion will stay in motion forever. Think, for a moment, about the spacecraft known as Voyager 1 and Voyager 2. They were launched from earth in 1977, and they are still traveling away from it! They ran out of fuel long, long ago, so there is nothing pushing them anymore. However, they continue to travel because they were in motion, and there is no outside force that can overcome their inertia. As a result, they will travel forever (unless they collide with something else in space or get captured by the gravity of a planet, moon, or star). In fact Voyager 1 is more than 18,000,000,000 kilometers (11,000,000,000 miles) from earth. It has traveled so far that it has left our solar system, but it is still moving, because of Newton's First Law!

LESSON REVIEW

Youngest students: Answer these questions:

1. What will an object at rest do until it is acted on by an outside force?

2. What will an object in motion do until it is acted on by an outside force?

Older students: Draw two illustrations of your experiment. The first should be from right before you hit the pie pan, and the second should be after you hit the pie pan and as the egg is falling into the water. Write down Newton's First Law and how it explains the behavior of the egg.

Oldest students: Do what the older students are doing. In addition, explain how Newton's First Law applies to the Voyager spacecrafts.

Lesson 72: More on Inertia

In the previous lesson, you saw that the egg was able to resist the slight frictional force between it and the tube and stay at rest, despite the fact that the tube pushed on it. However, the Ping-Pong ball was not able to stay at rest. Instead, it went flying in the direction that the tube pushed it. This was because the egg had more inertia (ability to resist changes in motion) than the Ping-Pong ball. But why is that? Perform the following experiment to find out.

An Inertial Balance

What you will need:
- A metal coat hanger
- A small plastic bottle, like the kind water comes in
- Tape
- A ¼-cup (or about 60 mL) measuring cup
- A funnel
- A marker
- An adult to help you
- A stopwatch or a watch with a second hand

What you should do:
1. Have the adult help you untwist the hanger and stretch it out so that there is about a meter (3 feet) of reasonably straight hanger.
2. Have the adult help you bend the straight end of the hanger into a "hook" that goes around the top of the bottle.
3. Tape the bottle to that hook so it is securely fastened to the hanger.
4. Have the adult hold the hanger at the edge of a table or counter so that the bottle is hanging about 60 centimeters (2 feet) from the edge of the table or counter.
5. Use the marker to make a mark on the hanger right where the edge of the counter or table is. In the end, your experiment should look something like the picture below:

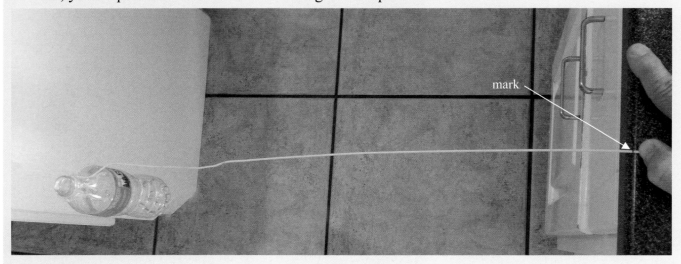

6. Pull down on the bottle and then release it. You should see it bounce up and down.
7. Get the stopwatch or watch with a second hand.
8. Grab the bottle and pull it down again, but this time start the stopwatch (or mark the second) when you release it.
9. Count how many times the bottle comes back to where you released it.

10. When you get to 10, stop the stopwatch or mark the second on the watch. Write down the time. This is the time it took for the empty bottle to make 10 complete bounces.
11. Use the measuring cup and funnel to add ¼ cup of water to the bottle and put on the lid.
12. Have the adult hold the hanger just like before, so the mark you made on the hanger is right at the edge of the table or counter, as it was before. Because of its weight, the bottle will be hanging down farther than before, but that's okay.
13. Once again, pull the bottle down and release it, starting the stopwatch or marking the second on the watch as you release it.
14. Once again, measure the time it takes for the bottle to make 10 complete bounces. Write it down.
15. Add another ¼ cup of water to the bottle and put on the lid.
16. Repeat steps 12-15 again.
17. Clean up your mess and put everything away.

Look at the three times you wrote down in your measurement. How do they compare to one another? If things went well, the first time you wrote down should be the shortest, the second time should be longer, and the third time should be the longest. Why is that? Well think about what is involved in bouncing. Once you released the bottle, it started moving upwards. However, the hanger started applying a force to the bottle, and eventually, the bottle stopped moving upwards and started moving downwards. In other words, every time the bottle changed direction, *its motion changed.*

So the bottle bouncing up and down experienced a lot of change in its motion. It changed from moving upwards to moving downwards, but then after it moved downwards for a while, it started moving upwards again. Of course, after a while, it stopped moving upwards and started moving downwards again. Each full bounce involved two changes of motion. Well, remember what inertia is all about. It is about how well an object resists changes in its motion!

What was different about the three times you did the experiment? The first time, the bottle was empty. The second time, the bottle had some water in it. The third time, the bottle had more water in it. So each time, the bottle got heavier. The heavier the bottle was, the longer it took to make 10 full bounces. That's because the heavier the bottle got, the harder it was for the hanger to change its motion.

What does that tell you? It tells you that *an object's mass determines its inertia.* The more mass an object has, the better it resists changes in its motion. Think about the experiment you did in the previous lesson. The egg was able to resist the tube's attempt to get it moving. However, the Ping-Pong ball was not. The Ping-Pong ball was smaller than the egg, but more importantly, it was lighter. In

Assume the small boat and the cruise ship in this picture are traveling at the same speed. Which would be easier to stop? The small ship would be easier to stop, because it has less mass and therefore less inertia.

other words, it had less mass. Because it had less mass, it did not have as much inertia, so it was unable to resist the tube's attempt to change its motion!

Now let's go back to your experiment for a moment. The time it took for the bottle to bounce 10 times depended on the mass – the larger the mass, the longer it took for the bottle to bounce 10 times. Well, it turns out that this can actually be used to measure an object's mass. If you set up a rigid rod that can bounce up and down (like the hanger in your experiment) and attach a container to the end (like the bottle in the experiment), you can measure the time it takes for the container to make a certain number of bounces, and using some mathematics, you can determine the mass of what's in the container! This is called an **inertial balance**, and what you made in your experiment is a simple version of one.

Now why in the world would you go to all that trouble to measure an object's mass? Why not just use a scale or a regular balance? Well, a scale that you step on (like the scale you might have in your bathroom) uses the strength of earth's gravitational pull on you to measure how heavy you are. A regular balance also requires gravity, because it compares the pull of gravity on one side of the balance to the pull of gravity on the other side (like your candle experiment in Lesson 70). However, suppose you are somewhere (like in a spaceship in outer space) where there is no gravity. A scale or regular balance won't work there. That's where you would need an inertial balance. The picture on the left, for example, shows two inertial balances built by NASA, the National Aeronautics and Space Administration of the United States. Since their astronauts do experiments in space, they need inertial balances to measure the mass of the objects they are testing.

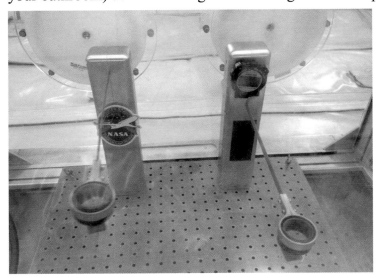

This is an inertial balance developed by NASA for use in space. It works exactly like the one in your experiment, although it is a lot more accurate!

LESSON REVIEW

Youngest students: Answer these questions:

1. Fill in the blank: The lighter an object, the _____ its inertia.

2. What can an inertial balance do that the scale in your bathroom cannot do?

Older students: Draw a picture of what you made in the experiment. Explain what happened in the experiment and use those results to explain what makes an object have more or less inertia.

Oldest students: Do what the older students are doing. In addition, explain why NASA would use an inertial balance to measure an object's mass.

Lesson 73: Still More on Newton's First Law

Newton's First Law is very important, because it explains a lot about what we observe when we study things in motion or at rest. Do the following experiment to see what I mean.

More on Newton's First Law
What you will need:
- 🖐 A wagon or anything else with wheels that you can stack things on and push (Even a chair with wheels will work)
- 🖐 A driveway or other long, flat surface over which the wagon can roll (If it is too cold or snowy to do the experiment outside, clear a large space in your garage or home. You just need room for the wagon to roll around.)
- 🖐 Several books that can be easily stacked on top of one another

What you should do:
1. Stack several books in the wagon so they form a stack that is at least 30 centimeters (1 foot) tall.
2. Push the wagon as hard as you can so it quickly rolls away. Watch what happens to the books. Note the way they fell.
3. Stack the books in the wagon again.
4. Push the wagon slowly at first, and then slowly increase the speed. You should be able to get the wagon moving fairly quickly and keep the books in their stack.
5. Stop the wagon suddenly, as quickly as you can. What happens to the books? Once again, note the way they fell.
6. Stack the books in the wagon again.
7. Push the wagon slowly at first, and then slowly increase the speed so the books remain stacked. Then, stop the wagon slowly and gently. Once again, you should be able to stop the wagon slowly and gently enough to keep the books stacked.
8. Clean up your mess.

What happened in the experiment? When you pushed the wagon quickly, the stack of books fell, didn't it? Which way did it fall? It should have fallen backwards, opposite of the way the wagon was moving. Why? Once again, it is because of Newton's First Law. The books were at rest, as was the wagon. Everything would have stayed at rest except that you applied a force to the wagon. That caused the wagon to start moving.

However, the books were at rest and resisted that change. Friction between the bottom book (and maybe one or two more books) was strong enough to overcome that resistance to motion, so those books started moving with the wagon. However, the force of friction on the books higher up on the stack wasn't enough to overcome their inertia. As a result, they stayed unmoving as the wagon and the books at the bottom of the stack started to move. This caused them to appear to fall backwards off the stack. They didn't actually fall backwards, however. Instead, the cart and other books moved forward, and since they didn't move with the cart and other books, it looked like they fell backwards.

When you started the wagon more slowly, you were able to keep the books stacked together. Why? Because when you pushed the wagon slowly, friction could work on all the books. The more slowly you pushed the wagon, the easier it was for friction to overcome the books' inertia. If you pushed slowly enough, then, friction was strong enough to overcome the books' inertia, and the books remained stacked together.

What happened when you stopped the wagon quickly? Once again, the stack of books fell, didn't it? But which way did the books fall? This time, the books fell forward, in the same direction you had been pushing the wagon. Why? Once again, it's Newton's First Law. As you were pushing, the wagon and the books were moving in the direction you were pushing. When you stopped the wagon, that was a change in its motion. That change happened because you applied a force that stopped the wagon.

The books, however, were still moving. In order for them to stop moving, Newton's First Law says a force must be applied to them. The only force available was the friction between them. Once again, friction was only strong enough to force one or two of the bottom books to stop. It wasn't strong enough to force all the books to stop. As a result, most of the books continued to move forward. This caused the stack of books to fall forward.

You've probably experienced something similar to what happened in your experiment. At some point, you were probably riding in your family's car when the driver had to stop really quickly.

What happened? You were thrown forward, weren't you? Once again, that's because you were moving along with the car. When the car stopped suddenly, you continued to move until a force could stop you. The friction between you and the car's seat wasn't strong enough to overcome your inertia, so you kept traveling forward, even though the car stopped. Hopefully, you had your seat belt on, and it applied a force to stop you so you remained in your seat.

That's why you should always wear a seat belt when you are in an automobile. If the driver has to stop suddenly, you will be thrown forward, and if the seat belt isn't there to apply a force that will overcome your inertia, you'll keep moving forward. That could cause you to smash against the seats in front of you, the dashboard, or even the window!

These boys are wearing their seat belts because Newton's First Law tells us that if the van stops suddenly, they will continue moving forward unless there is something to apply a force that will stop them.

Now, of course, your seat belt usually doesn't have to stop you, because most of the time, the driver doesn't have to stop quickly. If the driver can stop the car slowly, the friction between you and your seat is strong enough to slow you down with the car. In your experiment, you saw that when you stopped the wagon slowly. The books remained in their stack as long as you stopped the wagon slowly enough, because under those conditions, friction was strong enough to overcome the books' inertia and stop them along with the wagon.

In the end, a lot of things that happen to you when you are in motion can be explained by Newton's First Law. For example, have you ever been in a car when the driver had to turn really quickly? What happened? You ended up feeling like you were being pulled to the side of the car, didn't you? Actually, you weren't being pulled at all! In fact, the reason you ended up sliding (or leaning) into the side of the car was because you weren't being pulled enough!

Think about it. When the car was still traveling straight, you were traveling straight with it. When the car turned, however, you continued to travel straight. If the friction between you and your seat was strong enough, it would have made you turn with the car. However, if the car turned quickly enough, friction wasn't strong enough to force you to turn with the car, so you continued to move straight. Since you moved straight while the car was turning, you ended up sliding or leaning into the side of the car.

This is actually a very important point. In a situation like that, you really feel like a force is being applied to you, but until you hit the side of the car, there isn't much of a force working on you. Instead, it is the *absence of a strong enough force to overcome your inertia* that causes you to slide or lean into the side of the car. Of course, once your body presses against the side of the car, the car can apply enough force to overcome your inertia. At that point, a force is being applied, and that force actually stops you from sliding or leaning.

So sometimes, the reason an object moves suddenly is not because a force is applied to it. It's because there isn't a strong enough force to overcome its inertia, and as a result it resists changes to its original motion. In the case of the books in your experiment or you in a car, this can make it look like the object changed its motion. However, the opposite is true. Sometimes when an object doesn't change its motion, it looks like it suddenly has started moving, because everything else around it has changed.

These children have to hold on to the merry-go-round so that it can apply enough force to constantly change their motion. Otherwise, they will continue to move straight and fall off the ride.

LESSON REVIEW

Youngest students: Answer these questions:

1. When a car stops suddenly, in what direction do the passengers move?

2. Fill in the blank: Passengers slide or lean into the side of the car when it takes a curve quickly because of _____.

Older students: Use Newton's First Law to explain why the stacked books fell the way they did when the wagon started or stopped abruptly. Also, use it to explain why people should wear seat belts.

Oldest students: Do what the older students are doing. In addition, suppose you are in a car that is stopped. Another car rams into the back of your car. Explain which way you will move, and explain why. Check your answer and correct it if it is wrong.

Lesson 74: Isaac Newton and Acceleration

Since Isaac Newton has a First Law of Motion, he probably has a Second Law of Motion, right? In fact, he has three laws of motion. Before you can learn about his second law, however, you need to learn about **acceleration** (ak sel' uh ray' shun). Let's start with an experiment.

Acceleration

What you will need:
- A marble (A "shooter" marble that is larger than a standard marble is best. However, a standard marble will work.)
- Two cardboard tubes from rolls of toilet paper
- Three cardboard tubes from rolls of paper towels
- Tape
- A few uncooked eggs (The maximum you need is five.)
- A pie pan or paper plate with a lip around the edge

What you should do:
1. Put the pie pan on a table or counter.
2. Put an egg in the center of the pie pan.

3. Put one of the cardboard tubes from a roll of toilet paper on top of the egg. One end should be on top of the egg, and you should hold the tube straight up, as shown in the picture on the left.
4. Hold the marble in the center of the top opening of the cardboard tube and drop it so that it falls through the tube and hits the egg.
5. Pull the tube away and look for any damage that the marble did to the egg.
6. Use the tape to stick the second cardboard tube from a roll of toilet paper onto the one you just used. Now you have a cardboard tube that is twice as long as the one you used in step 4.
7. If you saw damage to the egg, roll it over so the damaged part is touching the pie pan.
8. Put the double-length tube on the egg, just as you did in step 3 with the single tube.
9. Repeat steps 4 and 5.
10. If the egg still has a side that is undamaged, roll it in the pie pan so the undamaged side is on top. If not, use a fresh egg.
11. Repeat steps 3-5, this time using a cardboard tube from a roll of paper towels.
12. Now tape two cardboard tubes from paper towel rolls together so you have a tube that is twice as long as the one you used in step 11.
13. Use a fresh egg and repeat steps 3-5 with the tube you just made.
14. Tape one more cardboard tube from a roll of paper towels to the tube you just used so you now have a tube that is three times the length of a normal cardboard tube from a roll of paper towels.
15. Use a fresh egg and repeat steps 3-5 with the tube you just made.
16. Clean up your mess.

What did you see in the experiment? Most likely, there was little or no damage when you dropped the marble down the cardboard tube from the roll of toilet paper. However, you probably saw at least some damage in the next step, where the marble dropped through two of the cardboard tubes. When you dropped it through the cardboard tube from a roll of paper towels, the damage should have been greater. When you dropped in through a tube twice as long, there should have been even more damage. If the egg wasn't completely broken in that step, there was even more damage when you dropped it through a tube that was three times as long.

Why did the marble damage the egg? Sure, it hit the egg, but why did that cause the egg to break? Well, when the marble hit the egg, it was moving. According to Newton's First Law, it wouldn't change its motion until it was acted on by an outside force. When it hit the egg, the egg applied a force to the marble, trying to stop it. The more force the egg had to exert to stop the marble, the more likely it was to get damaged, because the shell wasn't strong enough to exert that force.

So what does this tell us? It tells us that the farther the marble dropped, the larger the force the egg had to exert to stop it. This should make sense, of course, but why? Why was it harder for the egg to stop the marble the farther it dropped? The mass of the marble stayed the same, no matter how far it dropped. What changed? The *speed* of the marble changed. The farther it dropped, the faster it was moving when it hit the egg. The faster it was moving, the harder it was for the egg to stop it, so the more likely it was that the egg would break.

But why does the distance over which the marble fell affect its speed? Because gravity was pulling on the marble the entire time, and that force increased the marble's speed. The longer gravity had to pull on the marble, the faster it could make the marble go. So when the marble fell for a short amount of time, gravity could speed it up only a little. However, when the marble could fall for a longer amount of time, gravity was able to speed it up even more! When an object's speed changes, we say that it is being **accelerated**. So another way to say this would be that the longer gravity could pull on the marble, the more it could accelerate the marble, so the faster it would travel.

Now before I go on, I have to introduce you to a new term: **velocity** (vuh los' ih tee). Many people think velocity means the same thing as speed, but it does not. Speed tells you how quickly an object is moving. The higher its speed, the more quickly it is moving. Velocity tells you how quickly an object is moving *and* the direction in which an object is traveling. So if you are in a car and the driver tells you that the car is moving at 55 miles per hour, the driver is telling you the car's *speed*. On the other hand, if the driver says that the car is moving *west* at 55 miles per hour, he is telling you the car's *velocity*.

This train is traveling at a speed of 70 miles per hour. Its velocity is 70 miles an hour west. Speed tells you only how fast an object is traveling. Velocity tells you how fast *and* in what direction.

Why is this important? Because acceleration is determined by an object's *velocity*, not its speed. If an object's *velocity* changes, it is being accelerated. So acceleration is a change in an object's *velocity*. But wait a minute. Is it really possible for an object's velocity to change without its

speed changing? The answer might surprise you, but it is most certainly, "Yes!" Think, for a moment, about a car driving down a road. The road is going straight north, but then it curves so that it is eventually going west. The driver takes the curve, but the curve is so gentle that he doesn't slow down at all. In other words, his speed stays the same. However, he is changing his direction, because he is turning with the curve. So even though his speed isn't changing, his velocity is changing. As a result, even though his speed stays the same, he is accelerating, because his direction is changing, which means his velocity is changing!

When this car takes the curve ahead, it will be accelerating, even if its speed doesn't change. That's because acceleration is defined as a change in an object's *velocity*, and since the car will be changing its direction as it takes the curve, that means its velocity will be changing.

So, acceleration is a change in an object's velocity. It could mean either a change in speed or a change in direction. In your experiment, the marble accelerated because its speed was changing. Its direction didn't change, because it fell straight down the entire time, until it hit the egg. However, as pictured above, there are times when the velocity can change even though the speed does not. Even during those times, the object is still accelerating. The other important thing to realize about the term acceleration is that it refers to *any change in velocity*. Often, people use the word "accelerate" to mean "speed up," but that's not the only way acceleration happens. Even when an object slows down, it is being accelerated, because its velocity is changing. That might sound weird to you, but only because people tend to use the term "decelerate" to mean slow down. Scientifically, however, *any* change in velocity is an acceleration!

LESSON REVIEW

Youngest students: Answer these questions:

1. What's wrong with the following statement? "Acceleration is any change in an object's speed."

2. When an airplane pilot says, "We are heading due east at 560 miles per hour," what is she telling you?

Older students: Explain the difference between speed and velocity. Define acceleration. Use the terms "gravity" and "acceleration" to explain why the marble in your experiment traveled faster the longer it had to drop.

Oldest students: Do what the older students are doing. In addition, give three different ways acceleration can change an object's motion. For example, one way would be that acceleration can speed up an object. There are at least two other ways acceleration can change an object's motion.

Lesson 75: Isaac Newton and His Second Law of Motion

Now that you understand what acceleration is, you are ready to learn Newton's Second Law of Motion. Not surprisingly, the best way to start is with an experiment.

Acceleration

What you will need:
- A Ping-Pong ball
- A golf ball
- A straw (the kind you use to drink)
- Two eggs (You may need more if you miss in step 10.)
- A tall glass
- A ruler
- Water
- A sink
- Someone to help you

What you should do:
1. Place the Ping-Pong ball on a counter or table that is flat. If the ball rolls away when you set it down, the surface isn't flat. Find a counter or table where you can set down the Ping-Pong ball down and it stays where you set it.
2. Kneel or crouch so your mouth is at the same level as the ball.
3. Put one end of the straw in your mouth and hold it so the other end is aimed right at the center of the ball. It should be close to but not actually touching the ball.
4. Blow through the straw as hard as you can. What happens to the ball?
5. Repeat steps 1-4 with the golf ball. What's the difference between the way the golf ball moved and the way the Ping-Pong ball moved?
6. Use the ruler to measure the height of the glass or pitcher. Get an adult to help you if you don't know how.
7. Fill the glass (or pitcher) with water. Get it as full as you can.
8. Put the glass in the sink.
9. Hold an egg above the glass at about twice the height above the glass as the glass is tall. So, for example, if you measured that your glass is 18 cm (7 inches) tall, hold the egg 36 cm (14 inches) above the top of the glass. Your helper can hold the ruler so you can figure out where that is.
10. With the egg positioned right over the center of the glass, drop it. It should fall right into the water.
11. Carefully pour the water out of the glass and get the egg. Inspect it for damage.
12. Set the empty glass in the sink where it was before.
13. Hold the other egg above the glass at about the same height above the glass as the glass is tall. So, for example, if you measured that your glass is 18 cm (7 inches) tall, hold the egg 18 cm (7 inches) above the top of the glass. Once again, drop the egg so that it falls into the empty glass.
14. Compare this egg's damage to what you saw in step 11.
15. Clean up your mess.

What did you see in the first part of your experiment? You should have seen that the Ping-Pong ball rolled quickly away from the straw. However, when you did the same thing to the golf ball, you should have seen that it rolled much more slowly. Why? Well, each ball was initially at rest. As Newton's First Law says, each ball would have stayed at rest, but you blew on it. The force of the air hitting each ball overcame the ball's inertia, and the ball started rolling. However, the same force caused the Ping-Pong ball to roll away quickly but the golf ball to roll away slowly.

Newton's Second Law tells us why this happened. It says that the amount of acceleration a body has depends on two things: its mass and the total force acting on it. The stronger the force, the greater the acceleration. The larger the mass, the lower the acceleration.

When a net force acts on an object, its acceleration increases with increasing force and decreases with increasing mass.

Now this should make sense. Remember, mass is a measure of how much matter is in an object. The larger its mass, the heavier it is. Well, heavy things are harder to move than light things, so when something is heavy, the acceleration a force can produce is small. When something is light, the same force can produce a lot more acceleration.

That's what you saw in the experiment. The main difference between the Ping-Pong ball and golf ball was the mass. The Ping-Pong ball had only a little mass, while the golf ball had a lot more mass. You applied the same force to each of them by blowing on them as hard as you could through the straw. That force caused a lot of acceleration in the Ping-Pong ball, changing its velocity from zero to moving away from you really quickly. However, that same force couldn't produce nearly as much acceleration in the golf ball, because it had more mass. As a result, the golf ball's velocity couldn't change as much as the Ping-Pong ball's velocity.

But what about the other part of Newton's Second Law? It says that the larger the force, the larger the acceleration. That should make sense, too. The harder you push on something, the more drastically its velocity should change. That's what the second part of the experiment showed. When you dropped the egg, it started falling. By the time it hit the bottom of the glass, it had built up a large downward velocity. When it hit the glass, the glass stopped it rather quickly.

So the egg went from having a large downward velocity to having zero velocity in a short period of time. That means it had a lot of acceleration. Now remember, "acceleration" just means "change in velocity," so even slowing down is acceleration. Since the egg slowed down very quickly, the acceleration was very large.

When you dropped the egg in water, it fell the same distance before hitting the water, but it didn't stop nearly as quickly, did it? The water slowed it down over a longer period of time. Its velocity still went from large and downwards to zero, but it changed over a longer time period. As a result, its velocity didn't change as quickly. That means its acceleration was low.

So, when you dropped the egg into the empty glass, it experienced a very high acceleration. Newton's Second Law says that the larger the force, the larger the acceleration. Since the egg had a large acceleration, the empty glass must have exerted a large force on it. When you dropped the egg in water, it experienced a smaller acceleration. What does that mean about the force the water exerted on it? The force was smaller. Now do you see why the egg you dropped in water experienced a lot less damage than the egg you dropped in the empty glass? The egg you dropped in water experienced a smaller acceleration, which means it experienced a smaller force. That smaller force did less damage to the egg.

So in the end, Newton's First Law says that in order to change an object's velocity, you must apply a force. When you do that, the change in velocity is called acceleration. Newton's Second Law tells you that the acceleration you end up producing depends on both the strength of the force and the mass of the object. The stronger the force, the higher the acceleration. In addition, the smaller the mass, the higher the acceleration.

This forklift is carrying a load of books. The more force the forklift's motor can produce, the more the driver can accelerate, because acceleration increases with increasing force. If several boxes were taken off the load, the forklift could accelerate more quickly, because acceleration also increases with decreasing mass.

Now you might wonder why the word "net" is in Newton's Second Law. You will learn what the term "net force" means in the next lesson.

LESSON REVIEW

Youngest students: Answer these questions:

1. Fill in the blank: An object's acceleration increases when the net force acting on it _____.

2. Fill in the blank: A force will produce the largest acceleration when the object it is acting on has the _____ mass.

Older students: Write down Newton's Second Law. Describe the experiment you did and use the law to explain the results you observed.

Oldest students: Do what the older students are doing. In addition, there is a mathematical formula that can be used to describe Newton's Second Law. Find that formula and write it down. Can you see why it is another way of writing Newton's Second Law?

Section 6: The Revolution at the End of the 17th Century

This statue of Gottfried Wilhelm Leibniz adorns the University of Göttingen's auditorium.

Lessons 76-90: The Revolution at the End of the 17th Century

Lesson 76: More on Newton's Second Law

In the previous lesson, you learned about Newton's Second Law, which states, "When a net force acts on an object, its acceleration increases with increasing force and decreases with increasing mass." In that lesson, I didn't explain why the word "net" appears in the law. I want to do that now, and the best way to explain it is to start with an experiment.

Net Force

What you will need:
- A handheld hair dryer (It is best if the hair dryer has at least two settings, like "low" and "high.")
- A Ping-Pong ball
- A golf ball

What you should do:
1. If the hair dryer has a nozzle on it, remove the nozzle. You want the hair dryer to blow a column of air that is as wide as the face of the hair dryer.
2. Plug in the hair dryer and hold it so it is in front of you and is pointing straight up so that when you turn it on, it will blow hot hair straight up. Don't turn it on yet.
3. Place the Ping-Pong ball on the opening of the hair dryer, as shown in the picture on the right.
4. If the hair dryer has two or more settings, turn it on to the lowest setting. What happens?
5. If the hair dryer has two or more settings, increase the setting and see what happens. Continue to do this until you reach the highest setting.
6. Tilt the hair dryer a bit and see what happens.
7. Continue tilting the hair dryer more and more until the Ping-Pong ball falls.
8. Feel free to play with this. You can even start with the hair dryer on and drop the Ping-Pong ball from straight above the face of the hair dryer.
9. When you are done playing with the Ping-Pong ball, repeat steps 3-5 with the golf ball. What happens?
10. Put everything away.

Did the first part of your experiment surprise you? It was pretty cool to watch the Ping-Pong ball float above the hair dryer, wasn't it? The higher the setting, the higher the Ping-Pong ball floated. Even when you tilted the hair dryer, the ball continued to float off to one side of the hair dryer. In the end, you had to tilt the hair dryer pretty far before the Ping-Pong ball fell to the ground, didn't you? On the other hand, the results with the golf ball weren't very impressive, were they? Regardless of the setting you chose, the golf ball just sat on top of the hair dryer and did nothing.

What explains the results of the experiment? Not surprisingly, it's Newton's Second Law. When you placed the Ping-Pong ball on the hair dryer, gravity was pulling the ball down towards the earth. However, the hair dryer was holding it up, keeping it from falling. How did it do that? It applied a force on the ball that was directed *upwards*. In other words, the hair dryer applied a force to the ball that was *opposite* of the force that gravity was using to pull the ball down. So the ball had two forces acting on it: gravity was pulling it down with a certain amount of force, and the hair dryer was pushing it up with exactly the same amount of force.

What happens when you push on something with two equal but opposite forces? Nothing! The forces cancel each other out. So the Ping-Pong ball just sat there on the hair dryer because the two forces acting on it canceled each other out. In other words, the *net force* was zero! That's what "net force" means in Newton's Second Law. It means you have to consider all the forces acting on an object, and once you have tallied them all up, the resulting force is what determines the acceleration.

Now think about how this applies to the next part of your experiment. When you turned the hair dryer on, a new force appeared – the force of the air pushing up on the ball. That upward force was *larger* than the downward force with which gravity was pulling. So even though gravity was still pulling down on the ball, the air was pushing up with a greater force. As a result, there was a net force up, and the Ping-Pong ball started accelerating upwards.

In your experiment, the ball had two forces acting on it. Its acceleration was determined by the total or *net* force.

The Ping-Pong ball didn't continue to accelerate upwards, however. Eventually, it came to rest at some point above the hair dryer. It might have bounced around a bit, but it was essentially floating in the air, hardly moving at all. As a result, we can talk about it as if it were at rest. Why did it come to rest? Think about it. The hair dryer blows air out with a certain amount of force, but as the air gets farther and farther from the hair dryer, the force gets smaller and smaller. After all, if you put your hand right next to the face of the hair dryer, you feel the air hitting your hand pretty hard. However, the farther you pull your hand away from the hair dryer, the harder it is to feel the air hitting your hand, because the farther the air travels from the hair dryer, the weaker the force becomes.

So as the Ping-Pong ball continued to accelerate upwards, the upward force got smaller and smaller. Eventually, it got high enough so that the force with which gravity was pulling it down was equal to the force with which the air from the hair dryer was pushing it up. What happened then? The net force on the Ping-Pong ball was once again zero, and it stopped accelerating. Eventually, it came almost to rest at the point where the upward force from the air was equal to the downward force of gravity. At that point, the *net force* was once again zero, just like it was before you turned on the hair dryer!

Most of the time, an object is acted on by at least two different forces. When you throw a ball, for example, you are applying a force to it. However, gravity is also there, applying a downward force. You can still make the ball fly upwards, however, because you can apply a much greater force than gravity. As a result, the *net force* on the ball is still upwards, so the ball accelerates upwards while it is in your hand. So when you are using Newton's Second Law, you have to think about all the forces acting on an object and how they add together to make a net force. It's that net force which determines the acceleration of the object.

So why didn't the golf ball fly up in the air like the Ping-Pong ball? Well, remember that the force of gravity depends on the mass of the objects involved. A golf ball has a lot more mass than a Ping-Pong ball, so the force with which gravity pulls down on it is greater. It turns out that even on the highest setting, the air coming out of a hair dryer cannot exert more force on the golf ball than gravity. The air and hair dryer only manage to exert a force equal to gravity, so the golf ball has no net force acting on it. As a result, it just sits there.

Now please understand that there is more to your experiment than just the downward force of gravity and the upward force of air. After all, the Ping-Pong ball was really stable, wasn't it? You could tilt the hair dryer, and as long as you didn't tilt it too much, the Ping-Pong ball would continue to float in the air. That's because the Ping-Pong ball is very smooth and has a nice, round shape. As a result, the air flows around it very smoothly, as shown in the drawing on the right. As the air flows around the ball, it pushes sideways on the ball. However, because the air flows around the ball so smoothly, it pushes equally in all directions on all sides. Because of this, there is no *net* sideways force on the ball, and the ball doesn't accelerate to one side or the other.

The main point, of course, is that when you are trying to use Newton's Second Law, you must consider all the forces that are acting on an object, and you have to add them all together to get the net force in order to figure out how the object will accelerate.

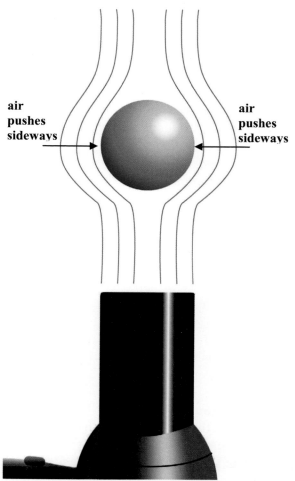

air pushes sideways   air pushes sideways

Because the Ping-Pong ball is smooth and round, the air envelopes it evenly on all sides. This means it is pushing equally on all sides of the ball, so there is no net sideways force. As a result, the Ping-Pong ball doesn't accelerate to the right or the left.

LESSON REVIEW

Youngest students: Answer these questions:

1. What two forces were acting on the Ping-Pong ball in your experiment?

2. When the Ping-Pong ball came to rest, what was the net force?

Older students: Make a drawing of what happened to the Ping-Pong ball in your experiment. Explain the forces acting on the ball and what the net force is. Use Newton's Second Law to explain where the ball came to rest above the hair dryer.

Oldest students: Do what the older students are doing. In addition, suppose you wadded up a piece of paper and used it instead of a Ping-Pong ball in your experiment? Explain what would happen when you turned the hair dryer on. Try it to see whether or not you are right.

Lesson 77: Newton's Second Law and Gravity

As you learned back in Lesson 70, Newton figured out that the force of gravity depended on two things: mass and distance. The greater the mass, the stronger the force of gravity; and the shorter the distance between two objects, the greater the force of gravity. So that means the earth pulls heavy objects to itself more strongly than it pulls lighter objects to itself. Does that mean (as Aristotle thought) that heavier objects fall faster than lighter objects? After all, if the earth pulls heavier objects to itself with a stronger force, they must fall faster than lighter objects, right?

You probably know that's not true. After all, in Lesson 26, you learned that Galileo used balls rolling down ramps to show that heavy objects fall at pretty much the same speed as lighter objects. In fact, we now know that heavy and light objects fall at exactly the same rate, as long as there is no air resistance. Perform the following experiment to see a very convincing demonstration of this fact.

Freely Falling Objects

What you will need:
- A paper or Styrofoam cup
- A stepladder
- A pen
- Water
- A large basin to catch water (if you can't do the experiment outside)
- An adult to help you

What you should do:
1. If the weather is okay, take the stepladder outside and set it up securely on a flat piece of ground.
2. If the weather is not okay, set the stepladder on a floor that your parents say can get wet. Put the basin at the bottom of the stepladder, on the side opposite of the side on which you climb.
3. Go inside and use the pen to poke a hole in the bottom of the cup. The hole should be as big around as the pen.
4. Have the adult use his or her finger to plug up the hole and fill the cup nearly full of water.
5. With his or her finger continuing to plug the hole, have the adult go to the stepladder and climb on it to the highest step that is safe.
6. Have the adult hold the cup so it is in front of him or her and the hole that is being plugged points down towards the ground.
7. If you are doing this indoors, have the adult hold the cup over the basin so that when water leaks out of the hole, it will fall into the basin. In addition, he or she will drop the cup, so the adult should make sure the cup will fall into the basin when it is dropped.
8. Stand in front of the stepladder so you are facing the cup and can easily see the finger the adult is using to plug the hole in the bottom of the cup.
9. Have the adult unplug the hole and watch the water start leaking out of the hole and falling down to the ground (or into the basin).
10. After you have watched the water leak out of the hole for just a moment, have the adult let go of the cup. As the cup falls, keep your eyes on the bottom of the cup where water was leaking out. What changes once the cup is in motion?
11. If you didn't notice a change, repeat the experiment. You can also record it with a phone camera.
12. Clean up any mess that might have been made, and put everything away.

What did you see in your experiment? You should have noticed that once the adult removed his or her finger from the hole, water flowed freely out of the hole. However, as soon as the adult dropped the cup, the water stopped flowing out of the hole. Why? Well, it was leaking out of the hole because gravity was pulling down on it. As a result, the water was accelerating towards the earth. However, when the adult let the cup go, the cup also started accelerating towards the earth. At that point, the water stopped leaking out of the cup, *because it was accelerating at the same rate as the cup.* As a result, it fell towards the earth at the exact same rate as the cup. In order to flow out the hole, it would have to fall to the earth faster than the cup. It couldn't do that, however, so as the cup fell, the water couldn't flow out of the cup.

Now this might bother you a bit. After all, the cup is really light, but the water is really heavy. Newton showed that the heavier something is, the stronger gravity pulls on it. That means the earth pulled on the water much more strongly than it pulled on the cup. Shouldn't that make the water fall faster than the cup? Not if you consider Newton's Second Law!

Remember, Newton's Second Law says that when a force is acting on an object, the acceleration depends on two things: the strength of the force and the mass of the object. When the force is greater, acceleration is greater, but when the mass is greater, acceleration is lower. So the earth pulled on the water with a stronger force than it pulled on the cup, but the water also had more mass. That means it was harder to accelerate!

If gravity pulled on the water and cup with the same force, the water would accelerate more slowly than the cup, because of its greater mass. Since gravity pulled on the water with a greater force, however, that made up for the water's greater mass, and as a result, the water and cup fell with the same acceleration.

In the end, then, the earth's gravity does pull harder on things that are heavier. However, because those things are heavier, it takes more force to make them accelerate. It turns out that the extra force with which gravity pulls on heavier objects is only enough to make up for the fact that their extra mass makes them harder to accelerate. This means that when both the force of gravity *and* the mass of the object are taken into account, earth's gravity accelerates all things at exactly the same rate. This means that as long as you ignore air resistance, all objects fall to earth at the same rate, regardless of how heavy they are.

The rocks falling off this conveyor belt are of various sizes and masses. However, they all fall with exactly the same acceleration, as long as we ignore air resistance.

Now, of course, I keep talking about ignoring air resistance, because as you should already know, air resists motion. For example, birds have to be streamlined in order to fly well, because air resists their motion as they fly through it. A feather will fall more slowly than a rock, but that's not because of the way gravity works. It is because air resists the feather's motion more effectively than the rock's motion. This makes the feather slow down as it falls. In situations like the dropping of a feather, then, you can't ignore air resistance. However, there are many situations in which air resistance is so small that you can pretty much ignore it.

For example, when things are fairly heavy, they can push the molecules in the air out of their way really effectively. As a result, when you are dropping fairly heavy things, you can pretty much ignore air resistance. When you drop a feather and a rock, you can't ignore air resistance, because the feather isn't good at moving the molecules in the air out of the way. However, when you drop a rock and a coin, you can ignore air resistance, because a coin is heavy enough to move the molecules in the air out of its way effectively. As a result, air resistance doesn't affect it very much.

Leaves (above) cannot overcome air resistance easily, so when they fall, they are not in free fall. A basketball (below) easily overcomes air resistance, so when it falls, it is in free fall.

Of course, there are lots of things that are heavy enough to overcome air resistance really well. As a result, there are lots of situations where you can ignore air resistance. Because of this, scientists have a term they use when describing the motion of falling things that aren't affected strongly by air resistance. We call it **free fall**. When an object is in free fall, the only important force acting on it is gravity. There might be other forces (like air resistance), but they are so small that they can be ignored. In such cases, we say that objects are in free fall.

Because Newton explained what affects the strength of the gravitational force, and because he also explained that the acceleration of an object depends on both the strength of the net force and the mass of the object, we can completely understand why most things fall to earth at the same rate, regardless of their mass. Even during Newton's time, there were still some natural philosophers who thought that Aristotle was mostly right in claiming that heavy objects fall more quickly than light objects. Newton's Second Law and his understanding of gravity, however, finally showed once and for all that Aristotle was wrong about that.

LESSON REVIEW

Youngest students: Answer these questions:

1. Compare the acceleration of a bowling ball and a golf ball that are dropped at the same time.

2. When can we say that an object is in free fall?

Older students: Write your own explanation of why objects fall at the same acceleration regardless of how heavy they are (ignoring air resistance), despite the fact that gravity pulls on the heavier things more strongly. Explain what free fall is.

Oldest students: Do what the older students are doing. In addition, suppose you were in free fall and had a coin in your hand. When you let go of the coin, what would you see the coin doing? Write down your answer and then see if it is correct. Fix it if it is wrong.

Lesson 78: Newton and His Third Law of Motion

Now that you've learned the first two of Newton's laws of motion, it is time to learn the third. Once again, the best way to introduce the law is by experiment.

Newton's Third Law

What you will need:
- A long piece of string or fishing line (Ideally, it should be long enough to stretch out along the longest hallway you have. You need something stronger than thread, but it needn't be really thick string.)
- A straw
- A balloon
- Tape
- Someone to help you

What you should do:
1. Thread one end of the string through the straw. This might be a bit tough, because it can curl up inside the straw. However, if you just keep pushing string into one side of the straw, it should eventually come out the other end.
2. Pull several inches of string through the straw and give the straw and tape to your helper. Tell your helper to make sure the string doesn't slide out of the straw.
3. You and your helper should now go to one end of the longest hallway in your home.
4. Blow up the balloon as big as you can, and then hold the opening with your fingers so the air doesn't come out.
5. Use your other hand to hold the balloon steady and have your helper tape the straw to the balloon. Your helper should use two pieces of tape, and he or she should position the straw so it is pointing in the direction of the balloon's opening, as shown in the picture on the right.

6. Once the straw is firmly taped in place, have your helper hold on to one end of the string while you hold on to the balloon and the other end of the string.
7. Have your helper walk to the other end of the hallway, keeping hold of the string at all times.
8. Once your helper has reached the end of the hallway, hold tightly to your end of the string and have your helper pull the string, so it stretches tightly across the entire hallway, keeping the balloon suspended.
9. Keeping the string tight, release the balloon and let the air escape. What happens? If the balloon didn't fly along the string to the end of the hallway, retry the experiment. Try to make sure the straw is as level as possible and aimed in the direction of the balloon's opening. Also, make sure the string is stretched tightly. Slack in the string will mess up the experiment.
10. Clean up your mess and put everything away.

As I mentioned in step 9, when you released the balloon, it should have sailed across the hallway along the string. Why? Well, the balloon was pushing on the air inside of it, and when you released the end of the balloon, the air was free to rush outside the balloon. That shouldn't have surprised you at all. Now the balloon moving in response to the air rushing out of it probably didn't surprise you, either. You have probably released an inflated balloon before and watched it fly all over the place. The only thing different in the experiment was that the string guided the balloon so that it moved in only one direction – down the hall.

The experiment probably wouldn't surprise many people, but most people have no idea why a balloon moves when its air is allowed to escape. Most people think the air that is escaping somehow pushes against the air that is on the outside of the balloon, and that's what causes the balloon to move. However, that's not true. The balloon moves because *the air that is escaping pushes the balloon in the direction that it moves*!

Why does the air push on the balloon in that direction? Because of Newton's Third Law of Motion, which says:

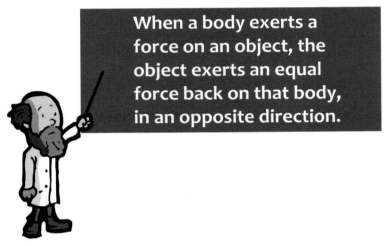

When a body exerts a force on an object, the object exerts an equal force back on that body, in an opposite direction.

In other words, suppose you push on a wall. You are exerting a force on the wall. In response, the wall exerts a force back on you, in the opposite direction. So you if you push forward on a wall, it pushes backward on you with a force equal to the one with which you are pushing.

This might sound a bit odd to you. How can the wall exert a force on you? It is just standing there. Well, when you aren't pushing on it, it can't push on you. As soon as you start pushing, however, the wall pushes back. The wall doesn't move in response to your push, because your push isn't strong enough to move the wall. You don't move in response to the wall's push, because the friction between your feet and the ground fights against the wall's push and keeps you from moving. However, if you put on roller skates and pushed against the wall, what would happen? You would roll backwards. Why? Because when you pushed on the wall, it pushed back on you. The roller skates made it much easier for the wall's force to move you, so when the wall pushed, you rolled in the direction of that push.

Now let's go back to your experiment. The entire time it was inflated, the balloon was pushing against the air inside it. According to Newton's Third Law, that means the air was pushing back on the balloon, in the opposite direction. Nothing happened at first, though, because you were holding on to the end of the balloon. That kept the air and balloon from moving in response to those forces. When you let go, however, the air was free to move, and the balloon was free to move as well. So the air went rushing out of the balloon in the direction the balloon was pushing the air, and the balloon went flying in the direction that the air was pushing on it! This happened because the balloon pushed on the air inside it, and in response, the air pushed back with an equal force that went in the opposite direction. That's Newton's Third Law!

Have you ever heard someone say, "For every action, there is an equal and opposite reaction"? That's another way to phrase Newton's Third Law. In your experiment, the action was the balloon pushing on the air inside it, which made that air rush out of the balloon in a certain direction. The equal and opposite reaction was that same air pushing back on the balloon. That equal and opposite reaction caused the balloon to go flying off in the direction opposite of the air.

Why did you need the string to guide the balloon in your experiment? Remember that the reaction is always opposite of the action. When you just let go of an inflated balloon, the air rushes out fast, and because of the way the opening flaps around, and other factors like air currents in the room, the air tends to rush out in slightly different directions as time goes on. That results in the balloon being pushed in slightly different directions, which is why an inflated balloon tends to fly all over the place when you release it. The straw and string forced the balloon to stay pointed in one direction.

Now, of course, this law applies in all situations. Consider, for example, a rocket being launched into space. Why does the rocket fly up when its fuel starts burning? The burning fuel produces hot gases, and those gases are pushed down by the rocket. Newton's Third Law requires that in response, the hot gases push on the rocket with the same force but in the opposite direction. As a result, the gases push up on the rocket, causing it to launch in the air.

1. The rocket pushes on the gases, causing them to fly down and out of the bottom of the rocket.

2. The gases push back on the rocket with an equal force in the opposite direction, causing the rocket to fly up.

Newton's Third Law explains how this rocket, which is carrying the space shuttle Atlantis, was launched.

LESSON REVIEW

Youngest students: Answer these questions:

1. In your experiment, what did the air that was rushing out of the balloon do to the balloon?

2. Fill in the blanks: For every action, there is an _____ and _____ reaction.

Older students: Write down Newton's Third Law of Motion. Draw a picture of a rocket being launched and use Newton's Third Law to explain how the launch works.

Oldest students: Do what the older students are doing. In addition, suppose your parents' car stalls on a cold, icy day. You get out to push, but when you push on the car, you end up sliding backwards. Explain why that happens. Check your explanation and correct it if it is wrong.

Lesson 79: Putting It All Together

Now that you have learned all three of Newton's Laws of Motion as well as his Law of Gravity, I want you to do an experiment that we can then analyze in terms of all four of the laws.

Colliding Coins

What you will need:
- Several (at least 5) coins of the same value
- A table or counter that is smooth

What you should do:
1. Stack four of the coins together so they are right on top of each other, forming a nice, neat column.
2. Place another coin on the table by itself several centimeters (a few inches) from the stack of coins.
3. Put your finger on top of the lone coin (which we can call the "shooter coin").

Shove this coin so it hits the bottom coin in the stack just a bit off center.

4. Use your finger to pull the shooter coin back away from the stack of coins, and then give the shooter coin a nice, hard shove forward, right towards the stack of coins. Lift your finger after you have given the coin a shove so the coin slams into the bottom of the stack of coins on its own. What happens?
5. Restack the coins and repeat steps 2–4. It is best to aim the shooter coin so it doesn't hit the bottom of the stack dead center. If you hit it dead center, the shooter coin will probably shove itself underneath the stack of coins. Ideally, you want to have the shooter coin hit the stack just a little off center, so it moves away from the stack at an angle after hitting it.
6. Once you have the technique down, start with a stack of at least 4 coins and try to use the shooter coin to knock each coin out of the stack one-by-one, until you are left with only one coin where the stack used to be.
7. Put away the coins.

If you got good at shoving the shooter coin into the stack, you should have seen that when it hit the stack, it shoved only the bottom coin out of the stack. The rest of the coins stayed stacked neatly on the counter. You should have been able to keep shoving the shooter coin into the stack, knocking out one coin at a time until you were left with only one coin where there used to be an entire stack.

Not surprisingly, we can use Newton's Laws of Motion and his Law of Gravity to explain how this experiment works. When you first put the coins on the table, they sat there at rest. That's because you put them there at rest, and Newton's First Law says that until an outside force acts on the coins, they will remain at rest. You then used your finger to apply a force to the shooter coin. At first, the force was directed backwards, so Newton's Second Law required the shooter coin to accelerate backwards, and then you pushed forward, so Newton's Second Law required the coin to accelerate forward.

As the shooter coin accelerated, it picked up speed. When you released the shooter coin, your finger was no longer applying a force to the coin. However, the coin continued to move because the force you had used put it in motion, and as Newton's First Law says, the coin will continue that motion until acted on by an outside force. As a result, the coin continued to slide across the counter, until it hit the stack of coins.

What happened when it hit the stack of coins? It applied a force, but the only coin it hit was the bottom coin, so it applied a force only to the bottom coin. As Newton's Second Law requires, that force caused the bottom coin to accelerate in the direction that the force was applied. This caused the bottom coin to slide out of the stack. Now, there was friction between the bottom coin and the rest of the stack, but that frictional force was small. It wasn't enough to overcome the inertia of the rest of the stack, so Newton's First Law required that the rest of the stack not move.

Now before the shooter coin hit the stack, each coin in the stack was being pulled down towards the earth by gravity, but the coin underneath (or the countertop in the case of the bottom coin) was fighting gravity, so the net force on the coins in the stack was zero. As a result, they did not move towards the earth. However, once the shooter coin knocked the bottom coin out of the stack, there was nothing fighting the force of gravity for the rest of the coins in the stack. As a result, gravity exerted a net force downwards, and the rest of the coins in the stack accelerated downwards according to Newton's Second Law until they hit the counter, where once again, the net force on each coin became zero.

What about Newton's Third Law? Where does that come in? Well, what happened to the shooter coin when it hit the stack of coins? It either slowed down or went sliding off in a different direction. Why? According to Newton's First Law, the shooter coin's motion wouldn't change unless it was acted on by an outside force. What applied the outside force to the shooter coin? The coin at the bottom of the stack! When the shooter coin hit the coin at the bottom of the stack, it exerted a force on the coin at the bottom of the stack. As required by Newton's Third Law, the coin at the bottom of the stack exerted an equal force in the opposite direction, and that's what changed the motion of the shooter coin.

The important point here is that Newton's Laws of Motion and his Law of Gravity can explain all sorts of motion that we see on earth. Have you ever played a game of marbles? If so, the marbles were obeying all those laws as you played. They stayed motionless until another marble hit them and applied a force. That's Newton's First Law. When you shot another marble, if it was a little bit off the ground as is the case in the picture on the right, it fell to earth, because of Newton's Law of Gravity. When it rolled into another marble, it applied a force that accelerated the other marble in the direction it was traveling, as required by Newton's Second Law. Finally, the marble that you initially rolled changed its motion, because as required by Newton's Third Law, the marble that was hit applied an equal and opposite force to the marble that you initially rolled.

When you play a game of marbles, all the motion can be explained using Newton's Laws.

So Newton's Laws can be used to explain all sorts of motion that occurs on the earth, but they can also be used to explain the motion that occurs in space as well. This was another brilliant insight on Newton's part. Do you remember reading about Kepler and his explanation of the tides in Lesson

34? He understood that the moon's gravity exerted forces on the oceans, and that's what explains the tides. Well, Newton had studied Kepler, and he realized that Kepler's idea could be expanded to the entire universe. He realized that the exact same laws which govern motion on earth also govern motion in the heavens!

Now, this might make sense to you and me, but it was a revolutionary idea in his time. Most natural philosophers thought the heavens operated by completely different rules, because they were so far from earth. Newton, however, realized that since God made the heavens *and* the earth, they should all operate on the same laws. With this realization, he was able to use his Law of Gravity to explain how the planets orbited the sun. He was also able to explain some oddities about the planets that no one had been able to explain before.

For example, he realized that as the planets orbited the sun, they would sometimes pass near one another. Since he believed that the laws of motion worked the same in space as they did on the

earth, he realized that when the planets passed near one another, they would exert a force that would change their motion. This should only be observable for the very heavy planets, because they would exert the greatest gravitational force. He wrote a well-known astronomer of the day (John Flamsteed) and asked him if Saturn had been observed changing speed as it passed by Jupiter. Flamsteed was amazed that Newton asked that, because that observation had been made and it was a mystery at the time. However, Newton explained it using the same laws he had developed for motion here on earth!

Newton used his laws of motion and gravity to predict that when Saturn got close to Jupiter, it should slow down in its orbit around the sun. Astronomers of Newton's day had already seen that happen, and they were puzzled by it. (Drawing is not to scale)

LESSON REVIEW

Youngest students: Answer these questions:

1. In your experiment, what caused the shooter coin to change its motion when it hit the stack of coins?

2. Fill in the blank: Newton realized that the laws which govern motion on earth also govern the motion that occurs in _____.

Older students: Explain what you did in your experiment, and then list the laws that governed the following results: (a) The fact that the bottom coin slid out of the stack, (b) The fact that the other coins did not move out of the stack, (c) the fact that the other coins fell down to the counter, and (d) the fact that the shooter coin changed its motion once it hit the stack.

Oldest students: Do what the older students are doing. In addition, explain the insight that allowed Newton to analyze the motion of the planets.

Lesson 80: Gravity, Newton's Laws, and Net Force

Because things move according to Newton's Laws, some surprising things can happen. Do the following experiment to see what I mean.

Don't Break the Mug!

What you will need:
- A coffee mug (The experiment is more dramatic if it's breakable!)
- A length of string that is about as tall as you and strong enough to stop the mug when it falls
- Scissors
- A nut (the kind that threads onto a screw)
- A pencil
- The cushion from a couch or a large pillow (not necessary, but encouraged at first)
- Someone to help you

What you should do:
1. Stand up straight and have your helper cut the string to a length that is about 30 centimeters (1 foot) shorter than the height of your shoulder.
2. Tie one end of the string to the mug's handle. Make sure the knot is strong and tight.
3. Tie the other end of the string to the nut. Once again, the knot needs to be strong and tight.
4. Put the couch cushion (or large pillow) on the floor in front of where you are standing.
5. Hold the pencil in front of you at your shoulder's height.
6. Holding the string by the end with the nut, drape the string over the pencil so the mug hangs from the pencil, as shown in the picture on the right. The mug should be hanging right over the cushion.
7. Pull the nut so the mug rises to where it is near but not touching the pencil.
8. Hold on to the pencil tightly and keep holding it tightly until the end of the experiment. The pencil will get jerked down hard. Be ready for that!

9. Let go of the nut so the mug can fall. What happens?
10. Hopefully, the mug never reached the cushion. If it did, the most likely culprit is that you dropped the pencil when it was suddenly pulled down really hard. Repeat the experiment, concentrating on holding the pencil hard so it doesn't come out of your hand.
11. Once you become confident, you should be able to do this experiment without the cushion, and the mug will not break.
12. Clean up your mess and put everything away.

Why didn't the mug fall to the ground and break into many pieces? At the end of the experiment, you should have seen that the end of the string that was tied to the knot had wrapped around the pencil several times. This, of course, kept the string from sliding along the pencil, which stopped the mug from falling. The surprising results of this experiment are all explained by Newton's Laws.

Think about the instant you released the nut. Gravity had been pulling down on the mug the entire time you held the nut, but the string was pulling the mug up with an upward force equal to the force of gravity. That meant the net force on the mug was zero, so the mug did not move. When you released the nut, however, the string could no longer exert an upward force on the mug. This meant the only force acting on the mug was gravity, so it started to accelerate downwards, which is the direction in which gravity was pulling it.

Gravity was also pulling on the nut. While you held it in your hand, you fought gravity with an equal upward force, so the nut didn't move. When you released the nut, gravity started pulling it down. However, that wasn't the only force acting on the nut. The string was also pulling on the nut because of the mug's weight. Once again, while you held the nut, your hand fought that force with an equal force pulling the other way, so there was no net force and no motion. However, when you released the nut, the string was free to pull the nut toward the pencil.

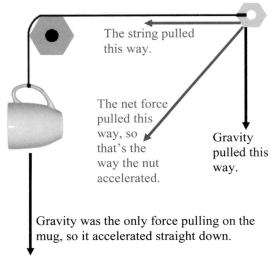

The string pulled this way.

The net force pulled this way, so that's the way the nut accelerated.

Gravity pulled this way.

Gravity was the only force pulling on the mug, so it accelerated straight down.

In your experiment, the net force on the mug was just the force of gravity, but the net force on the nut was the sum of the string's pull and gravity's pull.

So the nut had *two* forces acting on it. One force was gravity, and it was pulling the nut straight down. The other force was the pull from the string, and it was pulling the nut straight toward the pencil. Of course, remember that Newton's Second Law says the nut will accelerate according to the *net* force. Well, if one force is pulling down and the other is pulling towards the pencil, what is the net force? It is a force that is both down and towards the pencil. In other words, the force is diagonal, as shown in the illustration on the left.

Because the net force acting on the nut was diagonal, that's the way the nut started accelerating. So the mug accelerated straight down, and the nut accelerated diagonally down. Well, as this continued, both the mug and the nut picked up speed, moving faster and faster. Because the nut was moving diagonally, it eventually got to the point where it was right under the pencil. At that point, it had a lot of speed, so even though the string was pulling up and gravity was pulling down, it continued to move so it went to the other side of the pencil.

Once the nut reached the other side of the pencil, the string started pulling it back the other way, and (of course) gravity kept pulling it down. But the result of this net force was to keep the nut moving around the pencil. Eventually, it moved completely over and around the pencil, wrapping the string as it went. This happened several times, until the string couldn't slide along the pencil anymore, and the whole system came to a screeching halt.

So once again, the experiment can be explained completely by Newton's laws of motion and gravity. Obviously, gravity is pulling down on both the nut and mug the entire time. The mug has a lot more mass than the nut, so just as Newton's Law of Gravity says, the mug gets pulled down by gravity much harder than the nut. That's why it falls down, pulling the nut with it. Had you replaced the nut with something heavier than the mug, the experiment would have changed dramatically! The mug would have risen once the thing you had dropped had fallen far enough to tighten the string.

Newton's First Law applies to the experiment as well. The mug and nut started moving only when there was a net force acting on them. Of course, Newton's Second Law applies as well, because the nut accelerated in a diagonal direction, which was the direction of the net force. Newton's Third Law applies as well. After all, why did you have to hold on to the pencil so tightly? When the string wrapped around the pencil enough to stop sliding, the string pulled up really hard on the mug to stop its motion. As required by Newton's Third Law, the mug pulled down on the string with an equal force downward. That pulled the pencil down hard, which would have caused you to drop the pencil if you hadn't been holding it tightly.

If you got lost in some of the discussion, don't worry about it. The main point was to show you why it is important to consider the net force that acts on an object. When you did the Ping-Pong ball/hair dryer experiment, the two forces on the Ping-Pong ball were in opposite directions, so they ended up canceling each other out and the ball hovered in the air. However, as this experiment shows, that's not always the case. Often, forces are applied in different directions that are not opposite of one another. As a result, you have to figure out what the net force will be in order to understand the way the object will end up accelerating.

This man's kayak is being acted on by many forces. The waves are pushing it in several directions, and he is using the paddle to push the kayak in a specific direction. To determine how the kayak will accelerate, you need to consider all the forces and add them together to get the net force, which will tell you the direction and amount of acceleration.

LESSON REVIEW

Youngest students: Answer these questions:

1. In your experiment, what two forces acted on the nut?

2. What was the direction of the net force on the nut in your experiment?

Older students: Explain what you did in your experiment, and then list the laws that governed the following results: (a) The fact that the mug fell straight down and was pulled harder than the nut, (b) the fact that the nut moved diagonally and not straight down, (c) the fact that nothing moved until you let go of the nut, and (d) the fact that there was a hard pull on the pencil at the end of the experiment.

Oldest students: Do what the older students are doing. In addition, make a drawing of the experiment when the nut had moved so it was hanging straight down on the string, right alongside the part of the string tied to the mug. Draw the two forces acting on it at that point. What would be the direction of the net force? Why didn't the nut start moving in that direction?

Lesson 81: The Conservation of Momentum

When you were studying Christiaan Huygens in Lesson 50, you learned about the **Law of Momentum Conservation**. It turns out that this law is really just the result of Newton's laws of motion. However, it is treated as a separate law, because it is often easier to analyze a situation using just the Law of Momentum Conservation. To get an idea of what I mean, perform the following experiment.

Marbles on a Track

What you will need:
- Two rulers (You can use just a single ruler if it has a thin groove in the center that will act as a track down which marbles can be rolled.)
- At least five marbles, all the same size
- A flat counter or tabletop
- Two heavy books

What you should do:
1. If you have a ruler with a thin groove down the middle, lay it flat on the table. If not, lay two rulers side by side with just enough space in between for marbles to fit inside. The idea is that you want a track that will keep marbles rolling in a straight line.
2. Put five marbles on the track.

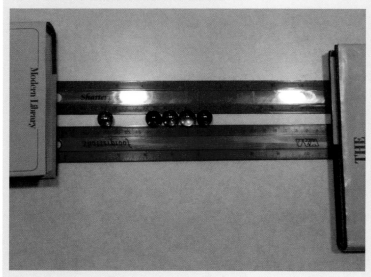

3. Arrange the marbles so there is a lone marble sitting at one end of the track.
4. Group the other four marbles so they are all touching one another and are a short distance away from the lone marble. (See the picture on the left.)
5. Flick the lone marble so it rolls quickly down the track and hits the other four marbles. What happens?
6. Arrange the marbles so there are two marbles touching each other where the lone marble was before, and the other three marbles are touching one another a short distance away.
7. Flick the marble that is nearest to the end of the track so the two marbles roll together and crash into the three marbles that are grouped together. What happens?
8. Arrange the marbles so there are three marbles touching each other where the two marbles were before, and the other two marbles are touching one another a short distance away.
9. Flick the marble that is nearest to the end of the track so the three marbles roll together and crash into the two marbles that are grouped together. What happens?
10. Arrange the marbles so there are four marbles touching each other where the three marbles were before, and the other marble is a short distance away.
11. Flick the marble that is nearest to the end of the track so the four marbles roll together and crash into the lone marble. What happens?
12. You can add more marbles to the system and continue to play with it if you want.
13. Put everything away.

What did you see in the experiment? If all went well, you should have seen that when the lone marble crashed into four marbles, it stopped, and a single marble on the other end of the group of four started rolling in the same direction the lone marble was rolling before it stopped. Now this can be easily understood in terms of Newton's Laws. When the lone marble crashed into the group of four, it applied a force to the marble it hit. Newton's Third Law says that in return, the marble it hit will apply an equal and opposite force back on it. That force caused the marble to accelerate according to Newton's Second Law, and the acceleration stopped the marble from rolling.

Now, of course, since the rolling marble applied a force on the first marble in the group of four, that first marble started to accelerate, as expected by Newton's Second Law. However, it then crashed into the next marble. Once again, using Newton's Third and Second Laws, you know that the marble stopped accelerating, and the marble it hit started accelerating. This continued until the last marble in the group was hit. Since it had nothing to hit, it continued to accelerate, rolling away in the same direction as the original marble.

Now, if you didn't quite follow that, don't worry, because it's confusing to apply those laws over and over again to different marbles down the chain of the collision. It is much easier to simply use the Law of Momentum Conservation. Remember, it says, "In a collision that is not affected by outside influences, the total momentum must always stay the same." So what was the total momentum of the system?

Well, the only thing that was moving was the lone marble, so its weight and speed gave it some momentum. When it hit the other marbles, its momentum went quickly to zero, since its speed went to zero. In order for momentum to be conserved, however, something had to start moving with the same momentum. That's why the one marble at the end started rolling in the same direction as the lone marble was rolling before the collision. Its weight and speed gave it momentum, and that momentum was the same as the lone marble had after you flicked it. In other words, the marble at the end started rolling so that the total momentum did not change in the collision.

Now before I go on, I want to clean up the language a bit. Momentum is actually the mass of an object times its velocity. Mass is a measure of how much matter is in an object, but it is a bit different from weight. The more mass an object has, the more weight it will have, so the two are related. However, they are not exactly the same. You will learn the specific difference between mass and weight if you continue to study science. Of course, you should already know the difference between speed and velocity. Speed tells you only how quickly an object is moving, while velocity also tells you the direction. So like velocity, momentum has a direction to it. If a truck is traveling down the street headed west, it has a momentum that is equal to its mass times its velocity, and that momentum has the same direction as the velocity – west.

These two trucks have about the same mass, but the one on the right is moving faster. That means its momentum is greater than the momentum of the other truck. However, since both trucks are traveling in the same direction, their momenta (the plural of momentum) have the same direction.

In the end, then, when the lone marble crashed into the group of four marbles, momentum was conserved because a single marble with the same mass started rolling away from the group at the same velocity as the lone marble had before it crashed into the group. But what about the rest of the experiment? When two marbles were rolled into a group of three marbles, what happened? Those two marbles stopped, and two marbles at the end started rolling away. Once again, this makes sense in terms of the Law of Momentum Conservation. You initially had two marbles rolling with a certain velocity. After the crash, momentum was conserved by having two marbles roll off the end with the same velocity.

In each part of your experiment, the number of marbles that started rolling after the collision was the same as the number of marbles you initially flicked. That way, the same amount of mass was moving with the same velocity both before and after the collision. As a result, the momentum stayed the same the whole time. There is actually a bit more to this experiment than momentum conservation, and you will learn about that in an upcoming lesson.

Your experiment was actually a simple version of something called **Newton's cradle**, which is pictured below. You might have seen one before, since they are popular desk toys. When you lift one

ball and allow it to fall, it will crash into the other balls. When that happens, one ball on the other end will rise, and the rest will hang motionless. Once the rising ball reaches roughly the height you lifted the first ball to, it will then fall and crash into the other balls, making the original ball rise again. This happens over and over until friction eventually stops all motion. If you lift two balls, the same thing happens, but this time, there will always be two balls in motion. As long as there is at least one ball left hanging, the number of balls you initially raise will be the number that keeps rising and falling after the collision. This is because of the Law of Momentum Conservation and one other thing you will learn about soon.

This Newton's cradle will behave much like your experiment, but the collisions will continue going back and forth.

LESSON REVIEW

Youngest students: Answer these questions:

1. What two things do you need to know to figure out an object's momentum?

2. (Is this statement True or False?) Momentum has a direction.

Older students: Make a "before" and "after" drawing of your experiment, showing the one marble rolling towards the group of four (before) and then the one marble on the end rolling away as all other marbles stayed motionless (after). Explain this in terms of momentum conservation. Write down what happened when you rolled more than one marble, and use momentum conservation to explain it.

Oldest students: Do what the older students are doing. In addition, suppose you rolled two marbles into a group of three and only one marble started rolling off the end. Explain how momentum could still be conserved if that happened. Check your explanation and correct it if it is wrong.

Lesson 82: More on the Conservation of Momentum

Before we leave the conservation of momentum, I want to show you how it works in a slightly different way from what you learned in the previous lesson.

A Boat Powered By Gravity

What you will need:
- A Styrofoam plate that has enough of a raised edge that it is a bit like a very shallow bowl (See the picture below.)
- A Styrofoam cup (the larger the better, but any size works)
- A straw
- A pen
- Scissors
- A small amount of Play-Doh or modeling clay
- A bathtub
- Someone to help you

What you should do:
1. Put the plug in the bathtub and start filling it with water. It needn't be warm, so save energy by using only the cold water. You want to fill it so there is about 2.5 centimeters (1 inch) of water in the tub.
2. Use the pen to poke a hole in the side of the Styrofoam cup near the bottom. It should be just barely large enough for the straw to fit through.
3. Stick the straw in the hole so that most of it sticks out away from the cup.
4. Use the Play-Doh to seal the hole around the straw so that water will not leak out of where the straw is inserted into the cup.
5. Once the bathtub has enough water in it, turn off the tap and allow the water to settle so it is not moving.
6. While you are waiting for the water to settle, fill the cup with water, using a finger or thumb to plug the straw so water doesn't come out of the straw yet.
7. Have your helper put the paper plate on the water at one end of the bathtub and hold it there.
8. Place the cup on the plate so the straw is pointed towards the nearest end of the bathtub and it reaches over the end of the plate. Your "boat" should now look a bit like the picture on the right.
9. Take your finger off the straw and have your helper let go of the plate.
10. What happens after a moment or two?
11. Play with your "boat" for a while, turning it with your hand to see what happens when the straw points a different way. You will need to refill the cup with water when it runs low.
12. Once you are done playing with the "boat," put everything away and clean up your mess.

What happened in the experiment? When you unplugged the straw and your helper let go of the plate, your "boat" should have started moving in the direction opposite of the way the straw was pointing. If you turned the "boat" around, it still moved opposite of the way the straw was pointing. What caused the "boat" to move that way?

Well, you could use Newton's Laws to explain why the boat moved, but as I mentioned in the previous lesson, it is often easier to use the Law of Momentum Conservation. Of course, that might have made sense in the previous lesson. After all, the Law of Momentum Conservation is about collisions, and in the previous lesson, you were colliding marbles into each other. Obviously, then, it made sense to use the Law of Momentum Conservation there.

But how does the Law of Momentum Conservation apply to this experiment? After all, it says, "In a collision that is not affected by outside influences, the total momentum must always stay the same." Your boat didn't collide with anything, so it wasn't involved in a collision, right? Even though it didn't bash into anything, its motion changed, which is the end result of a collision. After all, the "boat" was sitting still on the water, and the water was sitting still in the cup. However, once you and your helper let go, water started moving, and the boat started moving. Since motion changed, momentum changed, and the Law of Momentum Conservation still applies.

As long as this puppy stays still, its momentum is zero. As soon as it starts to move, however, its momentum will no longer be zero.

What was the momentum of the boat before your helper let go? Well, you don't know the mass of the boat, but its velocity was zero. In order to get momentum, you multiply mass by velocity. Anything times zero is zero. That means the momentum of the boat was zero. What was the momentum of the water? Once again, since its velocity was zero, its momentum was also zero. So the momentum of everything in the experiment was zero before you and your helper let go.

According to the Law of Momentum Conservation, then, the momentum should stay zero, even after you and your helper let things go. Did it? You might be surprised to learn that the answer is, "Yes!" But wait a minute? How can that be? After all, momentum is mass times velocity. Once you and your helper let things go, the boat and the water started moving. As a result, they each had velocity. They each also had mass, so they each had momentum. How could the momentum of the system be zero? Because even though each of them had momentum, the boat's momentum was *equal and opposite* of the water's momentum.

Remember, velocity doesn't just mean speed. It also includes direction. So when you multiply mass times velocity to get momentum, there is a direction in that as well (since velocity has direction). The water moved out the straw, towards the back of the bathtub. This means its momentum was in the direction of the back of the bathtub. The "boat," however, moved in exactly the opposite direction – towards the front of the bathtub. So its momentum was directed in exactly the opposite way. What happens when you have two things that are equal and opposite? They cancel each other out!

That tells us why the "boat" ended up moving when you and your helper let things go. Before you let things go, the total momentum was zero. When you unplugged the straw, however, water started moving. As a result, it got a momentum that was directed towards the back of the tub. But the Law of Momentum Conservation says that the momentum of the system needed to stay zero. In order for that to happen, the boat had to start moving in exactly the opposite direction! That way, the net (total) momentum of the system remained at zero!

So the important thing to take from this lesson is that Christiaan Huygens's idea of momentum conservation can be applied to situations besides just two objects colliding into each other. As long as the net force on a system is zero, it applies to any change that occurs in the system's motion. Consider, for example, an astronaut floating motionless in space. There is no net force acting on him. What will happen if he throws an object? He will start moving in the opposite direction! After all, before he threw the object, his momentum was zero. After he threw the object, the total momentum still has to be zero. However, by throwing it, he gave the object momentum. In order to keep the net (total) momentum zero, then, he must have the opposite momentum, which means he has to start moving in the opposite direction!

As he floats motionless, this astronaut's momentum is zero. If he throws an object, he will start moving in the opposite direction so the total momentum stays at zero.

LESSON REVIEW

Youngest students: Answer these questions:

1. In your experiment, what was the total momentum before you and your helper let everything go? What was the total momentum after you and your helper let everything go?

2. (Is this statement True or False?) The Law of Momentum Conservation applies only to collisions.

Older students: Explain what you did in your experiment, and then use the Law of Momentum Conservation to explain why the boat started moving once you and your helper let everything go.

Oldest students: Do what the older students are doing. Also, consider an ice skater. He is standing still on the ice wearing his skates and is carrying a bowling ball. He throws the bowling ball as hard as he can. What will happen to him? Check your answer and correct it if it is wrong.

Lesson 83: Isaac Newton and Viscosity

Newton studied all kinds of motion, including the motion of fluids. It was already well known at the time that some fluids moved easily, while other fluids did not. Perform the following experiment to see what I mean.

Viscosity and Temperature

What you will need:
- A Styrofoam cup
- A pen
- A stopwatch
- Water
- Karo corn syrup (Other brands would probably work.)
- A sink
- A pan
- A spoon for stirring
- A stove
- A pitcher, measuring cup, or some other container with a pour spout
- An adult to help you

What you should do:
1. Use the pen to make a mark near the top of the cup on the inside.
2. Use the pen to make a mark below the first mark you made, as close to the bottom of the cup as you can make it.
3. Use the pen to poke a hole in the bottom of the cup. The hole should be about as wide as the pen.
4. Cover the hole with your finger so water doesn't leak out, and fill the cup up to the mark you made that is nearest to the top of the cup.
5. Hold the cup over the sink, keeping the hole in the bottom plugged with your finger.
6. Have the adult hold the stopwatch. Tell her that she is going to time how long it takes the water to drain out of the cup. She should start the stopwatch and say "go" at the same time. Then, when you say "stop," she should stop the stopwatch.
7. When the adult says "go," unplug the hole in the bottom so the water drains into the sink. Look inside the cup, and when you see the water level reach the second mark you made, say "stop."
8. Write down the time it took for water to drain from the upper mark to the lower mark.
9. Put the container with a pour spout in the sink.
10. Repeat steps 4-8, but this time, use the Karo syrup rather than water. Also, don't let the syrup drain into the sink. Let it drain into the container that has a pour spout.
11. Pour the syrup that is in the container into the pan, and add some more Karo syrup to it. You want enough to fill the cup back up to the mark again.
12. Have an adult help you heat the Karo syrup on the stove. You don't want it to get very hot. Just start stirring it with the spoon, and when it gets much easier to stir, you have heated it up enough.
13. Repeat steps 4-8, this time using the warm Karo syrup and once again letting it drain into the container.
14. Clean up your mess, and ask your parents what to do with the syrup. If you didn't heat it too much, you can use it again, but getting it back into the bottle might be more trouble than it's worth.

What did you see in the experiment? You should have seen that the Karo syrup drained out of the cup much more slowly than the water. That's because Karo syrup has a lot more **viscosity** (vih skos' ih tee), which is the amount of resistance that a fluid has to flowing. A fluid that pours very quickly has a low viscosity, while a fluid that pours very slowly has a high viscosity. Since the Karo syrup has a high viscosity, it resisted flowing, and as a result, it drained out of the cup very slowly. Water, on the other hand, has a low viscosity. That means it doesn't resist flowing much, so it drained out of the cup really quickly.

If you go to the store to buy ketchup, you will find that it is often packaged in plastic bottles that can be squeezed in order to force the ketchup out of the bottom. Many of them can even be turned upside down when they are not being used. Why is that? Well, ketchup has a high viscosity. As a result, it can take a *long* time to pour ketchup out of a glass bottle. When the ketchup is in a bottle that can be squeezed, you can exert a lot of force on the ketchup by squeezing the bottle. That helps to overcome the ketchup's viscosity, allowing you to get the ketchup more quickly.

The bottles that can be stored upside down allow the ketchup to slowly slide down the bottle in between uses. So, when you are ready to use the ketchup, it is concentrated near the opening. That way, when you squeeze, it is ready to come out. Both the plastic nature of the bottle and the ability for it to be stored upside down allows you to better overcome the ketchup's viscosity.

Ketchup pours slowly because of its high viscosity (left). That's why you usually find it in squeeze bottles today (right). Squeezing the bottle allows you to apply force to the ketchup so as to better overcome its viscosity.

But what about the second part of the experiment? You should have seen that the warm Karo syrup drained out of the cup more quickly. It probably wasn't as quick as water, but it was quicker than before it was warmed. That's because as most liquids increase in temperature, their viscosity lowers.

This property is very important when it comes to automobiles. You probably know that an engine needs oil in order to run properly. What does the oil do? It gets in between the moving parts of an engine and keeps those parts from rubbing against one another. This is important, because if the parts rubbed against each other, it would take a lot of energy to move them, and they would wear out really quickly. In addition, friction would produce a lot of heat, melting some of the engine parts! In order to prevent that, you add oil to an engine.

The viscosity of motor oil is very important. If its viscosity is too low, it will not be able to resist motion well enough to keep the moving parts away from each other. If that happens, the parts will rub up against each other, and that would be bad. At the same time, however, if the viscosity is too high, its strong resistance to motion will make it more difficult for the moving parts to actually move. That means the engine will have to work harder for a given amount of motion, and that causes it to burn more fuel. As a result, there is a certain range of viscosities that work well in specific engines. If you ask your parents, you will find that their automobile's manual tells them to use a specific kind of oil, like 10W-30. The viscosity of the oil recommended in the manual is considered ideal for that kind of engine.

Motor oil is added to engines to keep the moving parts from rubbing up against one another. Its viscosity helps it do its job.

Of course, as the engine warms, the oil gets warm, and the viscosity changes. If the engine gets too hot, the oil's viscosity might get too low, and the moving parts might start rubbing against one another. Because of this, oils are made so that a change in temperature doesn't change their viscosity nearly as much as what you observed in your experiment. Isaac Newton helped us understand the principles involved in all of this, and he even developed a mathematical equation to describe viscosity. While the equation doesn't work for all fluids, it works for a lot of fluids, and it is still used today when dealing with specific kinds of fluids.

LESSON REVIEW

Youngest students: Answer these questions:

1. Fill in the blank: Viscosity is a measure of how a fluid _____ motion.

2. When most fluids are heated, what happens to their viscosity?

Older students: Define viscosity in your own words, and write how it typically changes with temperature. Explain what motor oil does in an automobile engine.

Oldest students: Do what the older students are doing. In addition, explain why motor oil should have a high viscosity, but not too high a viscosity.

Lesson 84: One More Lesson on Isaac Newton

In the past 16 lessons, you have learned a lot about Isaac Newton's scientific accomplishments. However, you haven't learned about all of them. For example, he designed a new kind of telescope known as a **reflecting telescope**. Rather than using two lenses, as all telescopes up to this point in history used, his used two mirrors and one lens. This design allows the viewer to see distant objects with more clarity, especially when those objects are rather dim. As a result, most telescopes used in research these days are reflecting telescopes. So not only did Isaac Newton provide us with laws that explain why the planets move in the night sky the way they do, he also invented a device that helped astronomers better study the objects in the sky.

Also, as I mentioned when I introduced you to him in Lesson 68, he made many advances in the field of mathematics. He discovered an entire field of mathematics called **calculus** (kal' kyuh lus). If you take a lot of math in your schooling, you might eventually reach calculus in your late high school years. It is a very important mathematical subject for scientists. Indeed, many scientists today couldn't do their research without it. In addition to inventing this field of math, he also showed how math could be applied to the study of motion and gravity.

Despite all these accomplishments in natural philosophy, there were some who thought Newton was wrong on some very important things. For example, even though he could use his Law of Universal Gravitation to explain how the planets orbit the sun as well as why things fall to the earth the way they do, there were some who thought he had to be wrong about it. Why? Perform the following experiment to get an idea.

Moving Foil Without Touching It

What you will need:
- A square of aluminum foil that is about 5 centimeters x 5 centimeters (2 inches x 2 inches)
- A sewing needle
- A lump of Play-Doh or modeling clay
- A balloon

What you should do:
1. Fold the square of aluminum in half.
2. Fold it in half again, this time folding in the opposite direction.
3. Unfold the square. The folds should separate it into four equal sections.
4. Make a small lump of clay and put it on a table or counter.
5. Put the sewing needle in the lump of clay so the sharp end sticks straight up in the air.
6. Put the square of foil on the sharp end of the needle right where the two fold lines cross each other.

7. Push down on the edges of the foil a bit so it forms an umbrella-like shape and work it until the square balances on the needle. At this point, it should look a bit like the picture above.
8. Blow up the balloon and tie it off.
9. Rub the balloon against your hair so it becomes electrically charged.
10. Hold the balloon far from the foil, but be sure the part of the balloon that you rubbed in your hair is pointed towards the foil.

11. Slowly bring the balloon towards the foil. You don't want to create a wind, so move the balloon very slowly.
12. Long before the balloon reaches the foil, you should see the foil react to the balloon by tilting. When you see that happen, slowly move the balloon in a circle around the foil. You should be able to make the foil spin simply by moving the balloon.
13. Play around with the system for a while, seeing how you can make the foil move with the balloon, even though the balloon never touches the foil. You may have to rub the balloon in your hair again to refresh its electrical charge from time to time, depending on how long you play with it.
14. When you are done, clean up your mess.

Why were you able to move the foil without ever touching it? If you remember what you learned in Lesson 48, you probably already know. When you rubbed the balloon in your hair, it became electrically charged. As Otto von Guericke showed, electrical charges can produce *a lot* of force. That force attracted the foil towards the balloon. By moving the balloon, you made that attractive force move the foil the way you wanted it to move.

While it doesn't bother you or me, this kind of motion really upset most natural philosophers of Newton's day. They didn't like the idea of one object pushing or pulling another object unless the objects were in contact with one another. You can push on a rock because you are touching the rock. You can twirl a toy on a string because the string connects you to the toy. In Newton's day, most natural philosophers thought all forces had to work that way. They assumed the earth pulled objects down to itself because the earth was connected to the objects in some way. For example, some thought that the air connected the earth to all the objects upon which it pulled.

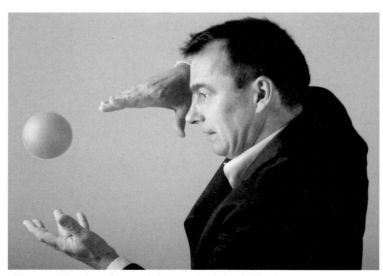

This magician is using a trick to make it look like he can control the ball without touching it. Many natural philosophers thought Newton's Universal Law of Gravitation was too much like magic.

The problem with Newton's idea of gravity, as far as these natural philosophers were concerned, was that it didn't explain how the sun was physically connected to all the planets, nor did it explain how the planets were connected to one another. Yet Newton's Law of Universal Gravitation said that everything with mass was attracted to everything else with mass. In some ways, this was almost like magic, and of course, that was not the way natural philosophers wanted to explain how the world worked! In fact, one of the natural philosophers you will learn about in an upcoming lesson **Gottfried** (got' freet) **Wilhelm** (vil' helm) **Leibniz** (libe' nits), said that Newton's Law of Universal Gravitation "…appears to me rather strange and I cannot believe it can be justified. If every body is heavy it follows necessarily (whatever his supporters say and however passionately they deny it) that gravity will be a scholastic occult quality or else the effect of a miracle." [*The Leibniz-Clarke Correspondence*, H. G. Alexander (Ed), Manchester University Press 1998, p. 184]

Do you know what the word "occult" means? It refers to magical, dark practices unrelated to the miracles that God does. So Leibniz was essentially saying that Newton's Law of Universal

Gravitation was either relying on magic or miracles from God. While Leibniz and most natural philosophers at that time had no problem believing that God performs miracles, they thought such things were rare and weren't required in order to keep the world running properly.

Of course, since he was a Christian, Newton believed that God does perform miracles. He also believed that God was intimately involved in each person's life. In fact, at one point in his life, he wrote a series of 12 statements that described what he believed. Here is the eighth:

> We are to return thanks to the Father alone for creating us, and giving us food and raiment and other blessings of this life, and whatsoever we are to thank him for, or desire that he would do for us, we ask of him immediately in the name of Christ. [Sir David Brewster, *Memoirs of the Life, Writings, and Discoveries of Sir Isaac Newton, Volume 2*, Thomas Constable and Company 1855, p. 349]

So Newton didn't have a problem with the idea that God worked supernaturally in the world.

At the same time, he didn't think gravity was a miracle that God had to keep doing. He was willing to believe that there was some natural way one object could apply a force to another object without being in contact with it, much like the natural way you were able to move the foil in your experiment. However, he did believe that God had to work continually to keep the universe running properly, because there were aspects of how the world worked that he couldn't understand without assuming that God was forcing it to work in that way.

That went against the views of many natural philosophers of his day. As you've already learned, many thought of God as such a great Craftsman that He could make the universe so that it runs completely on its own. As we have learned more science, we have learned that Newton's opponents were probably right on that point. God clearly performs miracles from time to time (like the resurrection of Jesus and the way He does miracles in people's lives), but the day-to-day running of the universe seems to happen naturally, without any direct intervention from God. Even though Newton was probably wrong on that specific point, he clearly taught us a lot about how the universe works, which is why he is considered one of the greatest scientists (if not the greatest) who ever lived!

LESSON REVIEW

Youngest students: Answer these questions:

1. (Is this statement True or False?) Objects must be physically connected for one to apply a force to the other.

2. Fill in the blank: Newton thought _____ had to continually act to keep the universe running.

Older students: Explain what some natural philosophers didn't like about Newton's Universal Law of Gravitation. In addition, discuss the difference between the way Leibniz saw God working in the universe and the way Newton did. Who was most likely correct?

Oldest students: Do what the older students are doing. In addition, do some research and find out how you can tell a reflecting telescope from the other kind of telescope, which is called a refracting telescope. Check your answer and correct it if it is wrong.

Lesson 85: Guillaume Amontons (1663 – 1705)

Newton had to deal with friction in all of his experiments. It fights against motion, and since Newton was studying motion, he had to continually think about how friction was affecting his work. Surprisingly, however, he wasn't the one who really advanced our understanding of friction. Instead, **Guillaume** (gee' ohm) **Amontons** (uh mahn' tahn) is considered the first person to really characterize friction well. However, it is important to note that some of that work had already been done by Leonardo da Vinci. If you learned about that great natural philosopher, you know that he studied friction and wrote down some details regarding how it works. However, like much of his work, it was never published, so most natural philosophers didn't know about it.

Based on what we know of history, it doesn't look like Amontons was aware of da Vinci's work and started using it as his own. Instead, it seems that he independently discovered what da Vinci had already discovered about 200 years before him. In case you didn't study da Vinci's work (or don't remember what you studied), let's start with a surprising experiment.

The Power of Friction

What you will need:
- Two paperback books that are roughly the same size and thickness (They should be small enough to be held easily in one hand.)

What you should do:
1. Hold one book in one hand and the other book in the other hand.
2. Open both books to the very end so you see the inside of the back cover.
3. Overlap the back covers so that about one-half of one book's cover overlaps with one-half of the other book's cover.

4. Flip the pages of each book so that the pages start overlapping just like the back covers. Don't worry about getting every page in one book to overlap with every page in the other book. Just make it so that lots of the pages overlap. See the picture on the left.
5. Once you have the books arranged so that lots of the pages overlap with one another, try as hard as you can to pull the two books apart.
6. Give the books to the strongest person around and have that person try to pull the books apart.
7. To get the books apart, you need to open them up and remove the overlap in the pages. Once you remove the overlap on most of the pages, the books will come apart easily.
8. Put the books away.

Were you surprised by the results of the experiment? Most people are. When you lay one piece of paper on another piece of paper, it is easy to slide them against one another. However, there is friction between them, fighting that motion. The friction isn't very strong compared to the force you are using to slide the papers, however, so the papers slide easily against one another. The more pieces of paper you pile on top of each other, the more force you have to use to overcome friction. When you get enough papers rubbing against each other, the frictional force is so great that you can't slide them against each other, even when you use all your strength!

This brings us to the first principle of friction. Remember, da Vinci discovered this first, but Amontons rediscovered it:

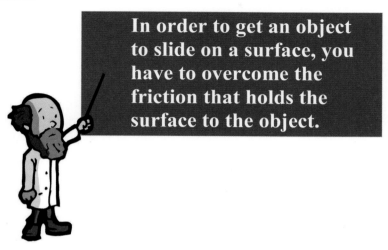

In order to get an object to slide on a surface, you have to overcome the friction that holds the surface to the object.

You couldn't pull the books apart because you couldn't overcome all the friction that was fighting the motion on every page. In terms of this principle, then, the pages of one book were the "object," while the pages of the other book were the "surface." You couldn't get the object to slide on the surface, because you couldn't overcome the friction between the object (one book's pages) and the surface (the other book's pages).

Amontons went further than da Vinci in trying to understand friction. He wanted to know what actually caused it, and so he developed what scientists today call a **model** for friction. When you hear that word, what do you think of? I think of a kit that comes in many pieces. When you put those pieces together just right, you get a miniature version of something in real life. For example, when you follow the instructions in a model car kit, you end up getting a miniature version of the car. Something that looks like the car, but isn't really the car. It is just a representation of the car.

Scientists use models as well. These models are supposed to help them understand what they are studying. Typically, they represent something that either can't be seen very well or studied directly. The model helps them visualize what they are studying so they can understand it better. So what was Amontons's model for friction? He thought that if you studied two surfaces sliding against one another, you would see that each one of them has tiny bumps and grooves in them. No matter how smooth they feel to the touch, if you could magnify them enough, you would see bumps and grooves, as shown in the drawing on the left.

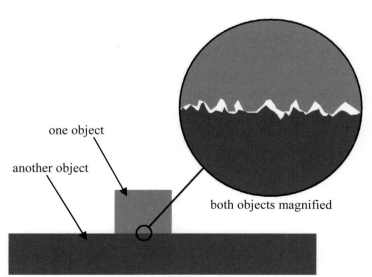

one object

another object

both objects magnified

In this drawing, the circle represents a region that is magnified. Even though the two objects look smooth, if you magnify them enough, you will find little bumps and grooves in them.

Amontons thought that these bumps and grooves would crash into each other when one or both objects started moving, and those crashes, of course, would make it harder for them to move. He called these bumps and grooves **irregularities** in each surface, and as far as he was concerned, they are what caused friction. If you could somehow make two perfectly smooth surfaces with no irregularities whatsoever, then there would be little or no friction between them, and they would slide across one another really easily.

This makes a lot of sense if you think about it. After all, the pages in the books you used in your experiment feel fairly smooth, but all you have to do is look at them through a magnifying glass to see that there are a lot of irregularities in their surface. As a result, there is a lot of chance for friction, and that's why it was so hard to pull them apart.

Also, it makes a lot of sense that smooth surfaces have very little friction. After all, think about the slipperiest surface you know. For most people, it's ice, and the smoother the ice is, the slipperier it becomes. Smooth ice is so slippery that you can easily fall and hurt yourself when you try to walk on it. Why is it slippery? Because you use the friction between your shoes and the surface upon which you are walking to keep a grip on the surface and maintain your balance. There is not much friction between your shoes and smooth ice, so you have a hard time keeping your balance.

Smooth ice produces very little friction with your shoes and is so slippery that it is hard to walk on it without falling.

It's important to realize that although Amontons's model makes a lot of sense, it isn't actually the main cause of friction. The irregularities on surfaces do contribute to friction, but they are not the main cause. It took a lot more study of how surfaces slide against one another (and lot more understanding of chemistry) before scientists learned the main cause of friction.

LESSON REVIEW

Youngest students: Answer these questions:

1. What must you overcome to get two surfaces to slide against one another?

2. Fill in the blank: Amontons thought that _____ on surfaces were the main cause of friction.

Older students: Explain what you did in your experiment, and then explain why it is easy to slide one piece of paper across another piece, but it was impossible to slide most of the pages of one book across the pages of the other book. In addition, explain what Amontons thought was the cause of friction.

Oldest students: Do what the older students are doing. In addition, explain what a scientific model is and why Amontons's view of friction is based on a model of friction.

Lesson 86: More about Guillaume Amontons and Friction

Friction is such an important concept that I want to spend two more lessons on it before we move on. There are two more things that Amontons discovered about friction, and we will cover them both in this lesson. Now remember, most of Amontons's work on friction was a rediscovery of Leonardo da Vinci's work on friction, and that's the case here. Both of these concepts were already worked out by da Vinci, but Amontons did a lot more verification of them than da Vinci did. To learn both of these concepts, let's start with an experiment.

Two Properties of Friction

What you will need:
- 🖐 An empty CD case
- 🖐 About a meter (about three feet) of string
- 🖐 Tape
- 🖐 A small plastic bag (like a Ziploc bag)
- 🖐 At least 30 pennies
- 🖐 A small plastic bottle with a lid (like the ones water comes in)
- 🖐 A funnel
- 🖐 A ¼-cup measuring cup
- 🖐 A flat counter or tabletop
- 🖐 A thin piece of cardboard (like you find on the back of a pad of paper)
- 🖐 Scissors

What you should do:
1. Tape one end of the string securely to the top of the CD case.
2. Tape the other end of the string securely to the top of the plastic bag.
3. Put the CD case on the counter so the side that doesn't have string taped to it is resting on the counter.
4. Drape the string across the counter so the bag hangs off the edge of the counter.
5. Use the funnel and measuring cup to put ¼ cup of water in the water bottle.
6. Put the lid on the bottle.
7. Place the bottle on the center of the CD case. Your experiment should now look something like the picture on the right.
8. Hold the bag in one hand.
9. With the other hand, add a penny to the bag.
10. Gently release the bag.
11. If the CD case and bottle don't start sliding across the counter, repeat steps 8-10. Continue to add pennies until you have enough pennies in the bag to make the CD case and bottle slide across the counter. Count the pennies as you go so you know how many pennies it took to get the CD case and bottle sliding.
12. Catch the CD case and bottle before they slide off the edge of the counter!
13. Write down the number of pennies it took to get the CD case and bottle to slide.
14. If the counter got wet, dry it off.
15. Use the funnel and measuring cup to add another ¼ cup of water to the bottle.
16. Add an additional ¼ cup of water to the bottle. You now have ¾ cup of water in the bottle.
17. Put the lid back on the bottle.

18. Put the bottle back on the CD case exactly like it was before.
19. You should still have the pennies in the bag from what you did before. Once you set the system up again, they should not cause the bottle and CD case to slide on the counter.
20. Start adding pennies again just as before, counting as you go. It is important to gently release the bag each time a new penny is added. Once again, catch the CD case and bottle before they slide off the counter, and write down the number of pennies it took to get them to slide.
21. Use the scissors to cut out a square of cardboard that is the same size and shape as the CD case.
22. Tape the cardboard to the bottom of the CD case (the side to which the string is not taped). Don't let the tape touch the bottom of the cardboard. Instead, curl the tape into a few tubes so it can be stuck to the bottom of the CD case. Then, push the cardboard onto the tubes of tape. That way, the tape is between the cardboard and the CD case but still holds the cardboard firmly in place.
23. Repeat everything you did before, starting with ¼ cup of water in the bottle.
24. Write down the number of pennies it took. How does that compare to the number of pennies for the bottle with ¼ cup of water and the CD case without cardboard?
25. Repeat everything one last time, but put two more ¼ cups of water in the bottle so that once again there is ¾ cup of water in the bottle.
26. Write down the number of pennies it took to move the CD case with cardboard on the bottom and the bottle with ¾ cup of water in it. How does that compare to the previous time without cardboard?
27. Clean up your mess, but keep the string and the attached bag. You will use them in the next lesson.

What did you see in the experiment? It should have taken more pennies to move the CD case when it had ¾ cup of water in it. Since the weight of the pennies was the force being used to pull the CD case and bottle, that means it took more force to get the system moving the more mass it had. That probably makes sense to you, but I need to make sure you understand why. This isn't the result of Newton's Second Law.

Most students think Newton's Second Law says it will take more force to get a heavier object *moving*, but it doesn't. Newton's Second Law says the *amount* that an object's motion changes is based on the force used. A small force changes an object's motion only a little, but a large force changes an object's motion a lot. Regardless of the force, however, motion changes. So Newton's Second Law would only say that the bottle would slide *more slowly* across the table the fewer the number of pennies in the bag. If there were no friction, even a single penny would move the bottle and CD case. They would move them slowly, but they would move.

If there were no friction between the rock and the ground, this baby could push it. It would just move very slowly.

The reason you had to put several pennies in the bag to get the system sliding is that you had to overcome the friction between the CD case and the counter. Thus, the number of pennies told you about how much *friction* was there. The more pennies it took to move the CD and bottle, the more friction there was. So the first part of the experiment showed you that the heavier something is, the more friction that exists between it and a surface. That's why it's hard to slide things that are heavy. Without friction, even the heaviest object would slide when pushed on with a tiny force. It would just slide very slowly. When friction exists, it takes force to overcome the friction, and the heavier the object is, the more friction there is between it and the surface over which you are sliding it. As a result, the larger the force required to move it.

So the first part of your experiment showed that the heavier an object is, the greater the friction between it and the surface upon which it sits. What about the second part of the experiment? The number of pennies required to slide the CD case and bottle when there was cardboard on the bottom of the CD case was different, wasn't it? That's because you changed the surface that sat on the counter. The plastic of the CD case was no longer touching the counter; the cardboard was.

So in the second part of your experiment, you were measuring the friction between the counter and the cardboard. It still took more pennies the heavier the bottle was, but each time it took a different number from what it took when there was no cardboard at the bottom of the CD case. This tells us that the amount of friction depends on the nature of the two surfaces that are sliding against one another. Thus, we have two more important things to remember about friction:

> **The amount of friction depends on the nature of the surfaces that are moving against one another. Also, the heavier the object, the more friction between it and any surface on which it sits.**

Once again, while da Vinci figured this out almost 200 years before Amontons, Amontons did a lot to confirm that it is true.

LESSON REVIEW

Youngest students: Answer these questions:

1. Fill in the blank: The amount of friction depends on the nature of the _____ moving against one another.

2. What happens to the amount of friction the heavier an object becomes?

Older students: Rewrite the statement in the green box above and explain how your experiment demonstrated it to be true.

Oldest students: Do what the older students are doing. In addition, in the experiment, you were asked to release the bag gently. Explain why that would be important. Check your explanation and correct it if it is wrong.

Lesson 87: One More Thing About Friction

Before we leave the subject of friction, I want to make it clear that while friction does resist motion, it can be used to aid motion in some situations. To understand what I mean, perform the following experiment.

Friction Can Aid Motion

What you will need:
- The string and bag from the previous lesson
- The counter or tabletop from the previous lesson
- Tape
- A toy car that doesn't have a motor
- At least 30 pennies

What you should do:
1. If the bag isn't still attached to one end of the string like it was in the previous experiment, use the tape to reattach it now.
2. Tape the other end of the string to the underside of the toy car.
3. Repeat the experiment you did in the previous lesson, but this time, determine how many pennies it takes to get the car to start rolling across the counter. Write down the number of pennies you determined.
4. Tape the sides of all four wheels on the car to the body of the car so they cannot spin. Tape them so that the tape you are using does not touch the counter in any way when you set the car on it. In the end, you want the tires to rest on the counter just like they did before. You just don't want them to spin.
5. Repeat the experiment again, determining how many pennies it takes to get the car to move across the counter without its wheels spinning. Write down the number of pennies you determined.
6. Clean up your mess and put everything away.

The results of the experiment probably didn't surprise you, did they? When the car's tires were free to spin, it took very few pennies to get the car rolling. In fact, the weight of the plastic bag might have been enough to get the car moving, so you might not have used any pennies at all. However, once the wheels were taped so they couldn't move, it took the weight of a few pennies to get the car moving, didn't it?

Even though the results probably didn't surprise you, it might be hard for you to explain *why* it is easier to move the car when its wheels are allowed to spin. After all, think about the friction involved in each situation. The surfaces stayed the same in both parts of the experiment, didn't they? The same wheels touched the same counter in both cases. Also, the weight of the car didn't change between the two parts of your experiment. However, even though the friction between the wheels and the counter was the same, it was harder to move the car in the second part of the experiment. Why?

Obviously, it has something to do with the wheels being able to spin, but what is it? What do spinning wheels do to help deal with friction? Well, when the car is pulled (or pushed) by an outside force, friction "grabs on" to the wheel, keeping it from sliding. However, since the wheel is free to spin, the thing to which the wheel is attached (the car, for example) can continue to move. As a result, the friction between the wheel and the surface doesn't hinder the motion of the car. The car doesn't have to overcome that friction to get moving. In fact, *friction holds onto the wheel so that the car can move.* In the first part of your experiment, then, the weight of the pennies and the bag didn't have to overcome the friction between the wheels and the counter.

Now, of course, there was still friction to overcome. The wheels are on an axle, a rod that connects the center of the wheel to the car. In order for the wheels to spin, that axle has to spin, and there is friction between the axle and the car. That's why the car will eventually come to a stop after you push it and let it start rolling on its own. The friction between the car and axle will work against the motion, eventually causing it to come to a halt.

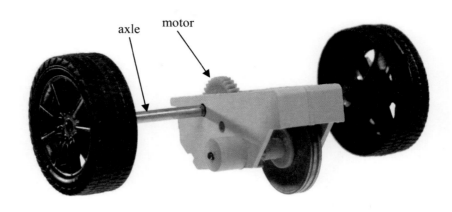

This is the back end of a toy car. Notice the rod that connects the wheel to the motor. That's the axle of the car. Even though the car in your experiment didn't have a motor, its wheels were still connected to the car by an axle.

What can you say about this friction, however? It's a lot smaller than the friction between the wheel and the counter. How can I say that? Well, think about the second part of your experiment. Once you taped the wheels so they could not roll, the only way to get the car moving was to let it slide across the counter. In order for that to happen, the weight of the pennies and bag had to overcome the friction between the wheels and the counter. That took more pennies, meaning it took more force to overcome that friction.

Because you needed less force to get the car rolling than you did to get the car sliding, you know that the friction involved in rolling (the friction between the axle and the wheel) was smaller than the friction involved in sliding (the friction between the wheels and the counter). The key, however, is to realize that without friction between the wheel and the counter, the car wouldn't roll at all. It would just slide. After all, the wheel rolls because the friction between it and the counter holds on to the wheel, forcing the axle to turn as the car moves. In the end, then, the wheels use friction to help move the car!

Now let's talk about a different kind of car. The car in your experiment didn't have a motor. It rolls only because it is pushed or pulled. However, some toy cars (and all real cars) have motors. What do the motors do? They spin the axle, which causes the wheel to start to turn. Look, for example, at the picture above. The motor is connected to the axle. As the gears in the motor spin, the axle spins, and that makes the wheels spin. When the wheels spin, the car moves.

But wait a minute. Why does the car move just because the wheels spin? If the car is not moving, Newton's First Law says that the only way it will start moving is if a force acts on the car. What force is acting on the car to make it move? Believe it or not, it's friction that is pushing on the car, making it move!

When the wheels on a car turn, they apply a force to the road. What does Newton's Third Law say must happen? It says the road has to apply an equal and opposite force on the wheel. What is that equal and opposite force? It's *friction*! The wheel pushes on the road, and friction pushes in the

The wheel spins this way.

The wheel pushes on the road this way.

Friction pushes this way, moving the car.

A car's wheels use friction to push the car in the direction opposite the direction in which the wheels are spinning.

opposite direction with an equal amount of force. So friction pushes on the wheel in the direction opposite of the way it is turning. That actually pushes the car forward! So once again, the wheels on a car are actually using friction to make the car move.

If you find this a bit hard to believe, think about what happens when a car gets stuck in snow and ice. The driver pushes down on the accelerator, which causes the motor to spin the axle, and the wheels start to spin. However, the car doesn't go anywhere, because there isn't enough friction between the tires and the road. As a result, there isn't a strong enough force to push the car in the opposite direction that the wheels are pushing, so even though the wheels spin like mad, the car doesn't go anywhere. Have you ever been in a situation like that before? I have. Do you know how I got out of it? I shoveled sand in between the wheel and the snow. Do you know what that did? It increased the friction between the wheel and the snow. With enough sand, the frictional force increased enough to produce a strong enough force to push the car, and I got out of the snow!

This is why the tires on cars have **treads** – the grooves and ridges you see when you look at your car's tires. Because there needs to be a lot of friction between the tires and the road, anything that reduces that friction must be eliminated. Well, when there is a lot of water on the road, the water can get in between the tire and the road's surface, reducing friction. That will cause the wheels to start spinning against the road, just as if they were on ice. This, of course, will reduce the control that the driver has on the car. Treads are designed to channel the water away from the tires so that doesn't happen.

LESSON REVIEW

Youngest students: Answer these questions:

1. (Is this statement True or False?) Wheels on a car use friction to produce the car's motion.

2. If a tire doesn't have good treads, what can happen to the car when it rains?

Older students: Explain how wheels on a motorized car use friction to produce motion and why a car's tires have treads.

Oldest students: Do what the older students are doing. In addition, explain what friction has to be overcome by a car in order to be able to move.

Lesson 88: Gottfried Wilhelm Leibniz (1646 – 1716)

As you've already learned, Newton discovered an entirely new kind of math that we now call calculus. Well, it turns out that he wasn't the only one who made that discovery. **Gottfried** (got' freet) **Wilhelm** (vil' helm) **Leibniz** (libe' nitz) was working during the same time period, and he independently came up with calculus. This led to some dispute between the two, but in the end, most people credit them both with the discovery.

Leibniz's father was a university professor, but he died when the boy was only six years old. The next year, Leibniz was given free access to his father's library, which contained books on a wide range of subjects. Most of those books were in Latin, however, so he had to learn Latin to make the best use of his father's library. He eventually went to the same university where his father had taught (the University of Leipzig) and received a degree in philosophy and then later went to the University of Altdorf to get a degree in law. He worked as an alchemist for a while, but eventually started working as an assistant to a statesman. He then met Christiaan Huygens, and with Huygens as a mentor, began making incredible contributions to both natural philosophy and mathematics. Even though he continued to do great things in those fields, he made a living by working in law and politics.

This is a statue of Leibniz that was put in the courtyard of the University of Leipzig, where his father taught and he got his first degree.

In addition to everything he did in mathematics, Leibniz discovered the Law of Energy Conservation, which says, "Energy cannot be created or destroyed. It can only be converted from one form to another." You have probably learned about this important law already, but there are so many ways to use this law it is important for you to study it in more depth. Let's start with an experiment.

Conservation of Mechanical Energy

What you will need:
- About a meter (3 feet) of string (not thread)
- Two marbles
- Tape
- Scissors
- Two chairs of the same height (or other heavy items to which string can be tied)

What you should do:
1. Place the chairs back-to-back with at least 46 centimeters (18 inches) between them.
2. Cut a length of string that can be tied to each chair and span the distance between them.
3. Tie one end of the string to one chair and the other end to the other chair.
4. Cut two more lengths of string about 15 centimeters (6 inches) long. They should be the same length.

5. Tie each length of string to the string that is strung between the chairs. They should be near the center and about 5 centimeters (2 inches) apart from one another.

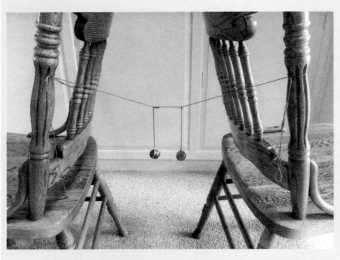

6. Tape a marble to the end of each string. Try to tape them so the marbles hang at about the same height.
7. Adjust the position of the two chairs so there is a slight bow in the string that is strung between the chairs. It shouldn't be a big bow, but the string should not be tight and straight. Your experiment should now look a bit like the picture on the left.
8. Slowly pull back on one of the marbles so it lifts up in the air towards you. Keep the string that is attached to the marble straight, and pull it straight back towards you so that when you release it, it will swing back and forth without hitting the other marble.
9. Release the marble and watch what happens.
10. After you have watched the system for a while, use your hands to stop all the motion so the marbles are hanging straight down again.
11. Repeat steps 8 and 9, this time using the other marble. Once again, watch what happens.
12. Clean up your mess.

What did you see in the experiment? At first, the marble you lifted should have started swinging back and forth. As you already know from Lesson 24, such a system is called a pendulum. But what happened after a little while? The pendulum started to slow down, and the *other* pendulum began to start swinging back and forth. If the string between the chairs was set with the right bow in it, the other pendulum should have gained speed while the first one slowed down. Eventually, the first one should have nearly stopped, while the other pendulum started swinging nearly as fast as the first one did. However, that shouldn't have lasted long, either. Eventually, the motion went back to the first pendulum. This exchange of motion should have continued for quite a while.

To understand the experiment, remember that when things are in motion, they have energy, which you may already know is called **mechanical energy**. When you lifted the marble, you added energy to it, and when you released it, it started swinging with that amount of energy. The height to which the marble rose (and the speed at which the marble swung) was determined by the amount of energy you gave to the pendulum.

However, because the two pendulums were connected with the string between the chairs, that energy could be transferred from one pendulum to the other. So as you watched, the first pendulum transferred its energy to the second pendulum. The Law of Energy Conservation says that energy can't be created or destroyed, so as the first pendulum started giving energy to the second one, it had to lose energy. That's why it slowed down as the other one sped up. Once again, if you had adjusted the string properly, you saw the first pendulum almost come to a halt, because it had given almost all its energy to the other pendulum. At that point, the other pendulum was swinging as fast and as high as the first one did just after you had released the marble.

This kind of motion would have gone on forever if there hadn't been any friction between the marbles and the air. However, because friction kept pulling energy out of the system, it eventually came to a halt. Even then, though, the energy wasn't lost. The friction just converted the mechanical energy into heat energy. The heat wasn't enough for you to feel, but it was definitely there. To see how friction can convert mechanical energy into heat energy, just rub your palms together back and forth really quickly. You will feel them warm up, because the friction between them converts the mechanical energy of your hands' motion into heat energy.

It's important to note that Leibniz's discussion of the conservation of energy applied only to mechanical energy. It took longer for scientists to determine the different kinds of energy in creation and how it was always conserved. Nevertheless, Leibniz started scientists thinking that way, and eventually, the Law of Energy Conservation was applied to all energy, regardless of the form it takes.

Do you remember crashing marbles together in Lesson 81? When you crashed one marble into a group of marbles, a single marble came out the other end. When you crashed two marbles into the group, two marbles came out the other end. This demonstrated the Law of Momentum Conservation. However, it also demonstrated the Law of Energy Conservation. After all, remember that momentum is just the mass of the object times its velocity. When you crashed two marbles into the group, momentum would have been conserved if a single marble came out the other side traveling at twice the velocity as the two original marbles. With twice the velocity, that single marble would have had the same momentum as the two marbles had before the crash. However, that single marble traveling at twice the velocity of the other two marbles would have had more mechanical energy. That can't happen, so your marble experiment behaved the way it did not only because of the Law of Momentum Conservation but also because of the Law of Energy Conservation!

Leibniz understood that the conservation of energy was a part of the order with which God created the world. He once wrote, "…in whatever manner God created the world, it would always have been regular and in a certain general order. God, however, has chosen the most perfect, that is to say, the one which is at the same time the simplest in hypothesis and the richest in phenomena." [Stuart Hampshire, *The Age of Reason*, Braziller 1957, p. 169]

LESSON REVIEW

Youngest students: Answer these questions:

1. What does the Law of Energy Conservation say?

2. What is mechanical energy?

Older students: Explain your experiment and how it demonstrates the Law of Energy Conservation for mechanical energy. In the process, define mechanical energy.

Oldest students: Do what the older students are doing. In addition, think about a car's engine. It gets so hot that it has to have a cooling system in it. Surprisingly, most of that heat doesn't come from the gasoline being burned. Where does it come from? Write down the question and your answer, and then check your answer. Correct it if it is wrong.

NOTE: The experiment in Lesson 90 (the next non-challenge lesson) requires a place outside that is reasonably flat and about 100 meters (100 yards) long. You will need to consider the weather, and you might need to plan a trip to a park, depending on what your surroundings are like.

Lesson 89: More on Gottfried Wilhelm Leibniz

As I mentioned in the previous lesson, Leibniz did a lot of work in mathematics as well as natural philosophy. While I don't often highlight the math that natural philosophers of the past did, I want to make an exception in this case. You will probably see why as the lesson proceeds.

Two Games of Twenty Questions

What you will need:
- Someone to help you

What you should do:
1. Sit down in a comfortable room with your helper.
2. Look around the room and choose something you see.
3. Tell your helper that he or she is supposed to figure out what object you are thinking about. Don't tell your helper it is in the room. Your helper can ask any question he or she wants, but each question must be answered with only "yes" or "no." Do not give any answers other than one of those two.
4. How many questions did your helper need to determine what object you had chosen?
5. Now think of something that you have never seen in person before. Perhaps you have only heard about it or seen pictures of it. It can be real or fictional, as long as it is something your helper has also heard of. Don't tell your helper it is something he or she has never seen.
6. Once again, have your helper ask you questions, and answer those questions only with a "yes" or "no."
7. How many questions did it take for your helper to guess what you were thinking of?

Computers run on instructions that are essentially questions which can be answered with either a "yes" or a "no."

Was your helper able to figure out what you were thinking of in both cases? Probably. Most likely, however, it took fewer questions to figure out what you were thinking of in the first game. That's because when you thought of something with which your helper was familiar, it was easier for him or her to figure it out. The less familiar the object is, the more questions it usually takes to figure out what object you are thinking of.

Why in the world did I have you play those two games? Because believe it or not, they illustrate how a computer "thinks." Computers don't really think, of course, but they do perform tasks based on a set of instructions, and those instructions boil down to a series of questions that are answered by "yes" or "no."

These instructions are built on a system of logic called **binary logic**. If you aren't familiar with the word "logic," it describes a very specific form of reasoning that allows you to come to correct conclusions as long as you start out with correct assumptions. The word "binary," means there are two parts. So binary logic is a system of reasoning built on only two parts: "yes" and "no."

Binary logic in computers is performed using **binary numbers**. What do you think a binary number would be? It is a number that has only two digits in it: 0 and 1. Believe it or not, any number in the world can be represented with just 1's and 0's! Consider, for example, the number 101. What does that number represent? Well, in the numbering system you are familiar with (called the **decimal** [des' uh mul] **system**), it means one hundred and one. However, in the binary system, it means *five*!

How does it mean five? Well, let's first understand how you know that in the decimal system, 101 means one hundred and one. Each digit in a number represents a value. In the decimal system, the digit on the right tells you how many 1's there are in the number. The digit to the left of that one tells you how many 10's there are in the number. The digit to the left of that one tells you how many 10x10's or 100's there are in the number. Here is an example:

This digit tells you how many 10x10's (100's) there are in the number. → 672 ← The end digit tells you how many 1's there are in the number.

This digit tells you how many 10's there are in the number.

You know there are six 100's, seven 10's, and two 1's. Thus, the number being represented is 6x100 + 7x10 + 2x1, or six hundred and seventy-two.

To make larger numbers, you just add more digits to the left. For each digit to the left, you multiply by another ten. In the decimal number 4,231, the right digit tells us the number of ones, the next digit to the left tells us the number of 10's, the next one to the left tells us the number of 10x10's (100's), and the next one tells us the number of 10x10x10's (1,000's). Thus, the number is 4x1,000 + 2x100 + 3x10 + 1x1, or four thousand two hundred thirty-one. Now let's look at the number 101. In the decimal system, that means there is one 100, no 10's, and one 1. So the number represented is 1x100 + 0x10 + 1x1, or one hundred and one.

But suppose the digits represented something other than 1's and 10's? Suppose they represented 1's and 2's? Let's look at the number 101 in that light:

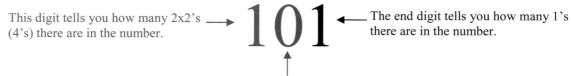

This digit tells you how many 2x2's (4's) there are in the number. → 101 ← The end digit tells you how many 1's there are in the number.

This digit tells you how many 2's there are in the number.

In the binary system, this number tells us there is one 1, no 2's, and one 4. So the number is 1x4 + 0x2 + 1x1, or five. Now if you don't understand all this, don't worry too much. I just want you to realize that there are many ways numbers can be represented. The numbers you are familiar with use the decimal system, which is based on 10's. However, numbers can be written in many different systems, including the binary system, which is based on 2's.

Guess who came up with the binary system? Gottfried Wilhelm Leibniz! Actually, that's not quite true. There were binary number systems around in ancient times. In fact, the Chinese used a binary system in 900 BC. However, Leibniz was the first to use it in its modern form. Why would Leibniz use such a numbering system? He obviously wasn't making computers!

There were two reasons. First, he wanted to reduce logic to exact statements. Exact statements are either completely true or completely false, so they could be answered with either a "yes" (represented by a "1") or a "no" (represented by a "0"). He developed a system of numbers that could deal with questions that only had "yes" or "no" answers, much like you used in the games you just played.

Second, he believed that binary numbers were the best representation of how God created the world. Christians believe that God created the world "*ex nihilo*," which is Latin for "out of nothing."

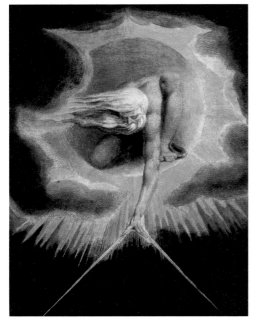

Since the only digits in the binary system are "0" (nothing) and "1" (something), the binary system best illustrates how God created something from nothing. Here is what Leibniz wrote about the binary system:

> After all, one of the high points of the Christian faith, which agrees least with the philosophers and is not easy to impart to pagans, is the creation *ex nihilo* through God's almighty power. Now one can say that nothing in the world can better present and demonstrate this power than the origin of numbers, as it is represented here through the simple and unadorned presentation of One and Zero or nothing. [Franklin Perkins, *Leibniz and China: A Commerce of Light*, Cambridge University Press 2004, p. 116]

This is a painting by poet-artist William Blake (1757 – 1827). It depicts God creating the world out of nothing (*ex nihilo*).

In a sense, then, we owe the invention of computers to Leibniz's desire to share the awesomeness of the Creator with those who did not know Christ (whom he calls pagans).

LESSON REVIEW

Youngest students: Answer these questions:

1. Fill in the blank: The system of numbers we use every day is based on _____.

2. What are the only two digits you will find in a binary number?

Older students: Explain the decimal system using the number 714. Explain what each digit means and how we know what number it represents. Explain the binary system using the number 101. Explain what each digit means and how we know what number it represents.

Oldest students: Do what the older students are doing. In addition, determine what is represented by the binary number 11001. Check your answer and correct it if it is wrong.

Lesson 90: Ole Christensen Rømer (1644 – 1710)

Because of Newton's amazing work, lots of natural philosophers of this time period were studying the heavens, trying to learn as much as they could about gravity and how it controlled the motion of the planets around the sun. One of these natural philosophers was **Ole** (oh' lay) **Christensen** (kris' ten sen) **Rømer** (rer' mur), a Danish astronomer who was educated at the University of Copenhagen. Once he graduated, he was hired to be the private tutor of the heir to the throne of France, but he later returned to the University of Copenhagen as a professor of astronomy. However, he also worked for the government. At one time, he was the royal mathematician, and later in his life, he was even the Chief of Police and Mayor of Copenhagen. Of course, regardless of the job he had, he spent a large part of his time studying the heavens and trying to understand how they worked.

This is a portrait of Ole Christensen Rømer.

Unfortunately, many of Rømer's observations of the heavens were lost when a huge fire broke out in Copenhagen in 1728. However, one of his most important accomplishments has not been lost, and like most things, it is best to illustrate that accomplishment with an experiment.

Light and Sound

What you will need:
- A place outside that is reasonably flat and about 100 meters (100 yards) long.
- A metal pan with a handle
- A metal spoon
- Someone to help you

What you should do:
1. Stand at one end of the long, flat area so that it stretches out in front of you.
2. Have your helper stand about 10 meters (10 yards) away from you, facing you. He or she should be holding the pan and spoon.
3. Have your helper hold the pan and spoon above his or her head and bang them together with one sharp bang. You should hear the sound they make as they hit each other.
4. Have your helper move so he or she is about twice as far from you as before and repeat step 3. Concentrate on both listening to the sound and watching the pan and spoon hit one another.
5. Repeat step 4 several times, each time concentrating on both watching the pan and spoon as well as hearing them. By the time your helper is as far away as possible and you can still see the spoon

and pan, you should notice something about the difference between seeing the pan and spoon hit and hearing the noise they make when they hit.

6.   Go inside and put away the pan and spoon.

What did you see in the experiment? You should have noticed that as your helper moved farther from you, there was a point at which you saw the pan and spoon hit each other *before* you actually heard the sound of them hitting each other. Why? Well, you see things because light reflects off them and travels through the air to enter your eyes. However, you hear things because sound waves travel through the air and enter your ears. So the fact that you eventually saw the spoon and pan hit before you heard them tells you that light travels faster than sound.

You can see a lightning strike before you hear the thunder it makes because light travels much faster than sound.

You might have already realized this if you live in an area that experiences a lot of thunderstorms. Have you ever noticed that in a thunderstorm you often see lighting before you hear the thunder that the lightning makes? That's because you can see lightning from a long way off, so often, the light from the lightning strike and the sound that it makes must travel a long way. Since light travels so quickly compared to sound, you often see the lightning several seconds before you hear the thunder it makes. As a general rule of thumb, you can tell how far away the lighting strike was by counting the seconds between when you see the lightning and when you hear it. For every second difference, the lightning strike was about 340 meters ($\frac{1}{5}$ of a mile) away. So, if you see the lightning flash and count to 5 seconds before you hear the thunder, the storm is about one mile away.

Natural philosophers in Rømer's day understood this, but one thing they didn't understand was whether or not light took any time to travel. Based on everything they experienced, it seemed that they could see things the instant they happened. As a result, there were many who thought that light was able to travel any amount of distance in no time at all. In other words, they thought light could go anywhere **instantaneously**.

Rømer determined that this was wrong. He realized that even though light travels very quickly, it does take *some* time to travel. How did he determine that? He carefully studied one of Jupiter's moons, **Io** (eye' oh). Do you remember studying about Cassini in Lesson 61? He had studied Io as it orbited around Jupiter, and he noticed that there seemed to be something odd about its orbit. Sometimes, it seemed to take less time for it to travel around Jupiter, and sometimes it seemed to take more time. That was odd, because the earth's moon doesn't vary in the time it takes to move around earth. There was no reason to expect Io to behave differently.

Rømer made a lot more observations of Io and confirmed its odd behavior. However, he also noticed that the odd behavior was related to where the earth was in its orbit around the sun. He realized that Io's motion wasn't odd at all. Instead, it was as regular as the moon's motion around the earth. The difference was that when earth was moving towards Jupiter, the distance between Jupiter and its moon Io was decreasing. This meant that as the earth traveled in that direction, it took less and less time for light from Io to reach earth. However, as the earth traveled away from Jupiter, the distance that light had to travel was greater and greater, so it took more and more time for light to travel from Io to earth. So what appeared to be odd motion on the part of Io was really the result of the fact that the distance between Io and the earth constantly changed, and light took different amounts of time to travel the distance to earth.

In order for an astronomer to see Io, light must travel from it to the earth.

As the earth travels away from Jupiter, the distance between it and Io increases, so light takes more and more time to travel to the earth.

As the earth travels towards Jupiter, the distance between it and Io decreases, so light takes less and less time to travel to the earth.

Rømer showed that Io's behavior only seemed odd because of the time it took for light to travel from Io to the earth.

This, of course, showed that light did not travel instantaneously. Instead, it took time to get from Io to earth. That meant that light had a definite speed, just like sound. Of course, light's speed is much greater than the speed of sound, but it still has a speed. With a long enough distance, the speed of light became apparent. We now know, of course, that Rømer was correct. Light travels very quickly. It covers 299,792 kilometers (186,282 miles) every second! That's really fast, but it is not instantaneous. In fact, it takes light about 8 minutes and 19 seconds to travel from the sun to earth.

Although Rømer is best remembered for demonstrating that it does take some time for light to travel from one place to another, he did other remarkable things in his lifetime. He developed a temperature scale that is no longer used anymore but formed the basis of the Fahrenheit temperature scale, which you will learn about as you study more science. In addition, when he was Chief of Police, he was the first to think of putting lights out on the streets to make them safer at night. The streetlights of his day burned oil, so they weren't as good as what we have now, but they did make the streets safer. As you can see, Rømer was a man of many talents!

LESSON REVIEW

Youngest students: Answer these questions:

1. Why do you often see lightning before you hear the thunder it makes?

2. What did Rømer discover about the way light traveled?

Older students: Explain why you can see lightning before you hear the thunder it makes. Also, explain why many natural philosophers thought light traveled instantaneously and what Rømer did to show that was wrong.

Oldest students: Do what the older students are doing. In addition, the distance around the earth is about 40,000 kilometers. How many times could light travel around the earth in one second? Check your answer and correct it if it is wrong.

Some Final Thoughts

Congratulations, you have reached the end of another science course! If you have been following the series this book is a part of, you now know what natural philosophers understood about creation up to the end of the 17th century. If you remember what you learned about how science progressed after the birth of Christ, you know that most of the natural philosophers whose work led to the development of the scientific method were Christians. This isn't surprising, because the Christian worldview fits so well with scientific thought. As Christians, we expect the universe to work according to natural laws, because it was created by a Lawgiver. Thus, it makes sense that we can learn about those laws to better understand how creation works.

As you went through this course, you probably once again noticed that most of the natural philosophers you studied were also Christians. This is important, because many history textbooks and history teachers try to make the claim that the Scientific Revolution started because natural philosophers stopped thinking about God and started thinking about how they could explain the natural world without reference to Him. However, as their own words indicate, the natural philosophers who started and continued the Scientific Revolution constantly and repeatedly discussed God and how He created the world.

Think about it. Copernicus thought the heliocentric view was better than the geocentric view because the universe "…has been built for us by the Best and Most Orderly Workman of all." Vesalius referred to God as the "Supreme Maker of all things" and often pointed out how the human body illustrates His craftsmanship. Galileo believed that the universe was written in a mathematical language because it was created by the Almighty Mathematician. Kepler said that God was being celebrated through his astronomical observations. Harvey's belief that God created the human body helped him figure out the way blood flows. Descartes championed the idea that God was so powerful He could create a universe that ran completely on its own. Huygens thought that plants and animals showed the very finger of God. Boyle said that natural philosophers must always remember to give credit to the "One who authored nature." John Ray was just one example of what historians call a "parson naturalist."

Newton's Law of Universal Gravitation illustrates what I am talking about. Newton was able to come up with that law because he believed the same laws of nature discovered on the earth applied to everything in the universe. Why would he believe that? As Dr. Morris Kline (a professor of mathematics) puts it, Newton believed that:

> God had designed the universe, and it was to be expected that all phenomena of nature would follow one master plan. One mind designing a universe would almost surely have employed one set of basic principles to govern related phenomena. [Morris Kline, Mathematics: The Loss of Certainty, Oxford University Press 1980, p. 52]

So in fact, the Scientific Revolution was really the result of natural philosophers understanding the consequences of God's existence. Once they understood that, they were able to make incredible discoveries about how creation really works!

Glossary

Absolute brightness – The brightness with which a star shines if you were right next to it

Absorb – To take in and not allow to escape

Acceleration – The change in an object's velocity

Acid – A chemical that reacts with bases and lowers the pH of a solution

Adhesive (ad he' siv) – The tendency of the molecules or atoms of different substances to be attracted to each other

Air pressure – The force per unit area with which air pushes on a surface

Air resistance – A force that opposes motion through the air

Albumen (al' byoo men) – The "egg white" that surrounds and protects the yolk

Altricial (al trih' shul) – An animal that is helpless (can't see, move well, or stay warm) when it is born or hatched

Alchemy – The attempt to turn inexpensive metals (like lead) into expensive metals (like gold).

Anal fins – The fins on the underside of the fish, near the rear, used to keep the fish rightside up in the water

Anesthetic – A substance that makes a person less sensitive to pain

Antenna – A long extension from an invertebrate's body that allows it to sense things

Anterior – Referring to the front of an animal (near the "head")

Apex – The point of a leaf farthest from the petiole

Apparent brightness – The brightness with which a star shines in the night sky from the perspective of earth

Arachnids – Invertebrates that share many common features such as eight legs and no antenna

Artery – A blood vessel that carries blood away from the heart

Asteroid (as' tuh royd) **belt** – A loose collection of large rocky bodies that orbit the sun between Mars and Jupiter

Astrology – The odd belief that the movements of the stars and planets affect a person's future

Astronomers – Scientists that study heavenly bodies

Astronomy – The study of the heavenly bodies

Atom – The smallest chemical unit of matter

Bacteria (bak' teer ee uh) – Microscopic creatures that are not plants or animals, they are considered the simplest form of life on earth

Balance – A device that compares the weight of two samples, one on each side of a bar

Barometer (buh rah' muh tur) – A device that measures air pressure

Base – A chemical that reacts with acids and raises the pH of a solution

Battery – A device that stores energy in the form of chemical energy but then converts it to electrical energy that can power an electrical device

Beak – A bird's bill that is sharp

Bill – The hard structure that leads to a bird's mouth; "beak" is often, but incorrectly, used to mean the same thing.

Binary number – A number that contains only 1's and 0's and uses a base of 2 to determine its value

Binocular vision – The ability to see the same object with both eyes at the same time

Blade – (of a leaf) The broad surface of a leaf

Bone marrow – Soft tissue found inside bones that is important for making blood

Boyle's Law – The volume of a gas times its pressure stays constant, as long as the temperature does not change

Capillaries (kap' uh lehr' eez) – Microscopic blood vessels that connect the arteries and veins

Carbon dioxide – A gas that people and animals breathe out; plants use it in photosynthesis.

Cartesian diver – A classic science experiment, named after Rene' Descartes, which demonstrates the principle of buoyancy

Cartilage – A firm but flexible tissue found associated with bones. It can also turn into bone.

Casting – The manure an earthworm leaves behind

Cell – (in biology) The basic unit of life; all living things have at least one cell.

Celsius – A temperature scale in which pure water freezes at 0 degrees and boils at 100 degrees

Chemical bond – What holds atoms together in a molecule

Chemical energy – The energy stored in chemicals, such as food

Chemistry – The study of substances and how they can be changed

Chlorophyll (klor' uh fill) – A green pigment found in most plants

Circulatory system – The system of organs involved in transporting blood throughout the body

Classification – The act of grouping things together based on their similarities

Clitellum – The large swollen region in the anterior part of an earthworm

Cloud – A visible collection of water or ice suspended in the air

Clutch – A group of eggs or baby birds produced by one adult at one time

Cohesive (koh hee' siv) – The tendency of the molecules or atoms of a substance to be attracted to each other

Cold-blooded – Referring to an animal that has no means by which to keep its internal temperature constant

Collision – The instance of one moving object striking another object

Comet – A collection of rocks, dust, frozen water, and frozen gases that orbits the sun; when it gets close to the sun, it brightens and often forms a tail

Comparative anatomy – The scientific investigation of similarities and differences in the anatomy of different organisms

Condensation (kon' den say' shun) – The process by which a gas turns into a liquid

Cones – Light-sensing cells in the eye; these cells detect color

Contract – To get smaller

Control – (in an experiment) A standard sample or trial to which all others are compared

Convert – To change or transform

Cornea (kor' nee uh) – The transparent outer covering of the eye

Cosmic rays – A stream of charged particles that comes from the sun

Cotyledon (kot' ul eed' un) – The means by which a plant embryo gets food until it can make food for itself

Counter intuitive (in too' ih tiv) – The opposite of what we expect based on what we know

Cranial nerves – Nerves that emerge directly from the brain

Crescent moon – The phase of the moon when only a small sliver of the surface is lit

Crest – The highest point on a wave (opposite of trough)

Decompose – To break down into completely different molecules

Deep – (in anatomy) A directional term meaning farther from the surface of the body

Depth perception – The ability to judge distance from visual observation

Detect – To discover or become aware of

Dicot – A flowering plant that sprouts with two seed leaves

Diffraction – The process by which a beam of light spreads out after encountering a small opening

Diffusion – The motion of atoms or molecules from high concentration to low concentration

Digestive system – The system of organs that process food so it can be used by the body

Digestive tract – The organs of the digestive system through which food actually passes

Displacement – The distance *and* direction in which an object is moved from a given point

Dissolve – To mix a solute with a solvent so that it seems that the solute disappears

Domesticated animals – Animals that people care for and use for food, clothing, work, or companionship

Dorsal (dor' sul) – Referring to the top of an animal (its "back")

Dualism – The belief that people have two natures: a physical one and a supernatural one

Dynamic sense of balance – The part of the balance sense that allows you to know how your head is moving

Eccentricity – (in an ellipse) The ratio of an ellipse's semimajor axis to its semiminor axis; when eccentricity is 1, the shape is a circle; the larger the eccentricity, the more oval the ellipse.

Ellipse – An oval shape defined as the collection of points in which the sum of the distances from two other fixed points is the same

Embryo (em' bree oh') – An unborn, unhatched, or ungerminated offspring in the process of development; a plant's seed contains a plant embryo, and a bird's egg contains a bird embryo, for example

Emerge – To come forth into view

Emission spectroscopy – A process by which scientists analyze the light emitted by a substance to learn more about it

Empiricism (em pir' ih siz' uhm) – The idea that the only way we can learn anything is through experiment and observation

Energy – The ability to do work

Epicotyl (ep' ih kot' uhl) – The part of a plant's stem that is above the cotyledons

Epicycle – A small circle whose center moves along a larger circle; Many were added to the geocentric system to make it consistent with observations

Equilibrium (ee' kwuh lib' ree uhm) – A state of balance brought about by the equal action of opposing processes

Evaporation (ih vap' uh ray' shun) – The process by which a liquid changes into a gas

Expand – To get larger

Expanse – Something that stretches out for a long way

Fahrenheit – A temperature scale in which pure water freezes at 32 degrees and boils at 212 degrees

Fat – A greasy or oily deposit found in many animals that is an excellent insulator

Fertile – Able to produce offspring

Fiber optic cable – A flexible transparent fiber which guides or transmits light with little or no loss of energy

Fibrous root system – A root system that is composed of many branching roots

Fin – A flattened structure used by fish to steer, guide, or propel themselves through water

Fossil – The preserved remains of a once-living organism; before Robert Hooke's work, the term referred to anything that was dug up from the ground

Free fall – The situation in which an object falls without significant hindrance to the earth

Freezing – The process by which a liquid turns into a solid

Freshwater organism – An organism that lives in water that has a low level of salt in it

Full moon – The phase of the moon when the entire surface that is facing earth is illumintated by the sun

Galilean moons – The four largest moons that orbit Jupiter; discovered by Galileo

Gas – One of the three phases of matter; this phase occupies the most volume

Gas planets – Planets that are mostly made of gas (in our solar system: Jupiter, Saturn, Neptune, and Uranus)

Genealogy (jee' nee awl' uh jee) – A line of decent traced from a specific ancestor

General sense – A sense that exists all over the body, such as the sense of touch

Geocentric System – The arrangement of the solar system in which the earth sits at the center

Germination (jur' muh nay' shun) – The process by which a seed develops into a plant

Gibbous moon – The phase of the moon when most (but not all) of the surface that is facing the earth is lit

Glacier – An accumulation of snow and ice that persists year round and is characterized by slow flow down a slope

Gland – A structure in a living organism that makes and releases a specific chemical or mix of chemicals

Glucose – A sugar that is produced through photosynthesis

Gravitropism – The process by which a plant alters its growth so that its leaves grow upwards and its roots grown downwards

Gravity – The force that attracts any object with mass to any other object with mass

Gregorian (grih gor' ee uhn) **calendar** – A calendar that uses the earth's orbit around the sun to track the passage of the seasons

Hallucinate (huh loo' suh nayt') – To see something that does not exist

Hatchling – A recently-hatched offspring

Heliocentric system – The arrangement of the solar system in which the sun sits at the center

Heterogeneous (het' uh roh jee' nee us) – Describes a substance or mixture whose composition is different depending on location

Homogeneous (ho' muh jee' nee us) – Describes a substance or mixture whose composition is the same regardless of location

Humus – The part of soil that is produced by living things that have decomposed

Hypothesis – An educated guess about how something in creation works or what will happen

Iceberg – A floating mass of ice that forms from a glacier; it has no significant amount of salt

Igneous rock – Rock that has formed by the freezing of lava

Immutable – Unable to change

Inclined plane – A flat surface that is tilted to form a ramp

Incubate (ink' yoo bayt) – To keep an egg warm until it hatches

Interia (ih nur' shuh) – A measure of an object's ability to resist a change in its motion

Infertile (in fur' tuhl) – Unable to produce offspring

Infrared (in' fruh red') **light** – Light that cannot be seen by human eyes but is emitted by objects that are warmer than their surroundings

Inner planets – The rocky planets in our solar system that are between the sun and the asteroid belt (Mercury, Venus, earth, and Mars)

Insects – Invertebrates that share many common features such as six legs and two antennae

Insulator – Something that tends to keep heat (or electricity) from being transferred from one place to another

Intuitive (in too' ih tiv) – What is expected based on what we know

Invertebrate (in ver' tuh brut) – An animal that does not have a backbone

Ion (eye' on) – An atom that has electrical charge due to the gain or loss of an electron

Jacobsen's organ – An organ found in some animals (like snakes) that enhances the sense of smell by sampling particles on the tongue

Jet propulsion – Being pushed along by forcing a stream of air or a fluid in the opposite direction

Law of Energy Conservation – Energy cannot be created or destroyed; it can only be converted from one form to another

Law of Momentum Conservation – In a collision that is not affected by outside influences, the total momentum must always stay the same

Law of Universal Gravitation – The force of gravity between two objects increases as the mass of either object increases, and it increases as the distance between them decreases

Leap year – A year in which there is an extra day added to make up for the fact that the earth takes slightly more than 365 days to make an orbit around the sun

Leaves – The part of a plant that makes its food

Lens – A device that bends light to focus or defocus an image

Lift – (aerodynamic) The upward force a wing feels due to there being more air below it than above it

Light pollution – Artifical light that interferes with ability to view objects in the night sky

Liquid – One of the three phases of matter; for most substances, this phase occupies more volume than the solid phase but less than the liquid phase

Locomotion – The act of moving from place to place

Lunar calendar – A calendar that uses the phases of the moon to track the passage of the seasons

Lunar eclipse – An event where the earth comes directly between the moon and sun, blocking the sun's light from falling on the moon

Lymphatic system – The system of organs that picks up fluid from in between the cells of the body, cleans it, and puts it back in the blood

Maggot – The immature form of a fly

Marine – Referring to a saltwater environment

Marine organism – An organism that lives in saltwater

Mechanical energy – The energy associated with motion and position

Melting – The process by which a solid turns into a liquid

Membrane – A thin layer of tissue

Metamorphic rock – Rock that is formed when sedimentary or igneous rock is changed by the application of heat and/or pressure

Meteorology – The study of weather

Microwaves – Light that cannot be seen by human eyes but is used in certain devices, like microwave ovens

Midrib – The central, most prominent vein in a leaf

Mixture – Two or more substances mingled together

Molecule (mol' ih kyool) – Two or more atoms linked together to make a substance with unique properties

Momentum – The mass of an object times its velocity; the larger the momentum (in absolute terms), the harder it is to stop the object

Monocot – A flowering plant that sprouts with just one seed leaf

Motor nerves – Nerves that are used to move muscles

Nasal cavity – The region where air goes when it is taken in by the nose

Nectar – A sweet liquid produced by plants, typically in their flowers

Nerve receptors – Structures through which animals and people sense the outside world

Newton's First Law of Motion – An object at rest will stay at rest until acted on by an outside force; an object in motion will stay in motion until it is acted on by an outside force.

Newton's Second Law of Motion – When a net force acts on an object, its acceleration increases with increasing force and decreases with increasing mass

Newton's Third Law of Motion – When a body exerts a force on an object, the object exerts an equal force back on that body, in an opposite direction

Observatories – Facilities located in places less affected by light pollution and atmospheric disturbances to facilitate the study of astronomical objects

Opposition – (in astronomy) Describing the times when the earth sits between a planet and the sun

Optic nerve – The nerve that sends information from the eyes to the brain

Optical illusion – An incorrect image that is produced by a trick of light or the surroundings

Organ – A structure in the body that performs a specific set of tasks

Organism (or' guh nih zuhm) – A general term that refers to anything that is alive, be it plant, animal, or something else

Osmosis – The tendency of a solvent to flow across a semipermeable membrane to where there is more solute

Oscillation – The regular, back-and-forth motion of an object across a fixed point

Otolith – An "ear stone" in the inner ear that allows the body to have a static sense of balance

Outer planets – The gaseous planets in our solar system that are farther from the sun than the asteroid belt (Jupiter, Saturn, Uranus, Neptune)

Oxygen – A gas that people and animals breathe in; plants produce it through photosynthesis

Ozone – A gas that is concentrated in a layer high above the surface of the earth; it blocks some of the sun's ultraviolet light

Ozone layer – A part of the atmosphere that is 15-50 kilometers (10-30 miles) above the surface of the earth and holds most of the earth's ozone

Parallax – The effect in which an object's position appears different because of the position from which it is viewed

Parson-Naturalist – A country minister or priest who spent a large portion of his time studying nature

Partial lunar eclipse – A lunar eclipse in which the earth blocks only a portion of the sun's light from hitting the moon

Partial solar eclipse – A solar eclipse in which only a portion of the sun's light is blocked by the moon

Pascal's Law – When pressure is exerted at one place in an enclosed liquid, the liquid transmits that pressure in all directions, pushing with that pressure against anything it touches.

Pascal's Wager – An argument to get people to believe in Christianity by showing it is the best bet

Pectoral (pek' tor uhl) **fins** – The frontmost fins of a fish that are used for steering

Pelvic fins – The fins on the underside of the fish, between the anal and pectoral fins, used to keep the fish rightside up in the water and also used by some fish to slow down

Pendulum – A weight hung from a fixed point so it can swing back and forth

Period – (in physics) The time it takes to complete a full cycle of motion

Petiole (pet' ee ohl) – (of a leaf) The small stem that attaches the leaf to the stem of the plant

Petrifaction – The process by which dead tissue is replaced by minerals to preserve a fossil

Phase – (in matter) One of the three ways matter appears: solid, liquid, or gas; (for the moon) A distinctive shape of the moon as seen in the night sky

Photosynthesis (foh' toh sinth' uh sis) – The process by which a plant makes food for itself from water, carbon dioxide, and light energy

Phototropism – The process by which a plant alters its growth so that it can be exposed to more light

Physics – The brand of science that studies the nature and properties of matter and energy

Pigment – A chemical that gives color to an object or organism

Planet – A bright light in the night sky that appears to "wander" among the stars

Plumule (plu' myool) – The part of a plant embryo that develops into the plant's first true leaves

Pod – (in biology) A protective case that holds one or more seeds

Population – A count of the number of living things in a region

Posterior – Referring to the rear of an animal (near the "tail")

Pore – A small opening or space

Porous – Full of holes

Precocial (prih koh' shul) – An animal that is not helpless (can see, move well, and stay warm) when it is born or hatched

Predator (pred' uh tor) – An animal that eats another animal

Preen gland – A gland in a bird that produces oil so that the bird can waterproof its feathers

Preening – The process a bird goes through to clean, straighten, and waterproof its feathers

Prefix (pree' fiks) – A group of letters put before a word, such as the "un" in "unfair."

Prey – An animal that is killed and eaten by another animal

Projectile – An object that is given an initial velocity but then travels through the air without anything powering its motion

Primary root – The main part of a plant's root system

Pulmonary circulation – The system that is involved in getting blood from the heart to the lungs and back again

Quarter moon – The phase of the moon when half the surface that is facing earth is lit

Radiant (ray' dee unt) **energy** – The energy of light

Radicle (rad' ih kul) – The part of a plant embryo that develops into the plant's root system

Reflect – To bounce off an object and change direction

Refraction (rih frak' shun) – A process by which light bends when it encounters a new substance through which it must travel

Respiratory system – The system of organs involved in breathing

Retina (ret' nuh) – The eye tissue that detects light

Retrograde motion – The motion of a planet when it reverses the direction it travels in the night sky

Rock cycle – The process by which rocks are broken down and reformed throughout creation

Rocky planets – Planets that are solid (In our solar system: Mercury, Venus, earth, and Mars)

Rods – Light-sensing cells in the eye; these cells detect only the presence or absence of light

Root system – All the roots and root branches in a plant

Scattered light – Light that has bounced off particles in various directions

Scientific method – A process of doing science in which you make observations, form a hypothesis, and test the hypothesis

Scientific Revolution – Beginning in 1543, the era of history in which natural philosophers began seriously questioning the authorities of the past and making their own observations to determine how nature works.

Sedimentary rock – Rock that has formed by the solidification of sediments, such as sand, silt, or clay

Seed leaves – A term often used to describe the cotyledons on a plant

Seedling – A plant that has recently sprouted

Semipermeable – An object that allows some things to pass through it, but not all things

Sensory Nerves – Nerves that provide information to the brain

Setae – Bristles on an animal, such as what exists on the ventral side of a worm

Shell – The outer covering of an egg; bird eggs have a hard shell, while reptile eggs have a leathery shell

Shell membrane – The thin membrane under the shell of an egg

Simple sugar – A small class of molecules of which glucose is a member

Skeleton – The system of support in an animal; for vertebrates, it is a skeleton made of bones; for invertebrates, it is a hard outer covering known as an exoskeleton

Soil – The upper layer of earth in which plants grow

Solar calendar – Another name for the Gregorian calendar

Solar eclipse – An event where the moon comes directly between the earth and sun, blocking the sun's light

Solar system – A system in which planets, their moons, and other astronomical objects orbit a sun

Solid – One of the three phases of matter; for most substances, this phase occupies the least volume

Solute – A substance being dissolved in a solvent; present in lesser amount

Solution – A mixture of at least one solute in a solvent

Solvent – The substance a solute is being dissolved into; present in greater amount

Special sense – A sense that depends on a specific organ, like the sense of sight, which depends on the eye

Species – A group of living organisms that can produce offspring which are also able to produce offspring

Spinal nerves – Nerves that emerge from the spinal cord

Star – A large body of gas that produces its own light

Starch – A molecule that is used to store food in plants

Static sense of balance – The part of the balance sense that allows you to know the position of your head

Stomata (stoh' mah tuh) – Tiny holes in a leaf that open and close to allow air into the leaf and oxygen to leave the leaf

Streamlined – Shaped to reduce air resistance or water drag

Sunburn – A burn on the skin caused by too much exposure to ultraviolet light

Sundial – A device that tells time by the movement of a shadow cast by the sun

Sunspots – Dark blotches on the sun that indicate a lower temperature than the rest of the surface

Superficial (anatomy) – A directional term meaning closer to the surface of the body

Supernova – An exploding star

Swim bladder – An inflatable sac in a fish that allows it to change its volume so as to change depth

Swimmerets (swih muh retz') – Small leglike parts of an animal that are used to swim

Taproot system – A root system that is composed mostly of a single root

Taste buds – The structures on your tongue that give you your sense of taste

Teem – To be full of

Tentacle – A slender, flexible extension of an animal, such as a jellyfish

Thermal (thur' muhl) **energy** – The energy associated with heat

Thermometer – A device that measures temperature

Thrust – A sudden push in a particular direction

Tides – The periodic variation of the height of the ocean at the shore caused by the position of the moon

Tornado – A quickly rotating column of air that can do a significant amount of damage

Total lunar eclipse – A lunar eclipse in which the earth blocks most of the sun's light from hitting the moon

Total solar eclipse – A solar eclipse in which almost all of the light from the sun is blocked by the moon

Transmission – The process by which light passes through an object

Transparent – Having the property of allowing light to pass through

Transpiration (tran' spuh ray' shun) – The evaporation of water through a plant's leaves

Trough – The lowest point on a wave (opposite of crest)

Ultraviolet light – Light that cannot be seen by human eyes but can cause tissue damage, such as sunburns; much of it is absorbed by ozone

Urinary System – The system of organs that cleans the blood and removes the water-soluble wastes

Vein – (in animals) A blood vessel that carries blood towards the heart

Veins – (of a leaf) The structures that carry water and other necessary items throughout the leaf

Velocity – A measure of an object's speed *and* the direction in which it is moving

Venn diagram – A chart consisting of two overlapping ovals that allows you to compare two things

Ventral – Referring to the bottom of an animal (its "stomach")

Vermicast – The manure an earthworm leaves behind

Vertebrate (ver' tuh brut) – An animal that has a backbone

Viscosity – A measure of the resistance a fluid has to flowing

Visible light – Light that can be seen by human eyes

Volume – A measure of how much room something takes up

Warm-blooded – Referring to an animal that has a means to keep its internal temperature constant

Water vapor – Water in its gas phase

Waterfowl – Birds that spend a lot of time on or in water

Weathered – (pertaining to a rock) Broken down by things that happen in nature

Woodcut – A block of wood that is carved to leave an image when inked and pressed against paper

Work – Exertion or effort directed to produce or accomplish something

Yolk – The center of an egg which serves as the embryo's food

Yolk sac – The thin membrane that holds the yolk

Zoology (zoh' ol uh jee) – The study of animals

Photo and Illustration Credits

Index

magnifying glass, 90, 97, 120, 121, 170, 260
Maker, 276
makers, spectacle, 90
Malpighi, Marcello, 169-172, 203
Malpighian layer, 170
man, 10
mandible, 18, 60
manual, 254
manubrium, 15
marbles, 241, 246-248, 267-269
Marcello Malpighi, 169-172, 203
Marco Severino, 140
marine animals, 59
Mars, 2-7, 93, 187
Martin Luther King, Jr., 11
mass, 214, 219, 220, 225, 228, 229, 231, 233-236, 247, 248, 250, 256, 262, 269
mass produced, 20
math, 47, 114, 115, 116
mathematician, 82, 137, 273, 276
Mathematician, Almighty, 276
mathematics, 50, 71, 81, 82, 96, 120, 123, 129, 134, 135, 142, 148, 172, 180, 206, 212, 214, 220, 255, 267, 270, 276
matter, 71, 87, 160-162, 247
mayor, 142
meat, 22, 192, 193
mechanic, 133
mechanical energy, 61, 71, 76, 267-269
medical uses (plants), 53
medicine, 47, 50, 71, 108, 120, 160
melt, 69

men, 15
merchant, fabric, 194
mercury (chemical), 124, 125, 129, 160
Mercury (planet), 2, 3, 4, 6, 70, 99-101
metacarpals, 60
metatarsals, 60
meteorology, 147
Metius, Jacob, 91
Michael Servetus, 62, 114
Micrographia, 172, 174, 181, 194
microscope, 169, 171-175, 178, 181, 192, 194-196
microscopic organisms, 196-199
miles, 275
milk, 59, 161, 162
mind, 127, 128
minerals, 85, 177
minister, 96, 104
minute hand, 83
miracle, 256, 257
mirrors, 255
mitral valve, 45
mitre, 45
model, 259
modern clocks, 85
modern physics, father of, 71
mold, 191, 192
molecules, 38, 161, 162, 235, 236
momentum, 152, 153, 246-251, 249, 250, 251, 269
Momentum Conservation, Law of, 153, 157, 246-248, 250, 251, 269
monastery, 172
monk, 172
monocots, 202
moon, 66, 69, 93, 99, 103, 104, 148, 181, 217, 274

moons, 71, 93, 149, 150, 187, 274
moons, Galilean, 93
Morris Kline, 276
motion, 5, 160-162, 215-217, 219-226, 238-255, 258, 262, 264, 265, 268, 273
motion, retrograde, 5, 6
motor, 265, 266
motor nerves, 28
mountains, 93
mouth, 31, 41
muscle, 23, 40
muscles, 19, 21, 22, 26, 28
muscles, deep, 19, 26
muscles, skeletal, 22
muscles, superficial, 19, 26
music, 47

-N-

NASA, 220
nasal bone, 17
National Aeronautics and Space Administration, 220
natural science, 120
natural state, 74, 76
naturalist, 50, 59, 200
naturalist, parson, 276
nature, 82, 120, 127, 160
neap tides, 104
nearsighted, 98
neck, 25
Nehemiah Grew, 203-205
Neptune, 93
nerve receptors, 140
nerve, optic, 28
nerves, 23, 28
nerves, cranial, 28
nerves, motor, 28
nerves, sensory, 28
nerves, spinal, 28
net force, 229, 232, 233, 236, 241, 244, 245, 251

sphere, 1, 22, 104, 143, 144
spheres, celestial, 70
spheres, heavenly, 66
spin, 264-266
spinal cord, 28
spinal nerves, 28
spine, 17
spirit, animal, 30
spit, 31
sponge, 176
spontaneous generation, 191-193, 199
spores, 192
spread of diseases, 49
spring, 178, 179, 186
spring tides, 104
squirrel, 175
stamen, 203, 205
stamp, 20, 62
star, 8, 66, 67, 217
stars, 7, 8, 9, 66, 71, 93, 148, 149, 154, 181, 185
state, natural, 74, 76
statesman, 65
steam, 186
steel wool, 121, 122
stems, 171
sternum, 15, 17
stomach, 31, 34, 35, 110, 190
stomach acid, 110
stones, 50, 175
strawberry, 205
streamlined, 235
streetlights, 275
Styrofoam, 68, 83-85, 87
subtractive primary colors, 208
sulfur, 146, 160
sulfur dioxide, 113
sun, 3, 4, 5, 6, 8, 66, 69, 93, 99-101, 128, 154, 182, 183, 186, 212, 214, 242, 255, 273-275

sun-centered system, 1
sundial, 83, 85, 154
sunflower seed, 53-55
sunny days, 124
sunspots, 93
superficial, 26
superficial muscles, 19, 26
supernatural, 126-128
supernova, 67
superstition, 185
surface, 259, 260, 263
surgeon, 140
Sweden, king of, 142
swing, 180
Switzerland, 13
Sydney, 154
sylvestre, gas, 112
system, binary, 271, 272
system, decimal, 271, 272
system, digestive, 31-34, 36, 110
system, earth-centered, 1
system, geocentric, 1-7, 10
system, heliocentric, 1-10, 13
system, lymphatic, 141
system, solar, 96, 217
system, sun-centered, 1
system, urinary, 37, 39

-T-

tablecloth, 216
tail, 60
tail, comet, 69
tarsals, 60
taste, 127
teeth, 16, 34, 60
telescope, 90, 91, 93, 96, 123, 149, 150, 187, 195, 212, 255
telescope, inventor, 90, 91
telescope, reflecting, 212
telescope, reflecting, 255

telescopes, 65, 128, 148, 150, 181
temperature, 86, 87, 254, 275
temperature scale, 275
tendon, 22, 23
testa, 55
Testament, New, 62, 118
Testament, Old, 62, 118, 119
The Natural History of Birds, 59
The Natural History of Strange Marine Fish, 59
The New Star, 66
The Restoration of Christianity, 62
The Sceptical Chymist, 160
The Wisdom of God as Manifested in the Works of Creation, 202
theologian, 10, 104
theology, 50, 62, 96, 117
theory, particle, 211
theory, wave, 211
thermometer, 86-88
Third Law of Motion, Newton's, 237-239, 241, 244, 245, 247, 265
Thomas Bartholin, 139-141
thoracic duct, 141
thread, 145, 146
throw, 232
throws, 251
thunder, 274, 275
tibia, 14, 16, 60
tide, high, 102, 104
tide, low, 102, 104
tides, 102-104, 242
tides, neap, 104
tides, spring, 104
time, 83, 84, 85, 154, 160
timer, 84
tires, 264, 266